KU-283-425

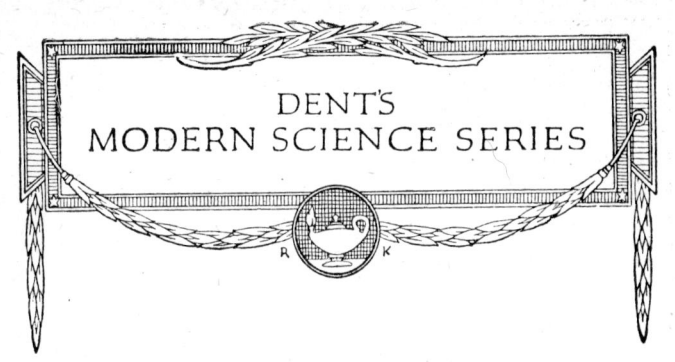

DENT'S
MODERN SCIENCE SERIES

HEAT, LIGHT
AND SOUND

BY THE SAME AUTHOR

MECHANICS & HYDROSTATICS

288 pages   3s. 6d.

ELECTRICITY & MAGNETISM

With 167 diagrams & 22 photographs.

288 pages   4s. 3d.

HEAT

For First M.B., H.S.C., etc.

352 pages   6s. 0d.

[By courtesy of the Director, Dominion Astrophysical Laboratory.

THE 72" REFLECTING TELESCOPE AT VICTORIA, BRITISH COLUMBIA.

HEAT, LIGHT AND SOUND

BY

R. G. MITTON

M.Sc., D.Phil.

Clifton College

Sometime Rhodes Scholar of South Australia
at Magdalen College, Oxford

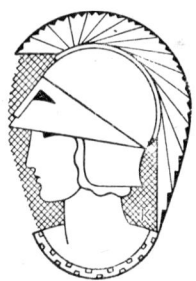

J. M. DENT AND SONS LTD.

BEDFORD ST. LONDON W.C.2

ALL RIGHTS RESERVED
MADE IN GREAT BRITAIN BY
BUTLER AND TANNER LTD., FROME AND LONDON
FIRST PUBLISHED 1936
LAST REPRINTED 1946

PREFACE

THIS book is intended primarily for the use of students preparing for School Certificate Examinations in Heat, Light, and Sound, and the subject-matter has been chosen with this end in view.

Two points call for comment regarding the part of the book which deals with Optics. The convention of signs for the distances of objects and images from mirrors and lenses differs from that generally used in elementary textbooks. In adopting the convention here used, I have followed the recommendation of the committee of the Physical Society (Report on the Teaching of Geometrical Optics, 1934). This convention offers such manifest advantages, both for elementary and more advanced work, that it appears certain to replace the Cartesian systems hitherto employed, and it is already doing so in many university courses. Teachers will find the new convention easy to use, and it promises to solve many of the purely mathematical difficulties encountered by the young student. Thus, the lens and the mirror formulæ are the same ; the formula for magnification is the same for both lenses and mirrors ; and none of these formulæ contains a negative sign. This last fact is of importance, for the beginner finds great difficulty in distinguishing between the negative sign in an equation, and the negative sign attached to a numerical quantity. With the new convention this difficulty does not arise. Finally, the new convention leads to the same signs for the powers and focal lengths of mirrors and lenses as those used by practical optical workers. The older convention did not do this, and the student who learned to use it at school was often compelled later to unlearn what he had with difficulty acquired.

The committee further recommend that the teaching of lenses should precede that of spherical mirrors. This has long been the practice in many schools, and is the order followed here. Since the student has probably handled various instruments which use lenses, he has an interest in learning how a lens works. His interest in spherical mirrors is seldom so great, but can be developed later by contrasting the action of such mirrors with that of lenses. For a similar reason, the chapter on refraction follows those on lenses. Having seen some of the effects of refraction when dealing with lenses, the student is better able to appreciate its importance.

I have to express my warmest thanks to Mr. W. C. Badcock, Head of the Physics Department, Clifton College, for much valuable advice and assistance, and for pointing out several errors and omissions. To Dr. E. J. Holmyard, the General Editor of this series of textbooks, my thanks are also due for his helpful advice and encouragement.

Several firms have lent pictures illustrating the application of physical principles in industry, and have assisted by supplying technical information. The Director of the Dominion Astrophysical Laboratory, Victoria, B.C., and Dr. A. H. Davis of the National Physical Laboratory, have also allowed me to reproduce photographs in their possession. The sources of the illustrations are acknowledged separately in the text, but it is a pleasure to record here my appreciation of their courteous help.

I am also indebted to the following examining bodies for their permission to use questions from past School Certificate Examination papers: The University of Bristol; The University of Cambridge Local Examinations Syndicate; The Joint Matriculation Board of the Universities of Manchester, Liverpool, Leeds, Sheffield, and Birmingham; The University of London; The Delegates of the University of Oxford, Local Examinations; The Oxford and Cambridge Schools Examinations Board.

R. G. MITTON.

CLIFTON COLLEGE, BRISTOL

CONTENTS

CONTENTS

SOUND

HEAT

CHAPTER 1

TEMPERATURE—EXPANSION OF SOLIDS

1.01. Although it is by no means easy to describe what we feel when we experience the sensation of warmth, everyone would agree that a poker which is removed from a fire feels hot, and that a block of ice feels cold. In physics, however, it is necessary not only to judge whether objects are hot, cold, or warm, but also to discover whether one object is hotter than another, and how much hotter it is. This we are unable to discover merely by feeling the objects, and instruments called *thermometers* are used to enable us to decide such questions.

A simple experiment shows how unreliable are our sensations of hotness and coldness. Three saucepans are filled with cold water. The first is heated for five minutes over a Bunsen burner, the second is heated for two minutes, and the third is not heated at all. If one hand is now placed in each saucepan in turn, the water in the first saucepan feels hot, that in the second warm, and that in the third feels cold. If, however, the left hand is placed in the hot water for one minute, while the right hand is placed in the cold water, and both hands are then transferred to the water in the third saucepan, this water feels much warmer to the hand which comes from the cold water than it does to that which comes from the hot. We do not believe that the water in the saucepan can be both hot and cold at the same time, so we are led to conclude that our feelings of hotness are in some cases unreliable.

When hotness or coldness is measured with a thermometer, it is usual to speak of the *temperature* of a body rather than its hotness, and temperature means the hotness or coldness of a body as measured with a thermometer.

Figure 1.01 shows the ordinary type of thermometer used in the laboratory. The position of the mercury in the stem of the instrument indicates the temperature, and a scale marked on

3

the stem enables the temperature to be measured in degrees on the centigrade scale, or degrees centigrade (° C.).

1.02. When an object is heated its temperature usually increases, but a number of other changes may occur. Thus ice changes to water when heated, a piece of wood commences to smoulder or burn, and a piece of iron may change its colour, first to red, and then to white, if its temperature is increased sufficiently. A rather less obvious change, but one which almost all substances share, is the increase of volume of the substance, or its *expansion*. In the present chapter we shall describe the expansion of solid materials.

It is not easy to observe the expansion of solid materials, because the increase of size is usually small. Nevertheless, it can be shown in various ways.

A brass ball (figure 1.02) is made of such a size that it will just pass through the hole in a brass stand when both are cold. When the ball is heated in boiling water it expands, and will then no longer pass through. As it is allowed to cool, the ball regains its original size, and falls through the hole.

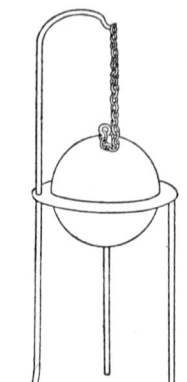

Fig. 1.01.
—Thermo-
meter.

Fig. 1.02.

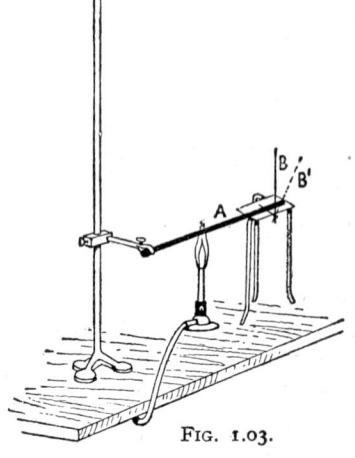

The expansion of a metal bar may be demonstrated with the apparatus shown in figure 1.03. A bar A is clamped at one end in a retort stand. The other end

Fig. 1.03.

rests upon a needle placed at right angles to the bar. The needle rests upon a plate of ground glass, so that it is rolled without slipping if the bar expands or contracts, and a pointer B, fastened to the needle, shows the movement of the latter. When the bar is heated with a Bunsen burner the pointer moves to some such position as B', returning to its original position as the bar is allowed to cool again.

If an attempt is made to prevent a bar expanding or contracting, the bar is able to exert very large forces on the apparatus holding it. Figure 1.04 shows a strongly built framework, into the sockets of which a red-hot iron bar can be inserted. Through a hole at one end of the bar a cast-iron rod is placed to prevent this end of the bar from moving, and the other end is screwed up tightly. As the bar cools, large forces are exerted by it, and the rod is finally snapped in two.

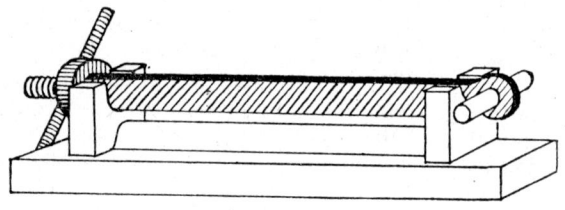

FIG. 1.04.

To avoid damage to railway lines by their expansion during hot weather, a small gap is left between each length of rail and the next. For the same reason, long steel bridges are not built rigidly into the piers which support them, but the ends of the steel structure rest on rollers, which allow the bridge to expand and contract with changing temperatures.

In some cases the expansion of a hot body is useful. Boiler-plates are riveted together with red-hot rivets, and as the rivets cool and contract they draw the plates so firmly together that even high-pressure steam is unable to escape at the seam. The steel tyres placed on the wheels of carts, locomotives, and railway carriages, are made too small to slip on to the wheels. When they are heated, however, they can be slipped into position, and on cooling are firmly held in place.

Different substances expand by different amounts when heated, and if a piece of metal is fused into glass, strains are set up as the joint cools, owing to the different contractions of the glass and metal. If the metal is soft (*e.g.* copper) it may take up the strain, but the glass is always liable to crack at the join if suddenly heated. It happens, however, that platinum expands by the same amount as glass, so strong airtight joins can be made when platinum is sealed into glass.

We have now to see how the expansion of a solid can be measured.

1.03. If a bar of a given material is heated equally throughout its length, one half of the bar expands as much as the other half ; so the increase of length of the bar varies directly as its initial length. It is found, moreover, that the length of any given bar increases by nearly the same amount, whether it is heated from 0° C. to 1° C., from 1° C. to 2° C., or through any other range of temperature of one degree centigrade. Hence the fraction

$$\frac{\text{the increase of length of the bar}}{\text{the length of the bar at 0° C.} \times \text{the rise of temperature}},$$

will be the same whatever length of bar is chosen, and whatever its increase of temperature may be. The fraction depends, however, on the *material* of the bar, and therefore gives useful information about the expansion of the *substance* of which the bar is composed.

The coefficient of linear expansion of a substance is :

$$\frac{\text{the increase of length of a piece of it}}{\text{the length of the piece at 0° C.} \times \text{the rise of temperature}}.$$

1.04. Figure 1.05 shows a piece of apparatus which may be used for measuring the coefficient of linear expansion of a metal —in this case brass.

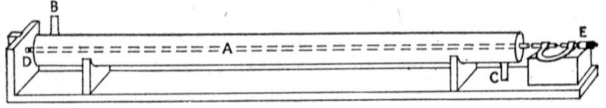

Fig. 1.05.—Apparatus for Measuring the Coefficient of Linear Expansion of Brass.

A brass bar A, about 1 metre long, is soldered into a tube made of the same material, and closed at both ends. Cold water or steam can be passed through this tube by means of the side tubes B and C, and, since the bar and its jacket are both of brass, their expansions are equal, so the expansion which occurs when steam is passed through causes no damage. At one end the bar rests against an ivory stop D, and when expansion occurs, this end remains stationary while the other end of the bar moves. This movement is measured by means of the screw gauge E. Cold water is first passed through the tube, and the temperature of the water is read with a thermometer. This gives the temperature of the bar. The screw gauge is screwed up to make contact with the end of the bar, its reading is noted, and it is then screwed back to allow space for the expansion. Steam is passed through the tube, and the temperature of the steam (and hence that of the bar) is calculated from the barometer reading. The screw gauge is now screwed up to make contact with the bar again, and the difference between this reading and the previous one gives the expansion of the bar. The apparatus is allowed to cool, and the length of the brass bar is measured with a metre scale.

The following data were obtained from an experiment of this kind :

Temperature of cold bar	= 17·3° C.
Temperature of steam	= 99·8° C.
∴ increase of temperature of bar	= 82·5° C.
Screw gauge readings (i)	0·216 cm.
(ii)	0·361 cm.
∴ expansion of bar	= 0·145 cm.
Length of bar (cold)	= 92·0 cm.

∴ coefficient of linear expansion

$$= \frac{\text{increase of length}}{\text{length at 0° C.} \times \text{rise of temperature}}$$

$$= \frac{0·145}{92·0 \times 82·5}$$

$$= 0·0000191 \text{ per centigrade degree.}$$

It is to be noticed that in this calculation the length at 0° C. has been taken as 92·0 cm., although this is really the length at about 20° C. The error is, however, so small that it is not worth taking into account. The expansion of the bar for 82·5 degrees increase of temperature was 0·145 cm., so if the bar had been cooled from about 20° C. to 0° C. the bar would have contracted about one-quarter of this amount, or 0·04 cm. Thus if the bar is 92·00 cm. long at 20° C. its length at 0° C. would be 91·96 cm. If this value had been used for the length at 0° C., the result for the coefficient of linear expansion would have been :

$$\frac{0.145}{91.96 \times 82.5} = 0.0000191 \text{ per centigrade degree.}$$

To three significant figures this is the same as before.

This calculation is a good example of an important principle of most measurements in physics. *It is no use taking one measurement in a given set much more accurately than others.* By " accuracy " here is meant percentage accuracy. Thus if the bar actually has a length of exactly 91.96 cm. at 0° C., and its length is measured as 92.00 cm., the error of measurement is 0.04 cm., which is about 0.04% of 91.96 cm.

When the increase of temperature is given as 82.5° C., the possible error is about 0.2° C. The percentage error in this measurement is thus probably 0.25%. In the same way, the percentage error in the measurement with the screw gauge is about 1.4%.

The error of 0.04% in measuring the length of the bar will cause an error of about 0.04% in the result. Similarly the temperature readings and the screw gauge readings cause errors in the result of about 0.25% and 1.4% respectively. Thus, by far the greater part of the error in the result is caused by the screw gauge readings, and it is useless to spend time in trying to measure the change of temperature and the length of the bar more accurately than we have done.

It is important, however, to try to improve the worst reading ; *i.e.* that which probably has the greatest percentage error. In this case we have done so by using an accurate measuring instrument (the screw gauge) to measure the small expansion of the bar. Even when the screw gauge is used, however, the error of the result arises chiefly from the small error in the measurement of the expansion.

Since the errors in the result are largely caused by the errors in the worst reading, the result should be quoted with sufficient figures to indicate approximately this percentage error. The error in this experiment is likely to be about 1.4%, so the result is quoted with three significant figures. The result is then given to 1 part in 191, or 0.5%.

The following table gives the coefficients of linear expansion of some common materials :

Substance.	Coefficient of Linear Expansion.	Substance.	Coefficient of Linear Expansion.
lead . . .	0·000028 per C. deg.	steel . . .	0·000011 per C. deg.
aluminium .	0·000023 ,, C. ,,	platinum .	0·0000090 ,, C. ,,
silver . . .	0·000019 ,, C. ,,	glass . . .	0·0000085 ,, C. ,,
brass . . .	0·000019 ,, C. ,,	invar . . .	0·0000009 ,, C. ,,
copper . .	0·000016 ,, C. ,,	fused silica .	0·0000005 ,, C. ,,

1.05. When a shell is fired from a big gun the gun must resist the enormous pressures (up to 20 tons per square inch) developed

[By courtesy of Vickers-Armstrongs, Ltd.

FIG. 1.06.—SHRINKING A TUBE ON TO A BIG GUN.

by the propelling explosive. The inner tube of the gun can best resist these pressures if it is being strained inwards by the outer casing when the gun is fired, and, to attain this end, the outer tubes are shrunk on by contraction after heating. Figure 1.06 shows the hot outer casing of a 15-in. gun being lowered over the inner tube, which projects from a pit. Water sprayed down the bore of the inner tube keeps this cool while the outer tube is lowered, and the latter is then cooled from the bottom upwards by water sprays, causing it to grip the inner tube tightly and strain it inwards.

In the case of the gun shown in the picture, the outside diameter of the partially built gun was 31·039 in. at 15° C., and the internal diameter of the outer tube was 31·000 in. at the same temperature. The outer tube was heated to 400° C. in order to slip it on. Let us calculate its diameter at this temperature.

The coefficient of linear expansion of steel is 0·000011 per centigrade degree, which means that the length of a piece of it increases by 0·000011 of its length at 0° C. for each centigrade degree its temperature increases. If d is the diameter of the tube at 0° C., its circumference is $\pi.d$, so its circumference increases when it is heated from 15° C. to 400° C., by an amount :

$$\pi.d \times (400 - 15) \times 0·000011.$$

We have seen, however, that in calculating the expansion no appreciable error is caused, if, instead of using the length at 0° C., the length at any given temperature is used. Hence, instead of using the circumference $\pi.d$ we may use the circumference at 15° C. in our calculation, and the increase of length of the circumference is, therefore :

$$\pi \times 31·000 \times (400 - 15) \times 0·000011$$

∴ circumference at 400° C.

$$= (\pi \times 31·000) + \{\pi \times 31·000 \times (400 - 15) \times 0·000011\}$$

∴ diameter at 400° C.

$$= 31·000 + \{31·000 \times (400 - 15) \times 0·000011\}$$
$$= 31·131 \text{ inches.}$$

This diameter is nearly $\frac{1}{10}$ in. greater than that of the inner tube, over which the outer casing has to slip.

1.06. The rate at which the hands of a clock move is regulated by a *pendulum*, and a clock runs at a steady rate only if the pendulum continues to make the same number of swings in each hour. It is found, however, that a pendulum does so, only if a certain point in it, called the centre of oscillation, is always the same distance below the axis about which the pendulum swings. If the pendulum expands, the centre of oscillation is lowered, and the pendulum swings more slowly.

There are several methods by which a clock pendulum may be made to adjust itself when the temperature changes. Figure 1.07 shows the arrangement known as the gridiron pendulum. The unshaded rods are made of steel, and those shown black are of brass. The middle rod, which carries the pendulum bob B, passes through holes in the two lower horizontal bars, and is not attached to them. It will be seen that an expansion of the steel rods causes the distance between the point of suspension S and the bob to increase, while they are brought closer together by an expansion of the brass rods. The centre of oscillation is usually in or near the bob B, so if the relative lengths of the steel and brass rods are properly chosen, the distance of the centre of oscillation can be made to remain the same distance below S whatever the temperature may be.

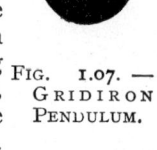

The coefficient of linear expansion of brass is 0·000019 per C. degree, and that of steel is 0·000011 per C. degree. That is to say, brass expands 0·000019 of its length at 0° C. for each degree its temperature is raised, and steel 0·000011 of its length at 0° C. Thus, if two rods of equal length are taken, one of brass and one of steel, and these are heated together, the brass expands $\frac{19}{11}$ times as much as the steel. If the steel rod is $\frac{19}{11}$ times as long as the brass, the expansions will be equal. Hence, in the gridiron pendulum the effective length of the steel rods should be $\frac{19}{11}$ times that of the brass rods.

FIG. 1.07. — GRIDIRON PENDULUM.

A more modern method of compensating a pendulum for the expansion caused by temperature changes is to make the rod R of the pendulum of invar, and the bob B of steel (figure 1.08). Invar is an alloy of steel and nickel, and has a very small coefficient of expansion. The bottom only of the bob is fastened to the rod passing through it, so that as the temperature increases the bob expands upwards, and compensates for the small expansion of the rod.

1.07. The rates of watches and some types of clocks are regulated by means of a balance wheel. This is a small wheel, which is caused to rotate backwards and forwards by a spring called a hair spring. If the wheel expands greater forces are required to turn it, and if the hair spring is of ordinary spring steel the watch will go more slowly. In many cases nowadays a special spring steel is used, and this exerts larger forces when the temperature increases, thus keeping the rate of the watch constant. In other cases a *compensated balance wheel* is used.

This is a wheel [figure 1.09(a)], the rim of which is made in two parts, each fastened at one point only. The inner and outer portions of the rim are made of different metals, and the outer expands more on heating, causing the wheel to change shape as shown in figure 1.09(b). Since the greater portion of the rim is now closer to the axle than before, the balance wheel is turned more easily, and this compensates for the smaller forces exerted by the hair spring.

FIG. 1.08.— INVAR PEN- DULUM WITH STEEL BOB.

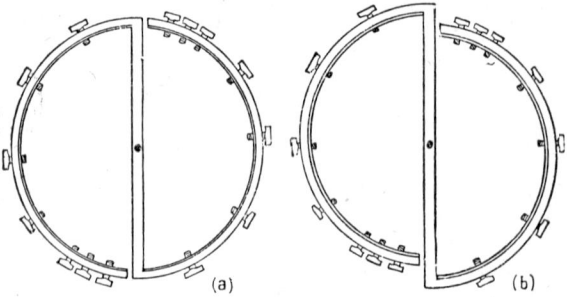

FIG. 1.09.—COMPENSATED BALANCE WHEEL.

1.08. The coefficient of linear expansion of a substance is

$$\frac{\text{the increase of length of a piece of it}}{\text{the length at } 0° \text{ C.} \times \text{ the rise of temperature}}.$$

Let a be the coefficient of linear expansion, l_0 be the length of the piece at $0°$ C., and l_t its length at $t°$ C.

The increase of length when the piece is heated from $0°$ C. to $t°$ C. is $l_t - l_0$

$$\therefore \ a = \frac{l_t - l_0}{l_0.t}$$

$$\therefore \ a.l_0.t = l_t - l_0.$$

$$\therefore \ l_t = l_0(1 + a.t).$$

This formula enables the length of a bar at any required temperature to be calculated from its length at $0°$ C. and the given temperature.

1.09. When a block of material such as glass is quickly heated, the temperature of the outer layers is raised more rapidly than that of the inner portions. Since the outer layers tend to expand more rapidly than the inner ones, strains are set up which may cause fracture of the block. If, however, a block of glass is *slowly* heated, so that the temperature of the whole block is raised at the same time, the block is not broken, because no strains are set up. The inner portion exerts no forces tending to prevent the outer layers expanding, and the outer layers expand as they would do if the block were hollow. Hence, *when a hollow vessel is heated and expands, the internal volume of the vessel increases, and the increase of volume is equal to that of a block of the same material as that of the walls, and of the same shape as the inside of the vessel.*

The coefficient of cubical expansion of a substance is

$$\frac{\text{the increase of volume of a piece of it}}{\text{the volume of the piece at } 0° \text{ C.} \times \text{the rise of temperature}}.$$

Let c be the coefficient of cubical expansion, V_0 the volume of the piece at $0°$ C., and V_t its volume at $t°$ C. The increase of volume when the piece is heated from $0°$ C. to $t°$ C. is $(V_t - V_0)$

$$\therefore \ c = \frac{V_t - V_0}{V_0.t}$$

$$\therefore \ c.V_0.t = V_t - V_0$$

$$\therefore \ V_t = V_0(1 + c.t).$$

This formula gives the volume at $t°$ C. in terms of the volume at $0°$ C. and the coefficient of cubical expansion, and as we have seen, it may be used to calculate the internal volume of a vessel, as well as the volume of a solid lump of material.

Let us consider the case of a measuring jar whose volume is

250 c.c. at 0° C., the jar being made of glass whose coefficient of cubical expansion is 0·0000255. The internal volume of the jar at 100° C. will be equal to the volume at 100° C. of a block of the glass whose volume at 0° C. is 250 c.c. Hence, we have :

$$V_t = V_0(1 + c.t)$$
$$= 250(1 + 0·0000255 \times 100)$$
$$\therefore V_t = 250·64 \text{ c.c.}$$

Although the volume increases by only 0·64 c.c., the expansion is important for many purposes, and it is necessary that coefficients of cubical expansion should be accurately determined to enable the volumes of vessels to be calculated at any given temperatures:

Coefficients of cubical expansion are difficult to measure. Fortunately, however, it is seldom necessary to measure the coefficient of cubical expansion of a substance, because it is easily calculated if the coefficient of linear expansion is known.

Consider any cube of the material, and let l_0 be its length at 0° C., and l_t its length at $t°$ C. The volume of this cube is l_0^3 at 0° C. and l_t^3 at $t°$ C. Using the same symbols as before, we have :

$$c = \frac{V_t - V_0}{V_0.t}$$
$$\therefore c = \frac{l_t^3 - l_0^3}{l_0^3.t}.$$

But,
$$l_t = l_0(1 + at)$$
$$\therefore c = \frac{l_0^3(1 + at)^3 - l_0^3}{l_0^3.t}$$
$$= \frac{(1 + at)^3 - 1}{t}$$
$$= \frac{3at + 3a^2t^2 + a^3t^3}{t}$$
$$\therefore c = 3a + 3a^2t + a^3t^2.$$

a is very small, and usually equal to 0·00002 or less, so a^2 is about 0·0000000004 or less, and a^3 is still smaller. Hence, the terms $3a^2t$ and a^3t^2 are so small that we need not take them into account.

$$\therefore c = 3a, \text{ very nearly.}$$

In words : **The coefficient of cubical expansion of a substance is three times its coefficient of linear expansion.**

1.10. Since most of the vessels used in the laboratory are made of glass, it is of particular importance that the coefficient of cubical expansion of glass should be accurately known. Unfortunately, however, glass happens to be one of the few substances whose coefficient of expansion can *not* be accurately calculated from its coefficient of linear expansion.

There are many varieties of glass and each has its own coefficient of linear expansion, so in calculating how much a given vessel will expand it is necessary to know the composition of the glass of which it is made. Even then, however, the difficulty is not entirely overcome, for the amount by which the given vessel expands depends also to a certain extent upon its previous heat treatment, and no two pieces of glass expand by exactly equal amounts. The best way of surmounting the difficulty is to use a silica vessel when great accuracy is required. The coefficient of cubical expansion of silica is known with sufficient accuracy. Silica vessels are still comparatively expensive, however. We shall see in a later chapter how the expansion of a glass vessel may be taken into account.

EXAMPLES 1

1. Calculate what gap should be allowed between successive lengths of rail on a railway line where 40-foot lengths are being laid when the temperature is 15° C. The maximum temperature to be allowed for is 70° C., and the coefficient of expansion of steel is 0·000011 per degree C.

2. How wide will be the gaps between the rails in the previous question on a day when the temperature is − 10° C. ?

3. Using the data given on page 10, calculate the temperature of the outer casing of the gun when this first fits tightly on the inner lining, assuming the latter to be maintained at a temperature of 100° C. by means of water sprays.

4. A steel tyre is to be slipped over the wheel of a locomotive. If the diameter of the wheel is 2 metres, and the tyre is to fit tightly when it is 100° C. hotter than the wheel, calculate the internal diameter of the tyre. [Coefficient of linear expansion of steel = 0·000011 per degree C.]

5. A steel ruler is exactly 12 in. in length at 20° C. Calculate its length at 0° C. Using this value, calculate its length at 100° C., and show that no appreciable error would be caused if its expansion between 20° C. and 100° C. had been calculated by means of the formula :

expansion = length at 20° C. × increase of temperature
× coefficient of linear expansion.

6. A glass vessel has a volume 200·00 c.c. at 0° C. Calculate its volume at 80° C., assuming the coefficient of linear expansion of the glass to be 0·0000085 per degree C. Explain why a knowledge of the coefficient of cubical expansion of glass enables the increase of volume of the vessel to be calculated.

7. A silica vessel has a volume of 200·000 c.c. at 0° C. Calculate its volume at 100° C. [The coefficient of linear expansion of silica is 0·0000005 per degree C.] If the coefficient of linear expansion of silica were assumed to be 10% larger, what percentage error would be caused in the result ?

SCHOOL CERTIFICATE QUESTIONS

The following abbreviations for the sources of School Certificate Questions are used throughout the book :

B	.	.	. University of Bristol.
C	.	°	. University of Cambridge Local Examinations Syndicate.
J	.	.	. Joint Matriculation Board of the Universities of Manchester, Liverpool, Leeds, Sheffield, and Birmingham.
L	.	.	. University of London.
O	°	.	. Oxford Local Examinations.
O.C	.	.	. Oxford and Cambridge Schools Examinations Board.

8. Explain what is meant by *the coefficient of linear expansion of a solid*. A rod of metal is 100 cm. long at 40° C. ; the coefficient of linear expansion of the metal is 0·000025 per degree C. Find the length of the rod at 100° C. correct to two places of decimals.

Why is it necessary to compensate clock pendulums ? Explain how it is done. (O)

9. Describe a method of measuring the coefficient of linear expansion of a metal. Find the ratio of the lengths of two rods of different metals A and B at 0° C., if the difference of their lengths is the same at all temperatures. The coefficients of linear expansion of A and B may be taken as 0·00002 per degree C. and 0·00004 per degree C. respectively. (C)

10. Define *coefficient of linear expansion* of a solid, and describe how you would obtain its value for a given metal bar. If the graduation on a brass scale is correct at 0° C., what would be the true length of an object that was read by the scale at 25° C. as 30·15 in. ? [Coefficient of linear expansion of brass = 0·000018 per degree C.] (L)

11. How would you measure the coefficient of linear expansion of a metal rod ? A steel tyre has a diameter of 99·7 cm. at 15° C. To what temperature must it be raised to enable it to be put on to a wheel 100 cm. in diameter ? [Coefficient of linear expansion of steel = 0·000012 per degree C.] (O.C.)

CHAPTER 2

THE EXPANSION OF GASES

2.01 When solids are heated, the actual amount of expansion they undergo is small; gases, however, such as air, coal-gas, oxygen and hydrogen, expand considerably on heating.

To prove this, we may use the apparatus shown in figure 2.01. A flask containing air or some other gas is fitted with a rubber stopper and a glass delivery tube which dips below the surface of some coloured water in a beaker. On heating the flask, bubbles of gas escape through the liquid in the beaker. When the flask is allowed to cool, the gas which remains in it contracts, and water is forced up the tube into the flask by the pressure of the atmosphere acting upon the liquid in the beaker.

When the flask is quite cool it may be removed from the beaker, and some coloured water then remains in the delivery tube. This can be forced into the flask by blowing with the mouth. In this case the gas in the flask is caused to contract, not because it is cooled, but merely because of the extra pressure exerted on it. It is therefore obvious that when we study the expansion caused by heating a gas, care must be taken to ensure that the pressure on it remains the same throughout our experiments; otherwise we shall be unable to decide what fraction of the volume changes are caused by heating, and what by changes of pressure.

FIG. 2.01

In the present chapter we shall study the changes of the volume of gases, (a) when the temperature is kept the same while the volume is altered, and (b) when the pressure is kept the same while the temperature is altered. We shall also have to discover, (c), how the pressure changes when the volume is kept the same and the temperature is altered.

2.02. The relation between the pressure and volume of a given

17

mass of gas, kept at constant temperature, may be investigated by means of the apparatus shown in figure 2.02.

Two glass tubes T_1 and T_2 are connected at their lower ends by a length of rubber tubing containing mercury. T_2 is closed at the top, and contains the gas whose pressure and volume are to be measured. T_1 is open to the atmosphere. The temperature of the gas in T_2 remains constant at the temperature of the room.

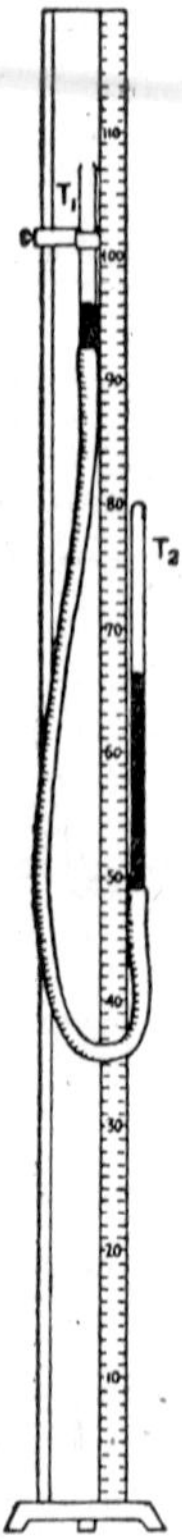

The pressure of this gas is altered by sliding the tube T_1 up or down the scale. The pressure on the surface of the mercury in the open tube is atmospheric pressure, and by adding the barometric reading to the scale reading of the mercury surface in the open tube, we obtain the reading of the mercury column which would exert a pressure equal to that exerted by the atmosphere together with the mercury on the left-hand side. To obtain the pressure on the gas in the closed tube, the scale reading of the mercury surface in this tube must be subtracted from the above value.

As the unit of volume, for measuring the volume of the gas in the closed tube, we use the volume of one centimetre length of the tube. In these units the volume is equal to the number of units of length of the closed tube occupied by the gas.

The results of an experiment with this apparatus are given on the opposite page.

From columns IV and V it is seen that the volume increases as the pressure decreases. Moreover, referring to lines 1 and 6 of the table, we see that when the volume is doubled the pressure is halved, so the product of pressure and volume remains the same. In column VI the products of pressure and volume are given, and it will be seen that, allowing for the small errors of measurement, these products are equal. This is true whatever gas is used in the closed limb of the apparatus.

FIG. 2.02.

This fact was discovered about the year 1660 by the Hon. Robert Boyle (1627–1691), and is known as **Boyle's Law.** The full statement of the law is:

The product of the pressure and the volume of a given mass of gas is constant if its temperature is kept constant.

Gas enclosed in T_2 dry air
Barometer reading $= 75\cdot8$ cm.
Top of closed tube remains at $70\cdot0$ cm.

I Mercury in Open Tube (cm.).	II Mercury in Closed Tube (cm.).	III Total height on Open Side = Barometer$+$I (cm.).	IV Pressure in cm. of Mercury.	V Volume.	VI $p \times v$.
87·7	59·6	163·5	103·9	10·4	1081
75·1	58·3	150·9	92·6	11·7	1083
62·8	56·8	138·6	81·8	13·2	1080
50·9	55·0	126·7	71·7	15·0	1083
38·0	52·4	113·8	61·6	17·6	1084
25·9	49·4	101·7	52·3	20·6	1077
14·0	45·6	89·8	44·2	24·4	1079
02·2	40·8	78·0	37·2	29·2	1086

When two quantities change in such a way that their product remains the same, the first quantity is said to *vary inversely* as the second. Hence, Boyle's Law may also be stated:

The volume of a given mass of gas varies inversely as its pressure if the temperature is constant.

Figure 2.03 is the graph obtained by plotting the volume of the gas in the above experiment against its pressure. A curved line on a graph is not so useful as a straight-line graph, where one point can be used to check another. When one quantity varies inversely as a second, the graph obtained by plotting one quantity against the reciprocal of the second is always a straight line passing through the origin. Figure 2.04 is the graph obtained by plotting volume against $\dfrac{\text{I}}{\text{pressure}}$.

2.03. Figure 2.05 (page 22) shows a piece of apparatus for measuring the expansion of a gas at constant pressure. A certain mass of gas is shut off in the bulb A by strong sulphuric acid poured into the limb B of the glass U-tube, and the volume of this gas can be measured by means of a scale on the tube C. The water which surrounds the gas can be heated by passing steam from a steam boiler through the inverted brass U-tube DD', which passes through holes in the rubber stopper E.

The pressure of the gas in A is adjusted before each reading to be equal to the pressure of the atmosphere, and thus always

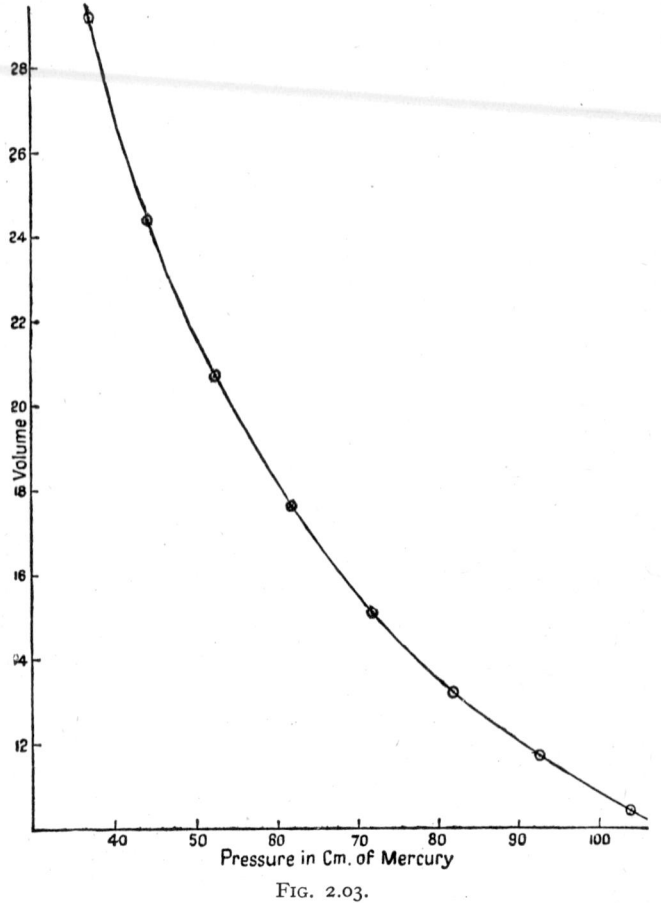

FIG. 2.03.

has the same value when a reading is taken. The adjustment is effected by running out sulphuric acid through the tap H until the acid stands at the same level in each limb of the

U-tube. Sulphuric acid is used in preference to any other liquid, because :

(*a*) It is less dense than mercury, so that a small error in the

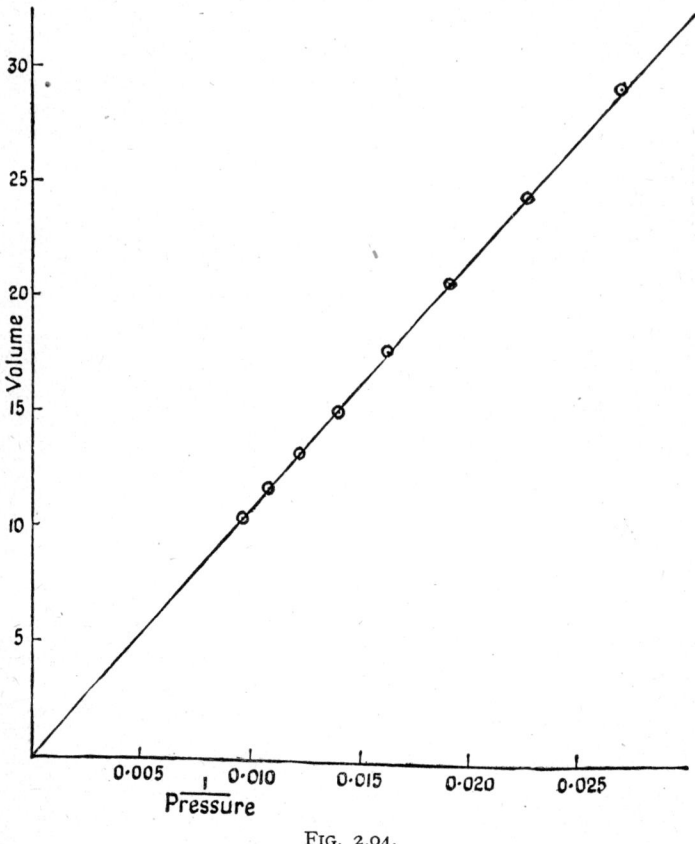

FIG. 2.04.

adjustment of the levels makes little difference to the pressure of the gas.

(*b*) It keeps the gas dry. Traces of moisture would cause large errors.

(c) Water and most other liquids would give off large quantities of steam or other vapour, and this would depress the liquid in C. Sulphuric acid gives off little vapour at the temperatures concerned.

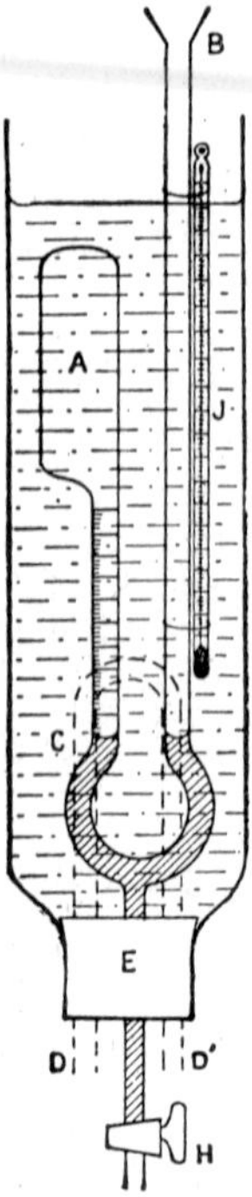

FIG. 2.05.

The procedure in taking a reading is as follows : The Bunsen burner is removed from the steam boiler, and the water is stirred vigorously with a stirrer. The levels of the sulphuric acid are adjusted, and the volume of the gas and its temperature are read.

The following table shows a set of readings obtained with this apparatus, and figure 2.06 is the graph obtained by plotting volume against temperature.

Temperature. (Degrees Centigrade).	Volume. (c.c.).
19·1	30·70
27·9	31·65
37·0	32·60
45·2	33·47
53·1	34·30
61·9	35·20
68·0	35·85
76·6	36·70

The graph is a straight line, and this shows that the volume of the gas increases by the same amount for each degree its temperature is raised. When the temperature increases from 0° C. to 70° C. the volume increases from 28·70 to 36·08 c.c. Hence, when the pressure of the gas is kept constant its coefficient of cubical expansion c is:

$$c = \frac{36\cdot08 - 28\cdot70}{28\cdot70 \times 70}$$

$\therefore c = 0\cdot00367$, or $\frac{1}{273}$ per ° C.

In view of the fact that each solid material has its own

coefficient of cubical expansion, and that the coefficient is different for different substances, it might be expected that the same would be true of gases. It is a remarkable fact, however, that experi-

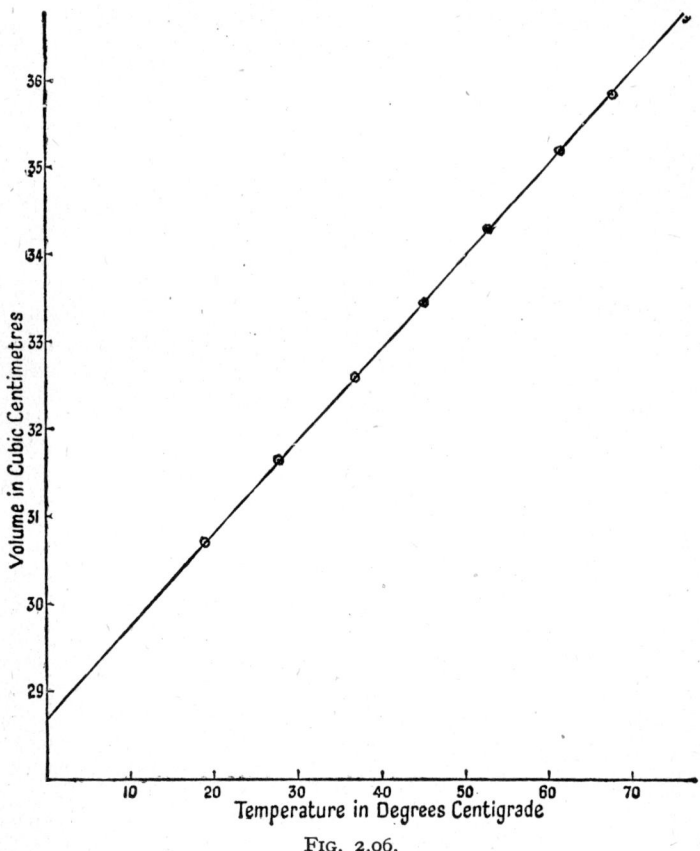

FIG. 2.06.

ment shows that all gases have the *same* coefficient of expansion. Hence, the following statement, known as **Charles's Law** (after the French scientist, J. A. C. Charles, 1746–1823), is true of any gas :

The volume of a given mass of gas increases by $\frac{1}{273}$ of its volume at 0°C. for each centigrade degree its temperature increases, provided its pressure remains constant.

2.04. We have now to investigate the changes of pressure of a gas whose volume is kept constant while its temperature is changed, and figure 2.07 shows a piece of apparatus suitable for this purpose.

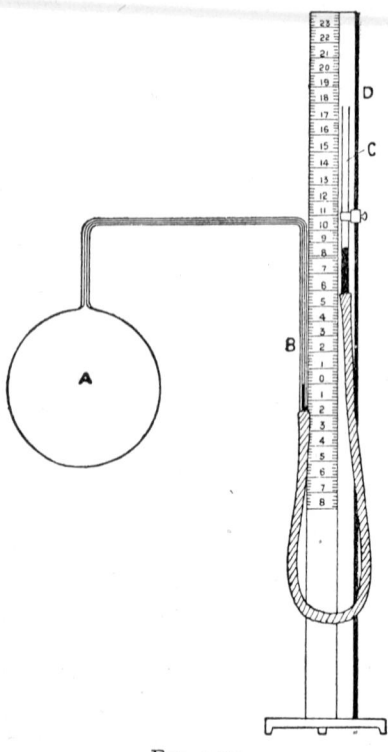

Fig. 2.07

The gas is contained in the large bulb A, and is shut off by mercury in the rubber tube connecting the capillary tube B with the tube C. The volume of this gas is kept the same throughout the experiment by sliding the tube C up or down the rod D until the mercury in B stands at the zero mark on the scale. As in the case of the Boyle's Law apparatus, the pressure of the gas is obtained by adding the barometer reading to the scale reading opposite the mercury surface in the tube C, and subtracting the scale reading opposite the mercury surface in B.

To perform the experiment, the bulb A is placed in a saucepan of water standing on a tripod, and this water is heated with a Bunsen burner. At suitable temperature intervals the burner is removed, the water is stirred, the mercury in B is brought back to the zero mark, and the temperature and pressure are noted.

The large bulb A and the narrow capillary B are essential parts of the apparatus. We should heat the whole of the gas contained in A and B, but since it is difficult to do so, it is arranged that as large a fraction of the gas as possible is contained in A where it can be heated, and as little as possible is in B where it cannot be heated.

Figure 2.08 is the graph obtained by plotting the pressures of the gas against the corresponding temperatures. The fact that the graph is a straight line shows that the pressure increases

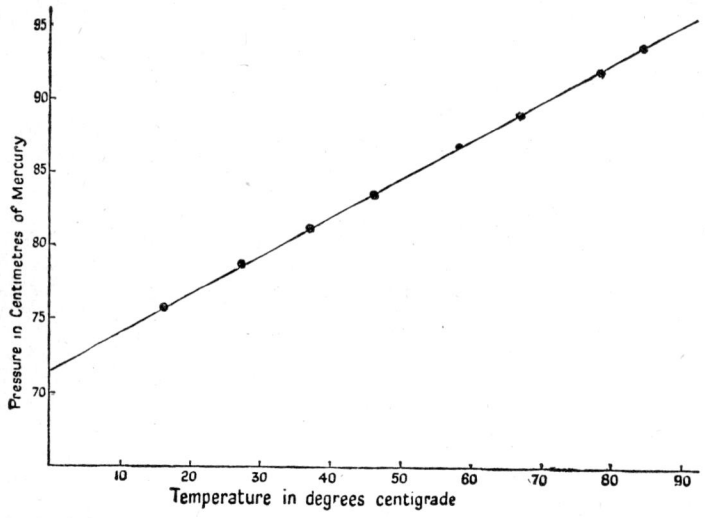

FIG. 2.08.

by the same amount for each degree rise of temperature. Let us calculate by what fraction of its pressure at $0°$ C. the pressure of the gas increases for a rise of temperature of one degree. From the graph the pressure is found to be 71.50 cm. of mercury when the gas is at $0°$ C., and 92.50 cm. when it is at $80°$ C. Hence :

$$\frac{\text{increase of pressure of the gas}}{\text{its pressure at } 0° \text{ C.} \times \text{rise of temperature}}$$

$$= \frac{92.50 - 71.50}{71.50 \times 80}$$

$$= 0.00367, \text{ or } \tfrac{1}{273} \text{ per C.}°$$

This figure is the same as that found for the coefficient of cubical expansion of a gas kept at constant pressure, and it is not difficult to guess that the above fraction has the same value for all gases. Hence :

The pressure of a given mass of gas increases by $\frac{1}{273}$ of its pressure at 0° C. for each centigrade degree its temperature is raised, provided its volume remains constant. This law is known as the **law of pressures**.

2.05. Let us suppose that a given mass of gas has a volume V_0 at 0° C., and V_1 at t_1° C. If its pressure does not alter, its volume increases by $\frac{1}{273}$ of V_0 for each degree centigrade its temperature is raised.

$$\therefore V_1 = \text{(volume at 0° C.)} + \text{(increase of volume)}$$
$$= V_0 + \frac{V_0 t_1}{273}$$
$$\therefore V_1 = \frac{V_0(273 + t_1)}{273}.$$

Similarly, if V_2 is the volume of the same gas at t_2° C., and its pressure is still the same,

$$V_2 = \frac{V_0(273 + t_2)}{273}$$
$$\therefore \frac{V_1}{V_2} = \frac{V_0(273 + t_1)}{273} \times \frac{273}{V_0(273 + t_2)}$$
$$\therefore \frac{V_1}{V_2} = \frac{273 + t_1}{273 + t_2}.$$

Hence, the ratio of the two volumes at temperatures t_1° C. and t_2° C. is equal to the ratio of the two numbers $(273 + t_1)$ and $(273 + t_2)$.

Although the thermometers used in the laboratory are usually marked in degrees centigrade, the numbers marked on the stem might equally well have been called 273 degrees, 274 degrees, etc., instead of 0° centigrade, 1° centigrade, and so on. Indeed, there is no reason why both sets of numbers should not be marked on a single thermometer. If a thermometer were graduated in this way we should say that it was graduated in degrees of the *absolute* scale of temperature, or in degrees absolute, as well as in degrees centigrade. If the mercury stands at the division marked t_1° C. on such a thermometer, its reading on the absolute scale will be $(t_1 + 273)$° Abs. That is to say, the thermometer reads T_1 on the absolute scale, where $T_1 = (t_1 + 273)$. Similarly, when the mercury stands at the division marked $t_2°$ C. it will be opposite the division $(t_2 + 273)$ on the absolute scale, and if this is called $T_2°$ Abs., we have: $T_2 = (t_2 + 273)$.

But,
$$\frac{V_1}{V_2} = \frac{273 + t_1}{273 + t_2}$$
$$\therefore \frac{V_1}{V_2} = \frac{T_1}{T_2}$$

In other words, **when a given mass of gas is kept at constant pressure, the ratio of its volumes at any two temperatures is equal to the ratio of the two temperatures, if these are measured on the absolute scale of temperature.**

2.06. The pressure of a given mass of gas whose volume is kept the same increases by $\frac{1}{273}$ of its pressure at $0°$ C. for each degree centigrade its temperature is raised. Let P_0 be the pressure of the gas at $0°$ C., and P_1 its pressure at $t_1°$ C. Then,

$$P_1 = \text{(pressure at } 0° \text{ C.)} + \text{(increase of pressure)}$$
$$= P_0 + \frac{P_0 t_1}{273}$$
$$\therefore P_1 = \frac{P_0(273 + t_1)}{273}.$$

Similarly, if P_2 is its pressure at $t_2°$ **C.,**

$$P_2 = \frac{P_0(273 + t_2)}{273}$$
$$\therefore \frac{P_1}{P_2} = \frac{P_0(273 + t_1)}{273} \times \frac{273}{P_0(273 + t_2)}$$
$$\therefore \frac{P_1}{P_2} = \frac{273 + t_1}{273 + t_2}.$$

But $(273 + t_1)$ is the temperature T_1 measured on the absolute scale of temperature, and $(273 + t_2)$ is the reading T_2 on the absolute scale, corresponding to t_2 on the centigrade scale.

$$\therefore \frac{P_1}{P_2} = \frac{T_1}{T_2}$$

In other words, **the ratio of the pressures of a given mass of gas, kept at constant volume, is equal to the ratio of the corresponding temperatures, if these are measured on the absolute scale of temperature.**

2.07. The temperature 0° C. corresponds to the temperature 273 degrees on the absolute scale. A temperature of − 1° C. corresponds to 272° Abs., − 2° C. corresponds to 271° Abs., and so on. A temperature of − 273° C. would therefore correspond to (273 − 273), or 0° Abs. Let V_1 be the volume of a given mass of gas at t_1° C. [*i.e.* at $(273 + t_1)$° Abs.], and let V_2 be the volume of the same gas measured at the same pressure and at − 273° C. [*i.e.* at 0° Abs.]

Since the ratio of the two volumes is equal to the ratio of the absolute temperatures, we have :

$$\frac{V_2}{V_1} = \frac{0}{273 + t_1}$$

$$\therefore \; V_2 = \frac{V_1 \times 0}{273 + t_1} = 0.$$

Hence, if a gas continued to change its volume in accordance with Charles's Law until its temperature was reduced to − 273° C. or 0° Abs. its volume would become zero. At any temperature lower than this, its volume would be less than zero ! Since it is impossible to imagine a gas occupying less than zero volume, we must conclude that :

   (*a*) Charles's Law is not obeyed at these low temperatures
      or,
   (*b*) it is impossible to obtain a temperature lower than − 273° C.

As a matter of fact no gas does obey Charles's Law at these very low temperatures, because all gases are converted into liquids or solids before the temperature of − 273° C. is reached. Nevertheless, a number of different facts have convinced scientists that it is impossible to produce a temperature lower than − 273° C. This temperature is accordingly known as the *absolute zero of temperature*. In recent years scientists have succeeded in cooling objects until their temperatures were only a few hundredths of a degree above the absolute zero, but the absolute zero never has been, and probably never can be, reached.

2.08. As examples on the use of the gas laws we may take the following problems :

   (1) *One gram of hydrogen gas occupies a volume of* 11,660 *c.c. at* 15° *C. and a pressure of* 750 *mm. of mercury. What is its volume at* 100° *C. and* 600 *mm. pressure ?*

The new pressure is 600 mm., and the initial pressure was

750 mm. By Boyle's Law, if the temperature had remained at 15° C.,

$$600 \times \text{new volume} = 750 \times \text{initial volume}$$

$$\therefore \text{ new volume, } v_1 = \left(\frac{750}{600} \times 11{,}660\right) \text{ c.c.}$$

The new absolute temperature, however, is $\left(\dfrac{273 + 100}{273 + 15}\right)$ times the old. Hence, by Charles's Law, the volume becomes $\frac{373}{288}$ times the volume v_1 given above.

$\therefore$ the volume of the gas at 100° C. and 600 mm. pressure will be :

$$\frac{750 \times 11{,}660}{600} \times \frac{373}{288}$$
$$= 18{,}880 \text{ c.c.}$$

(2) *A balloon is filled with gas at 15° C. and a pressure of 75 cm. of mercury. Assuming the pressure in the balloon is kept equal to that of the air outside, find what fraction of the gas has escaped when the balloon reaches a point where the pressure is 30 cm. of mercury and the temperature is — 20° C.*

Let V be the volume of the balloon.

If the pressure is changed from 75 to 30 cm. of mercury, keeping the temperature the same, the gas will occupy a volume v, where,

$$30 \times v = 75 \times V \text{ (Boyle's Law)}$$
$$\therefore v = \frac{75 \times V}{30}$$

If the temperature changes from 15° C. to — 20° C., the new absolute temperature is $\left(\dfrac{273 - 20}{273 + 15}\right)$ times the old. Hence, by Charles's Law, the volume becomes $\frac{253}{288}$ times the volume v given above.

$$\therefore \text{ new volume} = \frac{75 \times V}{30} \times \frac{253}{288} = 2 \cdot 20 V$$

The volume of the balloon is V, and the gas occupies a volume $2 \cdot 20 V$. Hence, a volume of gas $1 \cdot 20 V$ escapes, and this is a fraction $\dfrac{1 \cdot 20 V}{2 \cdot 20 V} = \frac{6}{11}$ths of the total quantity of gas.

(3) *A quantity of air at 17° C. and a pressure of 15 lb. per square inch is suddenly compressed to $\frac{1}{6}$ of its initial volume, and*

its pressure is then found to be 180 *lb. per square inch.   Find the final temperature of the gas.*

Let this temperature be $T_1°$ Abs., and let the initial volume of the gas be V_1.   If the temperature of the gas were unchanged during the compression, its pressure p would be given by:

$$p \times \frac{V_1}{6} = 15 \times V_1$$

$$\therefore p = 90 \text{ lb. per square inch.}$$

According to the law of pressures, the ratio of the pressures of a gas kept at constant volume is equal to the ratio of its absolute temperatures.   These are $(273 + 17)°$ Abs. and $T_1°$ Abs., so, if the pressure changes from 90 to 180 lb. per square inch, we have:

$$\frac{T_1}{(273 + 17)} = \frac{180}{90}$$

$$\therefore T_1 = 580° \text{ Abs.}$$

Hence the final temperature of the air is $(580 - 273) = 307° C.$

2.09. Let P_1 be the pressure, and V_1 the volume, of a given mass of gas whose temperature, measured in degrees absolute, is T_1, and suppose that its pressure is changed to p while the temperature is kept constant.   If V_2 is its new volume, we have, by Boyle's Law:

$$P_1 V_1 = p V_2.$$

Let us suppose that the gas is now heated at constant volume to the temperature $T_2°$ Abs.   According to the law of pressures, its pressure P_2 will then be given by the equation:

$$\frac{P_2}{p} = \frac{T_2}{T_1}$$

$$\therefore p = \frac{P_2 T_1}{T_2}$$

Substituting this value for p in the previous equation, we have:

$$P_1 V_1 = \frac{P_2 . T_1 . V_2}{T_2}$$

$$\therefore \frac{P_1 V_1}{T_1} = \frac{P_2 V_2}{T_2}.$$

The quantity $\frac{P_1 V_1}{T_1}$ will have a definite value for the given mass of gas chosen. Call its value R. The above equation shows that, however the pressure, volume, and temperature of the gas are altered, the fraction, $\dfrac{\text{pressure} \times \text{volume}}{\text{absolute temperature}}$, is equal to R, a constant. Hence, if P represents the pressure, V the corresponding volume, and T the corresponding absolute temperature of a given mass of gas, then, whatever changes may occur in the pressure, volume, and temperature of the gas,

$$\frac{PV}{T} = R, \text{ or}$$

$$PV = RT.$$

This equation is equivalent to those which embody Boyle's Law, Charles's Law, and the law of pressures, and may be used instead of these in calculations involving the gas laws. We shall use it to confirm the result obtained in example (3) above.

The initial pressure, volume, and absolute temperature were 15 lb. per square inch, V_1, and 290° Abs.

$$\frac{PV}{T} = R$$

$$\therefore \frac{15 V_1}{290} = R.$$

The final pressure, volume, and absolute temperature were 180 lb. per square inch, $\dfrac{V_1}{6}$, and T_1.

$$\therefore \frac{180 \times \dfrac{V_1}{6}}{T_1} = R$$

$$\therefore \frac{15 V_1}{290} = \frac{180 \times \dfrac{V_1}{6}}{T_1}$$

$$\therefore T_1 = 580° \text{ Abs}, \text{ which agrees with the previous result.}$$

EXAMPLES 2

1. One cubic foot of oxygen at 120 atmospheres pressure is allowed to expand until it is at atmospheric pressure. Assuming its temperature to be unchanged, what is then its volume?

2. A mass of air which occupies 1000 c.c. at 20° C. is heated to 100° C., the pressure being kept constant. Find the final volume.

3. The air in a bicycle tyre is at a pressure of 25 lb. per square inch at 10° C. What will be its pressure at 20° C., if the volume of the tyre remains unaltered ?

4. 1000 c.c. of air at 100° C. are heated at constant pressure to 150° C. Find the new volume of the air. What result would be obtained if the final volume of the air were calculated by means of the equation : expansion = volume at 100° C. × coefficient of expansion × rise of temperature ? Explain why this method of calculation is *not* applicable when dealing with gases.

5. The volume of 1 gm. of nitrogen at 20° C. and a pressure of 76 cm. of mercury is 860 c.c. What volume would it occupy at 57 cm. pressure and 500° C. ?

6. One end of a piece of capillary tubing is closed, the other end is open, and a thread of mercury 10 cm. in length is introduced into the open end, trapping some air in the capillary tube. The tube is held vertically with the open end downwards and a mark is made on the tube at the junction of the air and mercury columns. The tube is now inverted and heated. At what temperature will the air column again reach the mark ? Room temperature = 17° C. ; the barometric pressure is 75 cm. of mercury.

At what temperature would the length of the air column be increased by 20% ?

School Certificate Questions

7. State Boyle's Law, and describe how it may be verified experimentally. The mercury in a barometer tube stands at 75 cm. and the space above it is 5 cm. in length. 3 c.c. of air at atmospheric pressure are admitted to the tube, and the mercury falls 15 cm. Find the area of cross-section of the tube.   (B)

8. An airtight vessel of constant internal volume V cu. in. is connected with a pump. Initially the vessel is filled with air at a pressure of 31 in. of mercury. When 12 cu. in. of air at atmospheric pressure have been pumped into the vessel the pressure inside rises to 33 in. of mercury. Find V. If 12 cu. in. of the air inside the vessel are now pumped out, find the pressure of the remainder. [Take atmospheric pressure as equal to 30 in. of mercury.]   (B)

9. Describe with the aid of a diagram an experiment which you would carry out to find the relation between the volume of a given body of gas and its temperature, the pressure being kept constant throughout the experiment. Give a graph showing the results you would expect to get in such an experiment, and state the conclusions which can be drawn from these results.   (O)

10. What is meant by the statement that *the coefficient of increase* *of pressure of a gas at constant volume is* $\frac{1}{273}$ *per degree* C.? The mercury in a barometer stands at 76 cm. and the space above the mercury is 7 cm. long. A quantity of dry air at 15° C. is introduced at the top and depresses the mercury 2 cm. What is the pressure exerted by this air? To what temperature must this air then be raised in order to depress the mercury another $\frac{1}{2}$ cm.?   (J)

11. State *Charles's Law* for the expansion of a gas. How would you test the truth of this law by experiment?

The weight of a litre of air at 0° C. under a pressure of 76 cm. of mercury is 1·29 gm. What does a litre of air weigh at 800° C. under a pressure of 19 cm. of mercury?   (J)

12. State the laws which are found to hold for the relations between the pressure, volume, and temperature of a given mass of gas. Air is pumped into a motor tyre until the pressure is 80 lb. wt. per square inch. The air is then at a temperature of 17° C. Later in the day the temperature of the air in the tyre rises to 57° C. Assuming the tube does not stretch, what will then be the pressure?   (O.C)

13. How does the volume of a given mass of gas vary when its pressure and temperature are simultaneously changed? A man requires to breathe the same mass of air per minute at the top of a mountain as at the foot. The respective pressures and temperatures are 72 cm. and 17° C. at the foot, and 48 cm. and 2° C. at the top. If he breathes 15 times per minute at the foot, how often must he breathe per minute at the top, assuming that he always fills his lungs to the same extent?   (O.C)

14. State the relation connecting the pressure, volume, and temperature of a given mass of gas. A mass of air at 15° C. and at a pressure of 63 cm. of mercury occupies 25 c.c. On raising the pressure to 80 cm. the volume occupied is found to be 21 c.c. What is now the temperature of the air?   (L)

C

CHAPTER 3

THERMOMETERS

3.01. The expansion of liquids may be demonstrated by means of the apparatus shown in figure 3.01. Two similar flasks are fitted with lengths of glass capillary tubing passing through rubber stoppers. The capillary tubing is cut from a single length, so that the diameters of the capillaries are equal. The flasks are filled with water and methylated spirit, and placed in a vessel containing water. As this water is heated, the liquids in the flasks expand, and the levels in the capillary tubes rise. Two facts are shown by the experiment. *Liquids*, unlike gases, *do not all expand by equal amounts*, and *the expansion of a liquid is much smaller than that of a gas.*

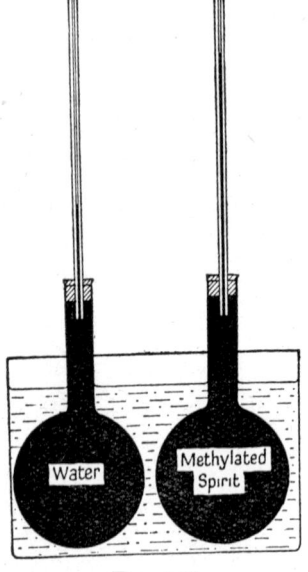

FIG. 3.01.

A further instructive experiment may be performed with the same apparatus. One of the flasks is removed, and held for an instant over a Bunsen flame. Instead of rising, the level of the liquid in the capillary tube first sinks. It then rises slowly until its level is higher than it was initially. A little thought will show why this happens. The heat from the Bunsen flame first raises the temperature of the glass, and causes the flask to expand. Since the flask can now contain more liquid, the liquid surface falls. As the heat passes to the liquid, however, and raises its temperature, the liquid expands sufficiently to fill the extra space in the flask, and some of the capillary as well. If the liquid happened to expand by the same amount as the flask, its level would be the same before and after the temperature had been raised. We have, therefore, to distinguish between the *apparent expansion* of a liquid and its *real expansion*. *The liquid really expands by an amount equal to that by which it appears to expand, plus the expansion of the vessel.*

It is, of course, true that when a gas expands, what is observed is the apparent, and not the real expansion of the gas. Gases expand by such large amounts, however, that the expansion of the containing vessel need be taken into account only for extremely accurate work. With liquids, on the other hand, the apparent expansion is considerably smaller than the real expansion.

3.02. We have now to describe the construction and calibration of a mercury thermometer.

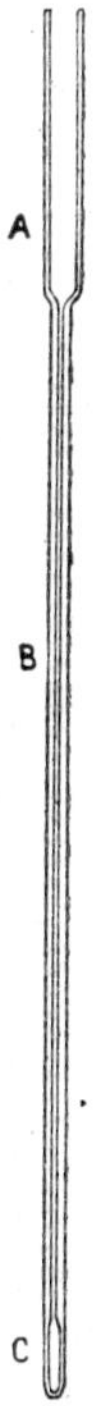

By melting the glass at the end of a capillary tube of very fine bore, a bulb is blown on the end of the tube. A tube of wider bore is then sealed to the other end of the capillary as shown in figure 3.02. A little mercury is now poured into the tube A. Although mercury is a heavy liquid, it is unable to force its way down into the bulb C, because the bulb is full of air, and this air is unable to escape through the capillary tube at the same time that the mercury passes down it. However, by heating the bulb, the air is caused to expand, and some of it is forced out, and escapes by bubbling through the mercury. The bulb then contains less air than before, and if it is allowed to cool, some of the mercury in A is able to force its way down the tube B, and into the bulb. By repeatedly heating and cooling it, the bulb can be almost entirely filled with mercury.

FIG. 3.02.—
MAKING A
THERMO-
METER.

A small bubble of air always remains, however. This is driven out by boiling the mercury in the bulb. As the mercury boils, its vapour, escaping through the capillary, carries away with it the last traces of air. When the bulb is again allowed to cool, mercury fills the bulb, the capillary tube, and the lower part of the tube A.

It is now necessary to seal off the top of the thermometer to prevent dust getting into the instrument, but this must be done in such a way that the correct amount of mercury is left in the thermometer. This will depend upon the uses to which the thermometer is afterwards to be put, but it can usually be done as follows.

The excess mercury in the tube A is poured out while the bulb is hot, and the bulb is then allowed to cool, and is placed in a vessel containing ice. If the thread of mercury then stands only a short distance above the bulb, the thermometer is ready for sealing off. If the mercury stands more than a centimetre or two above the bulb the latter must be reheated, and more mercury poured out until the thread stands at the required point when the bulb is surrounded by melting ice. The bulb is now heated until the mercury fills the entire stem. The glass is melted at the point where the tube A joins B, and the thermometer is sealed off while the mercury completely fills the bulb and tube. In this way, all the air is forced out of the instrument, and a vacuum is left when the mercury is again allowed to contract.

3.03. It is not possible to graduate thermometers by marking the stems in tenths of an inch or in millimetres, because the readings would then depend on the relative sizes of the bulbs and stems of various thermometers, and upon the amount of mercury contained in each.

To obtain thermometers whose readings agree with one another at all temperatures, it is necessary that the readings should be made to agree at two temperatures. The two temperatures chosen are known as the two fixed points. **The lower fixed point is the temperature of pure melting ice. The upper fixed point is the temperature of the steam from pure water boiling under a barometric pressure of 76 cm. of mercury.** The lower fixed point is called o degrees centigrade; the upper fixed point, 100 degrees centigrade. These numbers have not been discovered by experiment or calculation. Physicists have merely agreed to call these temperatures o° C. and 100° C. respectively.

The thermometer whose construction was described in the previous section might now have the fixed points marked, but if it is to be reliable, it should first be left for some weeks so that the glass bulb may contract to nearly its final volume. Glass continues to contract for a long time after being strongly heated, and contraction of the bulb will drive the mercury farther up the stem.

In order to calibrate it, the thermometer is first placed in melting ice in a vacuum flask (a thermos flask) as shown in figure 3.03, care being taken that the bulb is some distance from the sides, and that almost the whole of the mercury in the stem is surrounded by ice. A vacuum flask almost entirely prevents heat from the warmer objects in the room from reaching the mercury, and the thermometer is soon cooled to the same temperature as the ice. When the mercury ceases to sink in the capillary tube, a scratch is made at the level of its surface. This is the lower fixed point and may be marked 0° C.

The upper fixed point is found by means of the apparatus shown in figure 3.04. The steam from the boiling water A passes upwards through the inner tube B, down the outer tube C, as shown by the arrows, and escapes at the exit D. Thus, both the thermometer and the tube which surrounds it are kept at the temperature of the steam, so the temperature of the thermometer is unaffected by the temperatures of other objects. The whole of the mercury in the thermometer is in the steam, except for a small length of the mercury column which projects above the top of the apparatus, and enables the position of the meniscus to be observed.

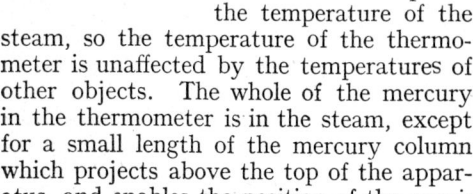

FIG. 3.03.—MARKING THE LOWER FIXED POINT.

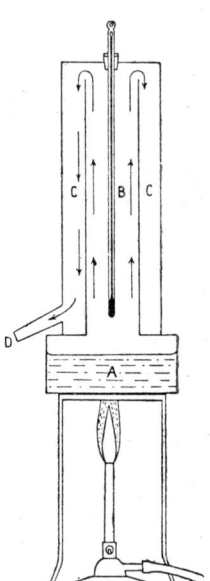

FIG. 3.04.—MARKING THE UPPER FIXED POINT.

The thermometer is placed in the steam, and not in the boiling water, because the temperature of the steam is found to depend only upon the pressure of the atmosphere, whereas the temperature of the boiling water depends upon a number of other factors as well.

The barometer is read, and if the pressure is 76 cm. of mercury, the position of the end of the mercury thread may be marked as 100° C. If the barometer reading is not 76 cm., a correction must be applied before the position of the mark 100° C. is engraved.

The two fixed points having been found in this way, the stem between them is divided into 100 equal divisions, each of which represents one centigrade degree, and these marks are numbered 0° C., 1° C., 2° C., etc. If necessary, divisions of the same size may now be marked off above and below the upper and lower fixed points, so that temperatures above 100° C. and below 0° C. can be read.

3.04. The upper and lower fixed points are called 100° C. and 0° C. respectively, because scientists have agreed to name these points in this way, and the scale of temperature so obtained is called the centigrade scale. There is, however, no reason why the fixed points should not be denoted by other numbers, and as we have seen, the absolute scale of temperature is the scale obtained by calling the upper fixed point 373° Abs., and the lower fixed point 273° Abs. Since there are 100 divisions between the upper and lower fixed points on both the centigrade scale and the absolute scale, the centigrade degree is the same size as the degree of the absolute scale. On the *Fahrenheit scale* of temperature, however, the divisions are smaller.

Fahrenheit, a German physicist living in the early eighteenth century (1686–1736), made many improvements to the thermometers of his day, among other things by introducing the use of mercury as the liquid in the thermometer. He is said to have calibrated his thermometers by placing them in a mixture of ice and salt to obtain the lower fixed point, which was then called 0° Fahrenheit (0° F.). The upper fixed point was taken as the temperature of the human body. Nowadays, thermometers are calibrated on the Fahrenheit scale by means of the fixed points used for calibrating centigrade thermometers. The temperature of pure melting ice is called 32° F., and the temperature of the steam from pure water boiling under a barometric pressure of 76 cm. of mercury is called 212° F.

In some of the northern European countries yet another scale of temperature is used, *viz.* the Réaumur scale, after R. A. F. de Réaumur (1683–1757). The freezing-point is called 0° Réaumur, and the upper fixed point 80° Réaumur. Since the use of this scale is confined to foreign countries, and is falling into disuse there, we shall not concern ourselves with it further.

The Fahrenheit scale, however, is used in English-speaking countries, except by scientists, so it is often necessary to convert temperatures from the Fahrenheit to the centigrade scale, and vice versa.

Examples :

(1) *The temperature of the human body is normally* 98·4° *F. What is this temperature on the centigrade scale ?*

When the mercury stands at 98·4° F., it stands (98·4 − 32) Fahrenheit divisions above the freezing-point. There are (212 − 32) = 180 Fahrenheit divisions between the fixed points and only 100 centigrade divisions.

∴ 180 Fahrenheit divisions = 100 centigrade divisions.

[Note that it is *not* true that 180° F. = 100° C.]

Hence, the mercury stands (98·4 − 32) × $\frac{100}{180}$ centigrade divisions above the freezing-point.

This is $\frac{66·4 \times 100}{180}$, or 36·9 centigrade divisions. The temperature is therefore 36·9° C.

(2) *Mercury freezes at* − 38·8° *C. What is the corresponding Fahrenheit temperature ?*

The mercury in the thermometer stands 38·8 centigrade divisions below the freezing-point of water. 100 centigrade divisions = 180 Fahrenheit divisions, so the mercury stands $\left(\frac{38·8 \times 180}{100}\right)$, or 69·8 Fahrenheit divisions below the freezing-point. The freezing-point is at 32° F., so the required temperature is (32 − 69·8) = − 37·8° F.

3.05. A mercury thermometer cannot be used to read temperatures below − 38·8° C., because mercury freezes at this temperature. For measuring lower temperatures, an alcohol thermometer is sometimes used. On the other hand, a mercury thermometer may be used up to temperatures of 450° C., which is a higher temperature than could be measured if another liquid were used in place of the mercury in a thermometer. In addition, mercury possesses the following advantages :

   (a) it is opaque, and therefore easily seen ;
   (b) it does not wet the inside of the thermometer, and there-
       fore quickly runs back along the stem when the ther-
       mometer is cooled ;
   (c) heat passes readily through the mercury in the bulb, so
       all the mercury quickly reaches the same temperature ;
   (d) the readings of a mercury thermometer agree fairly well
       with those of a gas thermometer (see section 4.05).

   3.06. When it is desired to measure the highest temperature reached in a given period of time, the **maximum thermometer** (figure 3.05) may be used. This thermometer lies in a horizontal

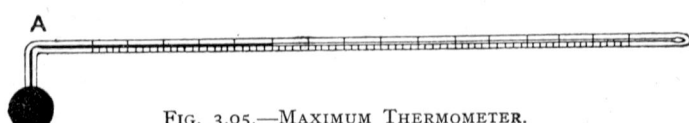

FIG. 3.05.—MAXIMUM THERMOMETER.

position during use. The bore of the thermometer stem is con-stricted at A. As the temperature rises, mercury is forced past this constriction, but the mercury thread breaks at this point as the temperature falls, and the thermometer continues to record the highest temperature reached.

   The **clinical thermometer** (figure 3.06) works on the same principle. Since this thermometer has to record temperatures near 98° F. only, its stem is short, and is graduated for a range of a few degrees only. In both these types of thermometer, the mercury thread is brought back after use by giving the instru-ment a sharp flick.

   The **minimum thermometer** (figure 3.07) records the lowest temperature reached in a given period of time. The thermo-metric liquid is in this case alcohol, and a small dumb-bell-shaped piece of steel rests in the stem. As the temperature rises, the alcohol flows past this indicator, but when the liquid contracts, the indicator is held at the liquid surface, and is drawn back with the liquid. Any subsequent expansion leaves the indicator at the position occupied by the meniscus when the thermometer was at its coldest.

   3.07. Liquid-in-glass thermometers, such as those described, are convenient instruments for measuring temperature because they are small and handy, and show the temperature without the need for any calculation. Nevertheless, they suffer from various disadvantages, and are not used as standard thermometers. The chief difficulty is that caused by the troublesome expansion of the glass of which they are made. Glass expands by an amount which depends upon its previous heat treatment, and since the position of the thread of liquid depends upon the apparent and not the real expansion of the liquid, the readings of a mercury thermometer are not entirely consistent. The errors are small, but to avoid them a gas thermometer is taken as the standard instrument, and a mercury thermometer which is to be used for accurate work must first be calibrated by comparison with one of this type.

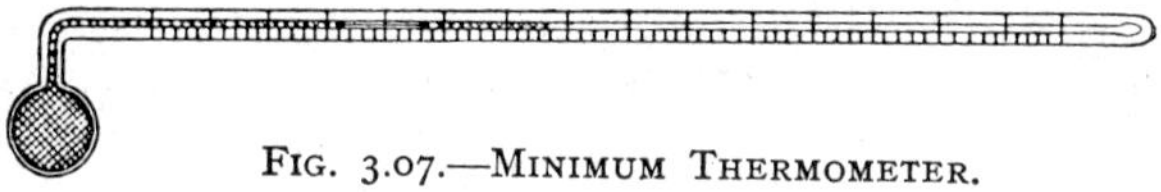

FIG. 3.07.—MINIMUM THERMOMETER.

A properly designed **gas thermometer** is a very complicated instrument, but the principle of the thermometer may be understood by reference to the apparatus shown in figure 2.07 (page 24). The gas in the bulb is kept at the same volume by moving the tube C up or down, and the pressure of the gas is found when the bulb is surrounded by pure melting ice, and also when it is surrounded by the steam from water boiling under a pressure of 76 cm. of mercury. If these pressures are p_0 and p_{100}, and the corresponding temperatures are called 0° C. and 100° C. respectively, the temperature will be said to be 50° C. when the pressure of the gas is half-way between p_0 and p_{100}. This temperature may or may not agree with the temperature of 50° C.

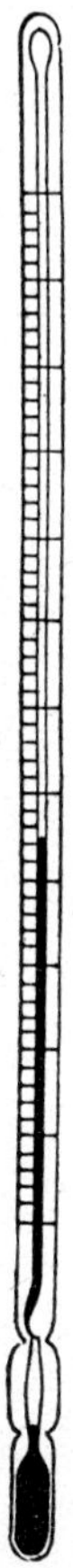

FIG. 3.06. CLINICAL THERMO-METER. found by means of a mercury thermometer. As a matter of fact it agrees with it very nearly, but not exactly, and it is therefore necessary to choose which of these nearly equal temperatures shall be called 50° C. For the reasons stated above, the gas thermometer

reading is said to be correct, and the mercury thermometer is said to have a small error. This error is so small that, for our experiments, it need not be taken into account. Nevertheless, it is important to realize that when the readings of a gas thermometer and a mercury thermometer are not in agreement it is the mercury thermometer which is in error, *because we agree to call true centigrade temperatures those registered by the gas thermometer.*

Other types of thermometer—platinum resistance thermometers, thermocouples, optical pyrometers, and vapour-pressure thermometers—are sometimes used for special purposes. Their construction and mode of working are, however, beyond the scope of this book.

EXAMPLES 3

1. Describe the construction and method of calibration of a mercury thermometer for use from − 10° C. to 110° C.

2. What are the fixed points of a scale of temperature ? Why are two, but not more than two, fixed points necessary ?

3. How would you calibrate a thermometer whose range was approximately 0° C. to 30° C. ?

4. It is suspected that the glass bulb of a mercury thermometer has contracted since it was calibrated. What steps would you take to find out whether this was the case ?

5. Convert the following into temperatures on the Fahrenheit scale : 75° C. ; − 45° C. ; 290° Abs.

6. Convert the following into temperatures on the centigrade scale : 100° F. ; − 10° F. ; 1000° F.

7. At what temperature would the reading of a centigrade thermometer be numerically equal to that of a Fahrenheit thermometer ?

8. The coefficient of linear expansion of lead is 0·0000279 per degree C. Express this as a fraction per degree F.

9. Express Charles's Law in terms of temperatures on the Fahrenheit scale.

10. Explain why the gas thermometer, although seldom used in practice, is yet taken as the standard thermometer. Why is the variable expansion of the glass bulb of a gas thermometer of small importance ?

SCHOOL CERTIFICATE QUESTIONS

11. Give a short account of the construction and graduation of a mercury thermometer. An ungraduated thermometer is attached to a centimetre scale, and is found to read 7·3 cm. in melting ice,

23·8 cm. in steam at 100° C., and 3·5 cm. in a freezing mixture. What is the temperature of the freezing mixture ?   (O.C)

12. Define the upper fixed point of a temperature scale. Describe, giving diagrams, how you would find where to mark both the upper and lower fixed points on an ungraduated mercury thermometer if you did not possess another thermometer. Why is glass not an ideal material for the bulb of a thermometer ?   (J)

13. How are temperature readings on the Centigrade, Fahrenheit, and Absolute scales related ?   " The boiling-point of alcohol, which is 78° C., is 43° C. higher than the boiling-point of ether." Rewrite the above statement, using (a) the Fahrenheit scale, (b) an absolute scale.   (L)

14. Describe and explain the action of a thermometer suitable for measuring the minimum night temperature in a greenhouse. Clinical thermometers are usually graduated to indicate a range of temperature from 95° F.–110° F. What would be the corresponding temperatures in degrees centigrade ?   (O.C)

15. Compare the properties of water and mercury as regards suitability for use as thermometric liquids. What special features are required in the construction of a mercury thermometer to make it suitable for (a) measuring the temperature of " freezing mixtures " down to − 20° C., (b) making maximum temperature determinations?   (J)

16. Describe with the aid of a diagram, a constant volume air thermometer. A thermometer of this kind is being used on a day when the barometer stands at 75 cm. of mercury. The bulb is placed in melting ice and the level of the mercury in the open limb is 5 cm. *lower* than that in the closed limb. Find (a) the pressure of the gas in the bulb, (b) the temperature of the gas in the bulb when the level of the mercury in the open limb is 65 cm. *above* that in the closed limb.   (O)

CHAPTER 4

REAL AND APPARENT EXPANSION—THE EXPANSION OF WATER

4.01. The coefficient of cubical expansion c of a solid was defined by the equation :

$$c = \frac{\text{the increase of volume of a piece of it}}{\text{the volume of the piece at } 0° \text{ C.} \times \text{the rise of temperature}}.$$

If V_0 represents the volume of the piece at $0°$ C. and the temperature is raised to $t°$ C.,

$$c = \frac{\text{the increase of volume}}{V_0.t}$$

$\therefore$ the increase of volume $= c.V_0.t$.

In the case of liquids, it is necessary to distinguish between the real and the apparent expansion, and two different coefficients of expansion have to be distinguished. The **coefficient of real expansion** c_r is defined by the equation :

$$c_r = \frac{\text{the real expansion of the liquid}}{\text{its real volume at } 0° \text{ C.} \times \text{the rise of temperature}}.$$

Hence, the real expansion of the liquid is equal to the product of c_r, the real volume at $0°$ C., and the rise of temperature.

The **coefficient of apparent expansion** c_a is defined by the equation :

$$c_a = \frac{\text{the apparent expansion of the liquid}}{\text{its apparent volume at } 0° \text{ C.} \times \text{the rise of temperature}}.$$

Hence, the apparent expansion is equal to the product of the coefficient of apparent expansion, the apparent volume at $0°$ C., and the rise of temperature. The coefficient of apparent expansion of a liquid depends, of course, upon the nature of the containing vessel as well as upon that of the liquid.

4.02. We have seen that, when a liquid is heated, the real expansion of the liquid is equal to the sum of the apparent expansion of the liquid and the expansion of the containing vessel. We have now to show that the *coefficient* of real expan-

44

sion is equal to the sum of the *coefficient* of apparent expansion and the *coefficient* of cubical expansion of the vessel ; *i.e.* that $c_r = c_a + c$.

We shall suppose that some liquid is contained in a glass vessel, such as a measuring jar, and that the vessel is correctly calibrated at $0°$ C. If the liquid fills the jar to the mark V_0 at $0°$ C., the real volume of the liquid and its apparent volume at $0°$ C. are both V_0. Figure 4.01(a) shows the liquid in the jar at $0°$ C.

Let the vessel and liquid be heated to $t°$ C. The vessel expands, so the volume up to any given mark is now greater than it was at $0°$ C., but in spite of this, the level of the liquid reaches a higher mark, since the liquid expands more than the vessel. We shall suppose that the vessel is filled to the division marked V_a, as shown in figure 4.01(b). V_a is thus the apparent volume of the liquid at $t°$ C. The real volume of the vessel up to the division numbered V_a is, however, not V_a, but a greater volume, since the volume up to this mark was V_a at $0°$ C., and the vessel has since expanded.

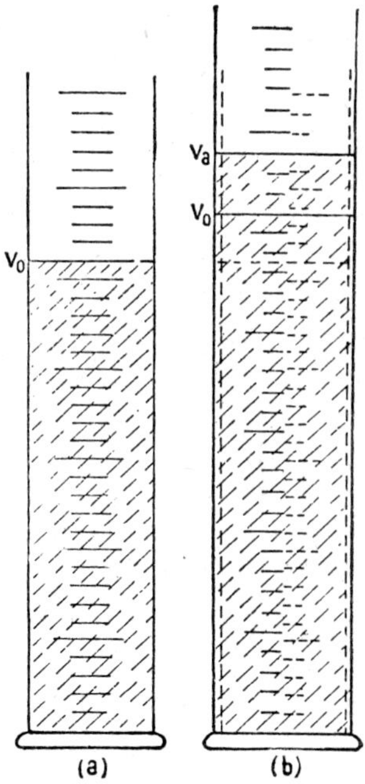

The real volume of the liquid was V_0 at $0°$ C., so the real expansion of the liquid is $c_r.V_0.t$. Since the apparent volume of the liquid was V_0 at $0°$ C., its apparent expansion is $c_a.V_0.t$. But,

Fig. 4.01.

(real expansion) = (apparent expansion) + (expansion of the vessel)
$$\therefore c_r.V_0.t = c_a.V_0.t + \text{(expansion of the vessel)}.$$

The liquid is at the mark V_a at $t°$ C., and has to fill the extra space in the vessel caused by the expansion of the portion of the vessel below this mark. The required expansion of the vessel is, therefore, $c.V_a.t$.

$$\therefore c_r.V_0.t = c_a.V_0.t + c.V_a.t.$$

Dividing throughout by $V_0 . t$

$$c_r = c_a + c . \frac{V_a}{V_0}.$$

In an actual experiment V_a is only a few per cent. greater than V_0, so $\frac{V_a}{V_0}$ is approximately equal to 1.

Putting $\frac{V_a}{V_0} = 1$ in the above equation, we have:

$$c_r = c_a + c.$$

That is: **the coefficient of real expansion of a liquid is approximately equal to the sum of its coefficient of apparent expansion and the coefficient of cubical expansion of the vessel.**

It may be asked why V_a is said to be equal to V_0 in the final step of this proof, whereas V_a has been treated as different from V_0 elsewhere. The reason is that the last term, $c . \frac{V_a}{V_0}$, is always small compared with the other two, so an approximate value for this term is sufficient. An example will serve to make this clearer.

In a typical experiment, c_a was 0·00101 per degree C., c was 0·000027 per degree C., while $\frac{V_a}{V_0} = \frac{10}{9}$. Hence,

$$c_r = c_a + c . \frac{V_a}{V_0}$$

$$\therefore c_r = 0 \cdot 00101 + 0 \cdot 000027 \times \frac{10}{9}$$

$$= 0 \cdot 00104.$$

Using the approximate equation $c_r = c_a + c$ we have

$$c_r = 0 \cdot 00101 + 0 \cdot 000027$$
$$= 0 \cdot 001037$$
$$= 0 \cdot 00104$$

to three significant figures ; and this result is the same as that given by the exact equation.

4.03. A measuring jar is not suitable for measuring the coefficient of apparent expansion of a liquid, because it does not allow of sufficient accuracy in the measurement of the small increase of volume of the liquid. A specific gravity bottle (figure 4.02) may be used, however. The ground-glass stopper of the bottle is bored with a fine hole, and if the stopper is put in when the bottle is full of liquid, the surplus liquid escapes through the hole. The narrowness of this hole ensures that the same volume of liquid is taken each time the bottle is filled.

The bottle is weighed empty, filled with liquid at temperature $t_1°$ C., and again weighed. The difference between the two weighings gives the weight of liquid in the bottle. The bottle is now immersed up to the neck in a vessel containing water at a higher temperature, and the temperature of this water is kept constant. When the liquid in the bottle reaches the same temperature as the water, it ceases to expand, and no more escapes through the hole in the stopper. The temperature of the water is then measured, the bottle is removed, dried and weighed, and the weight of liquid in the bottle at the second temperature t_2 is found by subtracting the first weight from the third.

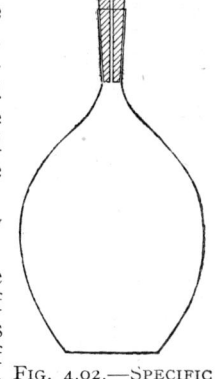

The coefficient of apparent expansion may be calculated as follows.

Let w_1 be the weight of the liquid in the bottle at $t_1°$ C., and let w_2 be the weight of liquid which remains when its temperature is raised to $t_2°$ C. Let c_a be the coefficient of apparent expansion, and call V_0 the apparent volume of 1 gm. of the liquid at 0° C., V_1 that of 1 gm. at $t_1°$ C., and V_2 that of 1 gm. at $t_2°$ C.

FIG. 4.02.—SPECIFIC GRAVITY BOTTLE.

By definition :

$$c_a = \frac{V_1 - V_0}{V_0 . t_1}$$

$$\therefore \; c_a . V_0 . t_1 = V_1 - V_0$$

$$\therefore \; V_1 = V_0 + V_0 . c_a . t_1 = V_0(1 + c_a . t_1)$$

Similarly,

$$V_2 = V_0(1 + c_a . t_2).$$

The apparent volume of 1 gm. of liquid at $t_1°$ C. is V_1, so that of the w_1 gm. will be $V_1 w_1$. Similarly the apparent volume of the w_2 gm. at $t_2°$ C. is $V_2 w_2$. These apparent volumes are equal, however, since each is equal to the apparent volume of the bottle.

$$\therefore V_1 w_1 = V_2 w_2$$
$$\therefore V_0(1 + c_a.t_1).w_1 = V_0(1 + c_a.t_2)w_2$$
$$\therefore w_1 + w_1.c_a.t_1 = w_2 + w_2.c_a.t_2$$
$$\therefore c_a(w_2.t_2 - w_1.t_1) = w_1 - w_2$$

$$\therefore c_a = \frac{w_1 - w_2}{w_2.t_2 - w_1.t_1}$$

4.04. The determination of the coefficient of apparent expansion of a liquid may also be carried out by means of the vessel A

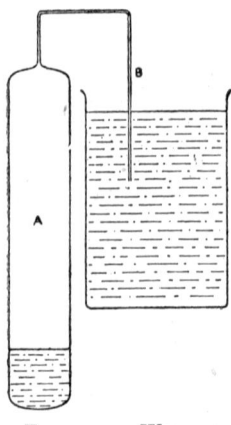

(figure 4.03). This vessel is filled with liquid by alternately heating it and cooling it while the tip of the capillary B is immersed in the liquid. When a sufficient quantity of liquid has entered the bulb, this liquid is boiled, and its vapour carries out the remaining traces of air. The rest of the experiment is then similar to that with the specific gravity bottle.

Filling this apparatus is a tedious process, but the apparatus possesses the advantage that the liquid expelled when the bulb is heated in the water bath can be caught and weighed separately ; so a number of measurements of the apparent expansion can be made during one experiment by catching and weighing the liquid which escapes between various pairs of temperatures.

Fig. 4.03.—Weight Thermometer.

In such an experiment :

$$c_a = \frac{w_1 - w_2}{w_2.t_2 - w_1.t_1}.$$

If the experiment is started at 0° C., t_1 is zero and $w_1.t_1$ will also be **zero**. Hence, in this case

$$c_a = \frac{w_1 - w_2}{w_2.t_2}$$

$$\therefore t_2 = \frac{w_1 - w_2}{w_2.c_a}.$$

All the factors on the right-hand side of this equation except c_a are measured during the experiment, and if c_a is known, the experiment would enable t_2 to be determined. The instrument may thus be used to measure temperatures, and is therefore called a *weight thermometer*. Since, however, the temperature can only be found in this way by means of a difficult experiment, the weight thermometer is seldom used for the measurement of temperatures.

4.05. The coefficients of real and apparent expansion of a liquid are related to the coefficient of cubical expansion of the vessel as shown by the formula :

$$c_r = c_a + c.$$

Hence, if the coefficient of apparent expansion and the coefficient of cubical expansion are known, the coefficient of real expansion may be calculated. The value so obtained, however, may not be accurate for two reasons :

(a) The formula given above is not exact. This difficulty can be overcome by using a more complicated equation.

(b) If specific gravity bottles or weight thermometers are made of glass, the coefficient of cubical expansion will probably be different for each bottle, and is seldom known accurately. This difficulty may be avoided by using a vessel made of silica, whose coefficient of cubical expansion is known with sufficient accuracy.

Thus, both sources of error can be avoided, and the coefficient of real expansion can be calculated. It can, however, be measured directly, although the experiment is not an easy one.

Let w_0 be the weight of unit volume of a given liquid at $0°$ C. and let w_t be the weight of unit volume at $t°$ C. Consider a mass of liquid whose volume is V_0 at $0°$ C. The weight of this liquid is $w_0.V_0$. If the liquid is heated to $t°$ C. its volume becomes V_t, where $V_t = V_0(1 + c_r.t)$. [The coefficient of real expansion is used because the real, and not the apparent, volume at $t°$ is required.] The weight of the liquid is $w_t.V_t$, or $w_t V_0(1 + c_r.t)$, and since the weight of the liquid is not altered by heating it, this weight is equal to that at $0°$ C.

$$\therefore \ w_0 V_0 = w_t V_0 (1 + c_r.t)$$
$$\therefore \ w_0 = w_t (1 + c_r.t).$$

Figure 4.04 shows a **U**-tube containing some of the liquid. The liquid in the left-hand tube is kept at $0°$ C., while that in the right-hand tube is maintained at the temperature $t°$ C. The pressure exerted by a liquid depends only upon the weight of unit volume of the liquid and its depth, and is found by multiplying these two quantities. Hence, if h_0 and h_t are the depths of the two liquid columns AB and CD, the pressure at B is $w_0.h_0$, and that at D is $w_t.h_t$. Since the liquid is stationary, the pressures at the two points B and D at the same horizontal level are equal.

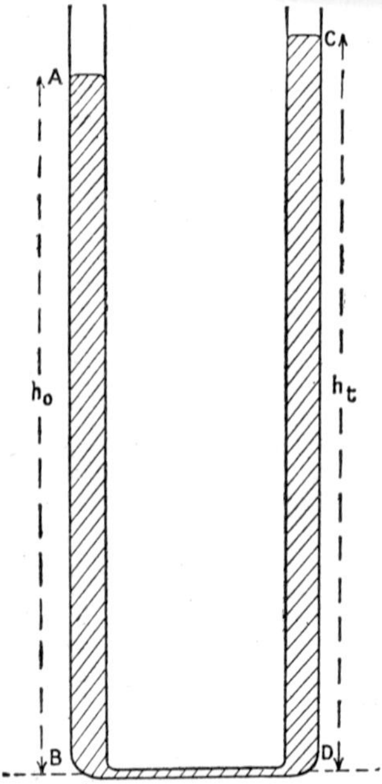

FIG. 4.04.

$$\therefore w_0.h_0 = w_t.h_t$$
$$\therefore w_t(1 + c_r.t)h_0 = w_t.h_t$$
$$\therefore h_0 + h_0.c_r.t = h_t$$
$$\therefore c_r = \frac{h_t - h_0}{h_0.t}.$$

Hence, if the factors on the right-hand side of this equation are measured, the coefficient of real expansion may be calculated.

The first accurate experiments of this kind were those performed by Dulong (1785–1838) and Petit (1791–1820), and their apparatus is shown in figure 4.05. The liquid chosen for the experiment was mercury, which possesses the advantage that it can be used over a wide range of temperatures. Moreover, since mercury is used in thermometers, it is particularly important that its coefficient of expansion should be accurately known. The two arms of the U-tube, A and A′, were connected by a capillary B. A was kept at 0° C. by means of melting ice. A′ was surrounded by an oil bath which was heated to any required temperature by the furnace, and the temperature was measured by means of the air thermometer C. The difference between the levels of the mercury surfaces in A and A′ was measured by sighting a telescope on each surface in turn. The telescope was clamped horizontally, and the amount of its vertical movement was accurately measured, thus determining the small quantity $(h_t - h_0)$.

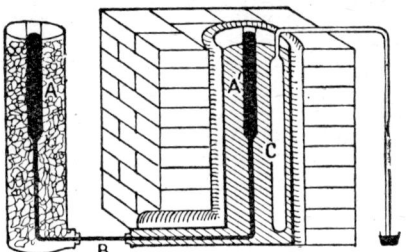

FIG. 4.05.—DULONG AND PETIT'S APPAR-
ATUS FOR MEASURING THE COEFFICIENT
OF ABSOLUTE EXPANSION OF MERCURY.

If a mercury thermometer were used as the standard thermometer, and its temperature were raised first from 0° C. to 100° C. and then from 100° C. to 200° C., the mercury would expand by the same amount in each case. There is no need to prove this, for the 200° C. mark is put on the stem at that point which is as far above the 100° C. mark as the latter is above the 0° C. mark. In other words, if a mercury thermometer were the standard, mercury would, *by definition*, expand by the same amount for each degree its temperature was raised. By using an air thermometer to measure temperatures, however, Dulong and Petit were able to show that mercury expands by very nearly equal amounts for each degree *when the temperatures are measured on the gas scale* (that is, on the centigrade scale measured by a gas thermometer). They found the following values for the average coefficient of real expansion of mercury :

between 0° C. and 100° C., 0·0001802,
,,   0° C. and 200° C., 0·0001843,
,,   0° C. and 300° C., 0·0001887.

These results show that mercury expands by *almost* the same amount for each degree centigrade, so a mercury thermometer agrees very nearly with the readings of the standard gas thermometer.

4.06. Let V_0 be the internal volume of the glass vessel shown in figure 4.06, measured up to a given mark on the stem. The expansion on heating to $t°$ C. is $V_0.c.t$ where c is the coefficient of cubical expansion of the glass. If the vessel contains some mercury whose volume is v_0 at 0° C. this mercury will expand at the same time by an amount $v_0.c_r.t$.

FIG. 4.06.—
CONSTANT
VOLUME
DILATO-
METER.

The expansion of the vessel will be equal to the expansion of the mercury if $V_0.c.t = v_0.c_r.t$, and in this case the empty space in the bottle will be the same at all temperatures. c for glass is 0·0000255 per degree C., and c_r is 0·00018 per degree C., so the empty space will remain of the same volume if,

$$V_0 \times 0·0000255 \times t = v_0 \times 0·00018 \times t$$

$$i.e. \text{ if } \frac{V_0}{v_0} = \frac{0·00018}{0·0000255} = 7 \text{ nearly.}$$

Hence, if a glass vessel is one-seventh full of mercury, the space in the vessel above the mercury will have the same volume at all temperatures. Such a vessel is called a *constant volume dilatometer*. It may be used to show the *absolute* expansion of other liquids. If the space above the mercury is filled with water (say), as in the figure, the movement of the water surface in the capillary tube will only depend upon the absolute expansion of the water.

4.07. The coefficient of real expansion of mercury varies slightly according as it is measured at low or at high temperatures, and most other liquids behave in a similar way. The expansion of water, however, is altogether peculiar. If some water at 0° C. in a constant volume dilatometer is slowly heated the water at first *contracts*. At a temperature of 4° C. the volume of the given mass of water in the vessel is smaller than at any other temperature. In other words, the density of the liquid $\left(\text{density} = \dfrac{\text{mass}}{\text{volume}} \right)$ is greatest at this temperature. After the temperature passes 4° C., the volume of the water begins to increase, the expansion becoming more and more rapid as the temperature rises. The graph, figure 4.07, shows the volume of 1 gm. of water at various temperatures.

Since 1 gm. of water occupies a smaller volume at 4° C. than at any other temperature, water at any other temperature can float on the surface of water at 4° C., just as oil floats on water, or water on mercury. This fact is used in Hope's experiment (T. C. Hope, 1766–1844). The middle of a tall metal vessel (figure 4.08) is surrounded by a trough containing a mixture of ice and salt. Such a mixture produces a temperature considerably below 0° C. Water is placed in the inner vessel, stirred, and then allowed to stand. Two thermometers enable the temperatures of the water near the top and bottom of the vessel to be read, and readings are taken at intervals of one minute for a period of half an hour or more. Figure 4.09 shows the graph obtained by plotting the thermometer readings against

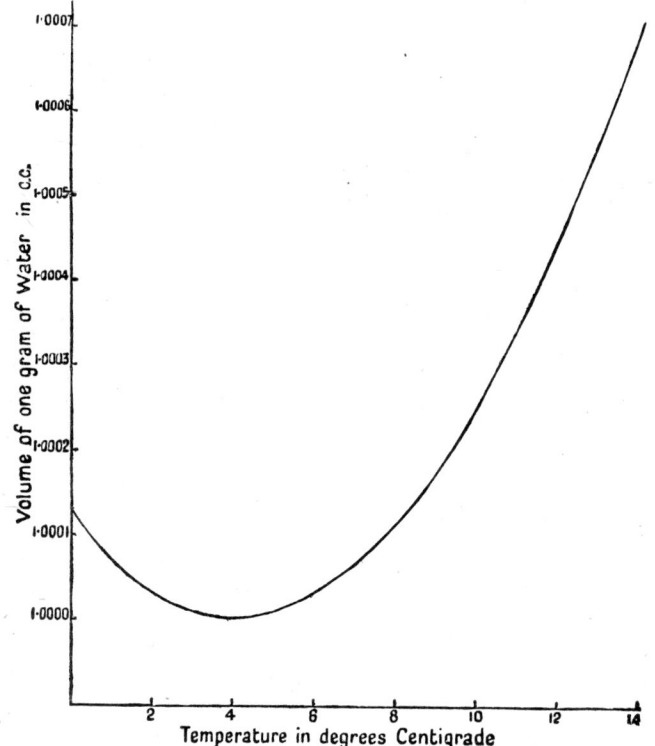

FIG. 4.07.—GRAPH SHOWING THE VOLUME OF 1 GM. OF WATER AT VARIOUS TEMPERATURES.

time. The dotted line shows the readings of the upper of the two thermometers, and the full line those of the lower one.

The reading of the lower thermometer quickly falls to 4° C., at which temperature it remains throughout the experiment.

The water near the top remains for a long time at its initial temperature. Its temperature then falls quickly to 0° C. The explanation is as follows.

The water near the trough is cooled and contracts. Its density is then greater than that of the rest of the water, and it sinks to the bottom, causing a decrease of temperature there, but no change near the top. This continues until the water at the bottom reaches 4° C., when it is at its temperature of maximum density. Any water which is cooled below 4° C. will float on the layer of dense water at 4° C., so the temperature at the bottom of the vessel remains at this value.

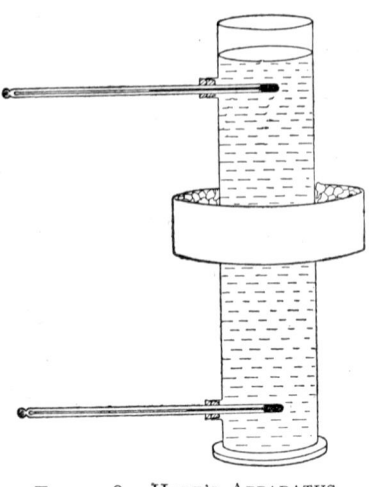

FIG. 4.08.—HOPE'S APPARATUS.

As cooling proceeds, the whole of the water below the trough is cooled in a similar way to 4° C., each layer in succession, from the bottom upwards, reaching this temperature. The layer of water near the trough is now cooled below 4° C., becomes less dense, and floats upwards until it reaches a layer whose density is less than its own. The quantity of cold water in the vessel thus continues to increase until finally the water round the upper thermometer is also cooled, and since water at a temperature below 4° C. is less dense than water at this temperature, the water here does not remain at 4° C., but its temperature is lowered by colder water from below until the temperature reaches 0° C., when ice begins to form on the surface.

Hope's experiment illustrates the cooling of ponds and lakes in cold weather. As the surface water is cooled, the heavy, cold water sinks to the bottom. When the temperature there reaches 4° C., however, the water is denser than that which is cooled still further at the surface, so the movement of the water ceases. Hence, the temperature near the bottom seldom falls below 4° C., even during long periods of frost, and ice forms at the surface only.

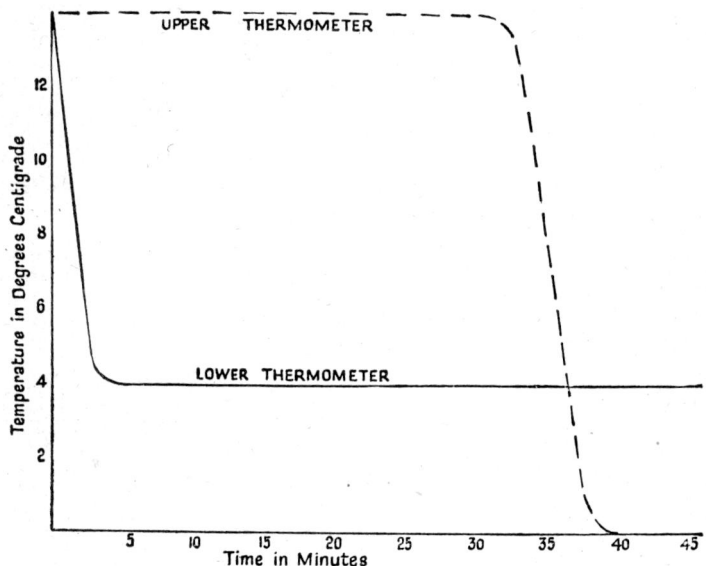

FIG. 4.09.—GRAPH ILLUSTRATING HOPE'S EXPERIMENT.

EXAMPLES 4

1. Define *coefficient of real expansion* and *coefficient of apparent expansion* of a liquid, and deduce the relation between these quantities and the coefficient of cubical expansion of the containing vessel.

2. A copper vessel contains 100 c.c. of liquid at 0° C. The coefficient of real expansion of the liquid is 0·00090 per degree C., and the coefficient of linear expansion of copper is 0·000016 per degree C. What will be the coefficient of apparent expansion of the liquid? What will be its apparent volume at 80° C. ?

3. In an experiment with a specific gravity bottle the following readings were taken:

Weight of empty bottle	=	15·49 gm.
Weight of bottle full of water at 14·4° C.	=	40·54 ,,
Weight ,, ,, ,, ,, ,, ,, 99·8° C.	=	39·57

Calculate the average coefficient of apparent expansion of water between the temperatures of 15° C. and 100° C. Assuming the coefficient of linear expansion of the glass of the bottle to be 0·0000085 per degree C., calculate the average value of the coefficient of real expansion of the water.

4. The coefficient of apparent expansion of mercury, as measured in an experiment with a specific gravity bottle, was found to be 0·000153 per degree C. Assuming the coefficient of real expansion of mercury between the same temperatures to be 0·000181 per degree C., find the coefficient of cubical expansion of the material of the bottle. The same bottle is now used to determine the coefficient of apparent expansion of alcohol. If this is found to be 0·00101 per degree C., calculate its coefficient of real expansion.

Why is it unnecessary that the coefficient of real expansion of more than *one* liquid should be accurately determined by the method of Dulong and Petit ?

5. It is required to make a constant volume dilatometer using olive oil (coefficient of real expansion 0·00070 per degree C.), as the liquid at the bottom of the dilatometer. What fraction of the bottle should be filled with the oil ? Coefficient of linear expansion of glass = 0·0000085 per degree C.

School Certificate Questions

6. Distinguish between real and apparent expansion in liquids. Describe how to determine directly the coefficient of real expansion of a liquid such as paraffin oil.

A glass vessel holds 50·00 gm. of paraffin at 0° C. How much will overflow if it is heated to 60° C. ? [Coefficient of linear expansion of glass = 0·000008 per degree C. ; coefficient of expansion of paraffin = 0·00100 per degree C.] (L)

7. Define *coefficient of expansion* of a liquid. Distinguish between real and apparent expansion. The bulb and stem of a mercury thermometer contain up to the zero mark 0·5 c.c. of mercury. If the stem is 0·2 mm. in internal diameter, what is the length of the degree on the scale ? [Coefficient of expansion of mercury = 0·00018 per degree C. ; coefficient of linear expansion of glass = 0·000008 per degree C.] (L)

8. Describe an ideal liquid for use in a thermometer. Explain what you understand by the coefficient of apparent expansion of a liquid.

The volume of a thermometer bulb is 0·85 c.c. Find the cross-section of the bore of the stem, if the mercury rises 1 mm. for 1° C. rise in temperature. [The coefficient of apparent expansion of mercury in glass is 0·000156 per degree C.] (B)

9. Distinguish between real and apparent expansion as applied to liquids, and show what is the relation between them. A specific gravity bottle weighs 15·44 gm. when empty, and 59·64 gm. when full of a certain liquid at 15° C. It is heated in a bath at 60° C., after which it is found that exactly 1 gm. of liquid has been expelled. Calculate the coefficient of apparent expansion of the liquid. If the coefficient of linear expansion of glass is 0·000009 per degree C., find the coefficient of real expansion of the liquid.   (B)

10. If the two arms of a U-tube are kept at different temperatures the levels of any contained liquid are not the same in the two arms. Explain why this is so and describe how it may be made the basis of a method of measuring the coefficient of expansion of the liquid. Will the coefficient so obtained be " real " or " apparent " ? (O.C)

11. Define *coefficient of linear expansion* and *coefficient of cubical expansion*, and prove that the latter is approximately three times the former.

Describe an experiment to show that water has a maximum density at 4° C., and explain two natural consequences of this.   (O.C)

12. Describe an experiment which shows that (a) in general liquids expand when they are raised in temperature, and (b) equal amounts of different liquids expand by different amounts when they are raised through the same temperature interval. Describe with a graph, how water behaves when raised from 0° C. to 16° C., and deduce from your description the temperature distribution with depth, in a pond during a period of hard frost in winter.   (O)

CHAPTER 5

5.01. When a kettle of water is placed over a fire, we say that the kettle is heated, or that heat passes from the fire to the kettle. When the kettle cools we say it is losing heat. We have now to see how quantities of heat are measured.

The thermometer does not measure quantities of heat, as the following experiment shows. A saucepan nearly full of water is heated until the water boils, and the temperature is measured with a thermometer. The temperature of some cold water in a small tin is also measured, and the tin of water is allowed to float for a minute in the saucepan. It is then removed, and the temperatures of the water in the tin and saucepan are again measured. In this experiment heat passes from the hot water in the saucepan to the cold water in the tin, and the heat gained by the latter is, at most, equal to that lost by the hot water. Nevertheless, the increase of temperature of the water in the tin is found to be several times as great as the decrease of temperature of the water in the saucepan. **Thermometers measure temperature ; they do not measure quantities of heat.**

If we wish to find which of two given Bunsen burners supplies most heat, the simplest method would be to take two similar saucepans containing equal masses of cold water, and to allow one burner to heat each saucepan. If the first saucepan is brought to the boil before the other, the burner under it is giving out more heat than the other. In other words, we should allow the heat from the flame to pass into a given mass of water, and should measure the change of temperature produced by the heat. This is the principle of all measurements of quantities of heat.

We may now perform the following experiments :

(1) 1000 gm. of distilled water are placed in a saucepan, are heated for 1 minute by an electric heater, and the rise of temperature is noted. The heater is switched on for a further minute, and the rise of temperature is again noted. The tem-

perature increases by equal amounts in the two cases, so a quantity of heat equal to that which will raise the temperature of the water from 15° C. to 25° C. raises its temperature from 25° C. to 35° C. More accurate experiments than the present one show that the quantities of heat required to raise the temperature of a given mass of water by one centigrade degree are nearly equal, whether the rise of temperature is from 0° C. to 1° C., from 1° C. to 2° C., or from any other temperature to one which is one degree higher.

(2) 500 gm. of water are heated in a smaller tin for $\frac{1}{2}$ minute. The temperature is found to increase by the same number of degrees as when 1000 gm. are heated for 1 minute, so, to heat 1000 gm. through a given temperature range, twice as much heat is required as that which heats 500 gm. through the same range. The quantity of heat required varies directly as the mass of water used.

In measuring quantities of heat, therefore, both the quantity of water and the rise of temperature must be known. **The unit of heat used in physics is called the calorie. The calorie is the heat required to raise the temperature of 1 gm. of water by 1° C.**

Two other units of heat are used by engineers. **One British Thermal Unit (B.Th.U.) is the heat required to raise the temperature of 1 lb. of water 1° F. One therm is a unit of heat equal to 100,000 B.Th.U.**

The heating value of coal gas is usually quoted in therms per thousand cubic feet. If the coal gas supplied gives 4·8 therms per thousand cubic feet, this means that, by burning 1000 cu. ft. of the gas, enough heat is produced to raise 480,000 lb. of water 1° F., or 3000 lb. of water 160° F.

5.02. In the above experiments there is a source of error which we have not yet considered. The temperatures of the tin and heater were increased during the experiments, as well as the temperature of the water, and some heat must have been used in heating these. Before we can calculate how much heat was so used, we must discover whether other materials, such as those of which the tin and saucepan are made, require the same amounts of heat as those necessary to heat similar masses of water.

Another rough experiment with the electric heater is suffi-cient to decide the point. Using the same tin as in the first experiment, 1000 gm. of paraffin are heated for 1 minute. The

increase of temperature is found to be about double that when
1000 gm. of water were used. Evidently each gram of paraffin
requires only about half as much heat to raise its temperature
1° C. as the same mass of water would require. The scientific
way of expressing this fact is to say that the *specific heat* of
paraffin is $\frac{1}{2}$.

The specific heat of a substance is the ratio :

$$\frac{\text{the heat required to heat a given mass of the substance}}{\text{the heat required to heat the same mass of water through the same}}$$
range of temperature

5.03. Quantities of heat are measured by means of an appar-

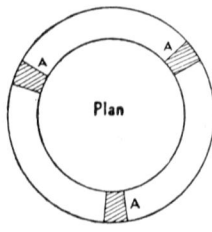

Plan

atus called a *calorimeter* (figure 5.01).
This consists of a copper beaker, supported
inside an outer jacket by three pieces of
wood attached to the latter. The inner
vessel can be removed for weighing. The
calorimeter is designed to reduce as far
as possible heat losses from the inner
beaker, and the means by which this end is
attained will be described later (page 94).

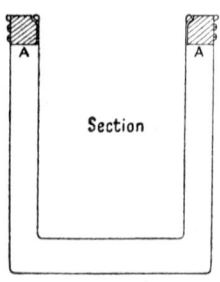

Section

When the calorimeter is used, some heat
is absorbed or given out by the inner
vessel, and this quantity of heat must be
known. It may be calculated if the
specific heat of the copper, of which it is
made, is known. The following experiment shows how the specific heat of copper is measured.

The inner vessel of the calorimeter is
weighed empty, and again about three-
quarters full of water. A block of copper
is weighed, tied to a piece of thread, and
immersed in some water which is kept

Fig. 5.01.—
Calorimeter.

boiling. The block is thus heated to a
known temperature. The temperature of
the cold water in the calorimeter is measured. The block of
copper is now removed from the boiling water by means of the
cotton attached to it, given a sudden flick to remove the hot water
clinging to it, and quickly transferred to the calorimeter.
The water is stirred by moving the block up and down, and its

temperature is measured with a thermometer. When the temperature ceases to rise, the highest reading reached is recorded. The results of such an experiment are given below :

Weight of calorimeter (empty)	= 53·9 gm.
Weight of calorimeter + water	= 162·9 gm.
∴ weight of water	= 109·0 gm.
Weight of copper block	= 180·8 gm.
Temperature of boiling water	= 99·5° C.
Temperature of cold water in the calorimeter	= 9·7° C.
Temperature of water after transferring block	= 21·2° C.

Let s be the specific heat of copper. During the experiment, 109·0 gm. of water are heated $(21·2 - 9·7)°$ C., and to heat this water $109·0(21·2 - 9·7)$ calories are required.

The calorimeter weighs 53·9 gm. and is heated $(21·2 - 9·7)°$ C. To heat 53·9 gm. of water $(21·2 - 9·7)°$ C., $53·9(21·2 - 9·7)$ calories would be required, and since the specific heat of copper is s, the calorimeter requires s times this amount of heat, or $53·9(21·2 - 9·7) \times s$ calories.

∴ heat taken up by the water and calorimeter

$$= 109·0(21·2 - 9·7) + 53·9(21·2 - 9·7)s \text{ calories}$$

If we assume that during the experiment no heat was lost to, or gained from, the surroundings, this is the quantity of heat given out by the block.

The latter weighs 180·9 gm., and its temperature decreases $(99·5 - 21·2)°$ C. 180·9 gm. of water, falling through this range of temperature, would give out $180·9(99·5 - 21·2)$ calories, and since the specific heat of copper is s, the block gives out s times this amount, or $180·9(99·5 - 21·2) \times s$ calories.

∴ $180·9(99·5 - 21·2) \times s = 109·0(21·2 \times 9·7) + 53·9(21·2 - 9·7)s$

Solving this equation, we have :

$$s = 0·092.$$

In the above experiment it is assumed that there is no loss of heat to the surroundings. There is always *some* gain or loss of heat, but this and other errors are made as small as possible, as follows :

(a) The block is transferred from the boiling water to the calorimeter as quickly as possible.

(b) As much water as possible is used in the calorimeter. A smaller amount of heat is then lost, because the water in the calorimeter is not heated much above the temperature of the surroundings. Moreover, the *whole* of the calorimeter is heated, as is assumed in the calculation.

(c) A block of metal of a suitable size is used. Its mass is sufficient to cause an increase of temperature which can be accurately measured, but the temperature is not raised so much that big heat losses are caused.

(d) The water in the calorimeter is stirred continuously, so that it all reaches the same temperature.

(e) By cooling the water in the calorimeter several degrees below room temperature, the final temperature is made nearly equal to room temperature (19° C. in this case). When the block is transferred to the cold water, the temperature of the latter quickly rises to within a degree or so of the final temperature, then more slowly to this temperature. Hence, during most of the time in which heat is passing from the block to the water, the temperature of the latter is nearly that of the surroundings, so little heat is gained or lost.

(f) The calorimeter itself is designed to minimize heat losses. The weighings quoted above are to the nearest tenth of a gram, which means that they are in error by $\frac{1}{5}$ of 1%, or less. Since the increase of temperature is only measured to 1%, it is a waste of time to weigh more accurately.

5.04. The result of this experiment may now be used in the determination of the specific heat of another substance—aluminium, say. The experiment is carried out as before, except that an aluminium block is used in place of the copper one. Since, however, a copper, and not an aluminium, calorimeter is used, the calculation is different. The method is as follows:

Weight of calorimeter (empty)	=	56·5 gm.
Weight of calorimeter + water	=	168·2 gm.
∴ weight of water	=	111·7 gm.
Weight of aluminium block	=	56·4 gm.
Temperature of boiling water	=	99·5° C.
Temperature of cold water in the calorimeter	=	10·2° C.
Temperature of water after transferring the block	=	18·7° C.
∴ temperature of block decreases (99·5 − 18·7)	=	80·8° C.
temperature of water and calorimeter increases (18·7 − 10·2)	=	8·5° C.

Let s be the specific heat of aluminium. 56·4 gm. of aluminium are cooled 80·8° C., and therefore give out (56·4 × 80·8 × s) calories. The specific heat of the copper of which the calorimeter is composed is very nearly 0·1.*

∴ heat taken up by the calorimeter of weight 56·5 gm. during a rise of temperature 8·5° C. = (56·5 × 8·5 × 0·1) calories.

Heat taken up by 111·7 gm. of water heated 8·5° C.

$$= (111·7 × 8·5) \text{ calories.}$$

If we assume that no heat has been lost to, or gained from, the surroundings, the heat given up by the block is equal to the heat gained by the calorimeter and water in it.

∴ (56·4 × 80·8 × s) = (56·5 × 8·5 × 0·1) + (111·7 × 8·5).

Solving the equation, we have :

$$s = 0·219.$$

In the previous experiment the value of the specific heat of copper was found to be 0·092, whereas the specific heat of the copper of the calorimeter has been taken as 0·100. The reasons for this are :

(a) 0·100 is nearly equal to 0·092, and the result would be very little altered if 0·092 were used in the above calculation.

(b) It is easy to multiply by 0·100.

(c) The thermometer, as well as the calorimeter and water in it, has to be heated. By taking the specific heat of the copper as 0·100 some allowance is made for the heat which passes into the thermometer.

5.05. In the above experiment the calorimeter weighed 56·5 gm., and the specific heat of copper was taken as 0·100. Hence, for each degree its temperature is raised, (56·5 × 0·100) = 5·65 calories have to be added to it. 5·65 calories, however, would raise the temperature of 5·65 gm. of water 1° C., so the calorimeter absorbs as much heat as 5·65 gm. of water would do, if both the water and calorimeter were heated through the same number of degrees. The calorimeter is said to have a *water equivalent* of 5·65 gm.

If the temperatures of a given body and a mass of water increase by equal amounts when equal quantities of heat are added to each, the mass of the water is called the water equivalent of the body.

* See below.

The thermal capacity of a body is the quantity of heat required to raise its temperature one degree centigrade. Thus the thermal capacity of the calorimeter considered above is 5·65 calories per degree centigrade.

5.06. The specific heats of many liquids can be found in a similar way to that in which the specific heat of aluminium was found. Thus, the specific heat of paraffin may be measured by heating some paraffin to a known temperature of 30° to 40° C., pouring the paraffin into a known weight of water in a calorimeter at a known temperature, and measuring the temperature of the mixture in the calorimeter. This method, whether a liquid or solid is transferred to the calorimeter, is called the "*method of mixtures*." A paradox of the method of mixtures, however, is that, in spite of its name, it can be used only for substances, such as paraffin or aluminium, which do *not* mix with (*i.e.* dissolve in) water. Sulphuric acid, or alcohol, if mixed with water changes the temperature of the water, even if the sulphuric acid or alcohol is at the same temperature as the water into which it is poured. It is therefore impossible to calculate the specific heats of these substances by equating the heat given out when they are cooled, to the heat taken up by the water and calorimeter.

The specific heat of such substances may, however, be calculated as below. The thermal capacity of a block of metal is first measured by means of measurements such as the following :

Weight of calorimeter (empty)	= 56·5 gm.
Weight of calorimeter + water	= 168·2 gm.
∴ weight of water	= 111·7 gm.
Temperature of boiling water	= 99·5° C.
Temperature of cold water in the calorimeter	= 10·2° C.
Temperature of water after "mixing" aluminium and water	= 18·7° C.
∴ temperature of block decreases (99·5 − 18·7)	= 80·8° C.
temperature of water and calorimeter increases (18·7 − 10·2)	= 8·5° C.

Let c be the thermal capacity of the block (*i.e.* the number of calories given out when its temperature decreases 1° C.)

Heat given out by block falling 80·8° C. = 80·8 × c calories.
Water equivalent of calorimeter = (56·5 × 0·1) = 5·65 gm.
∴ heat taken up by water and calorimeter
$$= \{5\cdot65 + 111\cdot7\} \times 8\cdot5 = (117\cdot3 \times 8\cdot5) \text{ calories.}$$

If we assume that there has been no gain from, or loss of heat to, the surroundings, the heat lost by the aluminium is equal to that gained by the water and calorimeter.

$$\therefore\ 80{\cdot}8 \times c = 117{\cdot}3 \times 8{\cdot}5$$
$$\therefore\ c = \left(\frac{117{\cdot}3 \times 8{\cdot}5}{80{\cdot}8}\right) \text{ calories per degree centigrade.}$$

The same calorimeter is now nearly filled with methylated spirit (say), weighed, and the temperature of the liquid is taken. The same block of aluminium is transferred from boiling water to the methylated spirit in the calorimeter, and the rise of temperature is measured.

$$
\begin{aligned}
\text{Weight of calorimeter} + \text{spirit} &= 141{\cdot}5 \text{ gm.} \\
\therefore\ \text{weight of spirit} = (141{\cdot}5 - 56{\cdot}5) &= 85{\cdot}0 \text{ gm.} \\
\text{Temperature of spirit before "mixing"} &= 10{\cdot}5°\text{ C.} \\
\text{Temperature of spirit after "mixing"} &= 26{\cdot}3°\text{ C.}
\end{aligned}
$$

Let the specific heat of methylated spirit be s. The aluminium block cools from $99{\cdot}5$ to $26{\cdot}3°$ C., and gives up heat

$$\left(\frac{117{\cdot}3 \times 8{\cdot}5}{80{\cdot}8}\right)(99{\cdot}5 - 26{\cdot}3), \text{ or } \left(\frac{117{\cdot}3 \times 8{\cdot}5}{80{\cdot}8} \times 73{\cdot}2\right) \text{ calories.}$$

Heat taken up by calorimeter whose temperature increases

$$(26{\cdot}3 - 10{\cdot}5) = 15{\cdot}8°\text{ C., is } (56{\cdot}5 \times 15{\cdot}8 \times 0{\cdot}1) \text{ calories.}$$

Heat taken up by methylated spirit

$$= (85{\cdot}0 \times 15{\cdot}8 \times s) \text{ calories.}$$

If we assume that there has been no gain or loss of heat, the heat given up by the aluminium is equal to that gained by the calorimeter and methylated spirit.

$$\therefore \left(\frac{117{\cdot}3 \times 8{\cdot}5}{80{\cdot}8} \times 73{\cdot}2\right) = (56{\cdot}5 \times 15{\cdot}8 \times 0{\cdot}1) + (85{\cdot}0 \times 15{\cdot}8 \times s.)$$
Whence, $s = 0{\cdot}60_4$.

5.07. The quantity of heat produced by burning a given weight of coal varies considerably. It depends upon the completeness of the combustion, but it also depends upon the quality of the coal, and where large quantities of coal are consumed it is of the utmost importance that the heating values of various samples should be known. The heat produced by burning 1 gm. of coal may be measured by means of the fuel calorimeter (figure 5.02).

About 1 gm. of coal is placed in the small nickel crucible A.

D

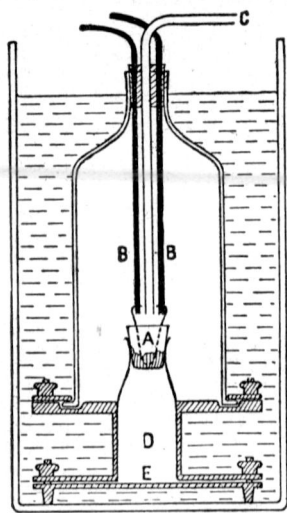

FIG. 5.02.—FUEL CALORIMETER.

and this coal is ignited by passing an electric current through the fine iron wire attached to the bottom of the leads BB. As soon as the coal commences to burn, the electric current is switched off. A steady stream of oxygen, entering through the tube C, passes over the coal in the crucible, and ensures complete combustion. Any unburned oxygen, together with the gases given off by the combustion of the coal, passes down through the broad brass tube D, and escapes through holes in the brass plate E. The whole apparatus stands in a large vessel of water, and the escaping gases, rising through this water, give up their heat to it. The increase of temperature of the water having been noted, the heat of combustion of the coal is calculated as follows :

Weight of nickel crucible (empty)	= 8·16 gm.
Weight of crucible + coal	= 9·10 gm.
∴ weight of coal burned	= 0·94 gm.
Temperature at beginning of experiment	= 15·70° C.
Temperature at end of experiment	= 19·69° C.
∴ increase of temperature	= 3·99° C.
Weight of water in the jar	= 1400 gm.
Water equivalent of apparatus	= 210 gm.
	1610 gm.

∴ heat given out = 1610 × 3·99 calories

∴ 1 gm. of coal burning gives out $\dfrac{1610 \times 3 \cdot 99}{0 \cdot 94}$

$= 6800$ calories.

5.08. We have already noted that in using a calorimeter the temperature of the water in it should never be raised more than 10 to 15° C. above the temperature of the surroundings if large heat losses are to be avoided. This is clearly shown by the graph, figure 5.03. The outer jacket of a calorimeter was removed to allow some hot water in the calorimeter to cool more rapidly, and the temperature of the water was taken at intervals of 1 minute. The figure shows these readings plotted against the corresponding times.

The graph AB is a curved line, steepest at the beginning, when the temperature of the water was high, and least steep

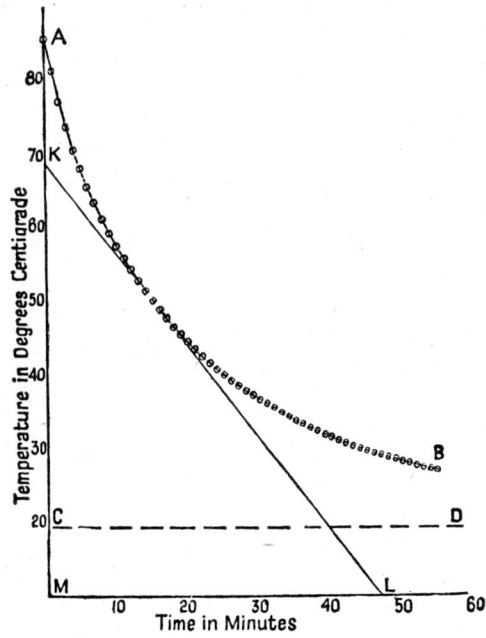

FIG. 5.03.—COOLING CURVE FOR WATER IN A CALORIMETER.

at the end when the temperature was approaching that of the room. Room temperature was 19·3° C. during this experiment, and is indicated on the graph by the dotted line CD.

From the graph it may be seen that during the first 10 minutes the temperature decreased from 85·8° C. to 57·5° C., so the average rate of cooling during this time was $\frac{85·8 - 57·5}{10} = 2·83°$ C. per minute. Similarly, during the last 10 minutes the average rate of cooling was only $\frac{29·8 - 26·9}{10} = 0·29°$ C. per minute.

Hence, the rate of cooling decreases when the temperature decreases. When the calorimeter finally reached the same temperature as its surroundings it would, of course, cease to cool, and the graph would then become parallel to the time axis.

The slope of the graph indicates the rate of cooling. At the beginning the rate of cooling is rapid, and the slope of the graph is steep; later, when the rate of cooling has decreased, the slope has also decreased; and when the water finally reaches room temperature, and its rate of cooling becomes zero, the slope of the graph also becomes zero. Hence, the rate of cooling can be found from the slope of the graph. Let us find the rate of cooling of the calorimeter at 50° C.

We at once meet with a difficulty. The slope of the graph is continually changing. How are we to discover the slope *at* 50° C.? To overcome the difficulty we may draw a tangent to the graph at the point representing a temperature of 50° C. The graph at this point has the same slope as the tangent, so the slope of the tangent represents the rate of cooling of the calorimeter at 50° C.

If a body continued to cool at the same rate as the calorimeter does at this temperature, its cooling graph would be the tangent KL, so the body would cool through the range of temperature represented by KM, in the time represented by ML. Its rate of cooling would therefore be $\dfrac{68\cdot3 - 10}{47\cdot2} = 1\cdot24°$ C. per minute, and this is the rate of cooling of the calorimeter and water at 50° C. The result so obtained is not very reliable, because it is difficult to draw a tangent to a curve accurately.

In the above experiment the water equivalent of the calorimeter and its contents was 94·7 gm. Hence, in cooling 1·24° C. the calorimeter gives out 94·7 × 1·24 calories, so at 50° C. it is losing heat at a rate of (94·7 × 1·24) = 117 calories per minute.

5.09. When similar calculations are performed for the rates of loss of heat at 30° C., 40° C., etc., the results shown in the following table are obtained. The first column gives the temperature of the calorimeter, column II the rate of loss of heat, and column III the difference between the temperature of the calorimeter and that of its surroundings. Referring to lines 1 and 3, we see that when this difference is doubled the rate of loss of heat is also about doubled, so the rate of loss of heat divided by the temperature difference is constant. Column IV

I	II	III	IV
Temperature of Calorimeter. °C.	Rate of Loss of Heat—Calories per minute.	Temperature of Calorimeter minus Room Temperature (°C.).	II ÷ III.
30	32	10·7	3·0
35	47	15·7	3·0
40	67	20·7	3·2
45	91	25·7	3·5
50	117	30·7	3·8
60	173	40·7	4·2
80	344	60·7	5·7

shows the results obtained by dividing the rate of loss of heat by the temperature difference. At temperatures up to 40° C. this quotient is nearly constant, but its value increases rapidly at higher temperatures. Hence,

When the temperature of a body is near the temperature of its surroundings, the rate of loss of heat from the body varies directly as the difference between the temperature of the body and that of its surroundings.

This fact was discovered by Newton (1642–1727), and is known as **Newton's Law of Cooling.**

TABLE OF SPECIFIC HEATS

Lead	0·030	Slate	0·20
Brass	0·089	Aluminium	0·220
Copper	0·093	Ice	0·502
Iron	0·119	Mercury	0·033
Glass	0·16	Sea water . . .	0·94

EXAMPLES 5

1. 1000 gm. of water at 80° C. are mixed with 2000 gm. of water at 15° C. Find the temperature of the mixture.

2. 200 gm. of paraffin at 40° C. are poured into 500 gm. of water at 10° C. Find the resulting temperature. [Specific heat of paraffin = 0·49; no heat is generated when water and paraffin are mixed.]

3. Find how many calories are equivalent to 1 B.Th.U.

4. 30 gallons of water are used for a hot bath, and the temperature of the water is to be raised from 50° F. to 105° F. Find the cost of heating the water by means of a gas heater, assuming that **85**% of the heat of the combustion passes into the water, the gas costing $7\frac{1}{2}d$. per therm. [1 gallon of water weighs 10 lb.]

5. A copper calorimeter weighed 71·9 gm. empty and 162·3 gm. when two-thirds full of water. A block of iron weighing 180·2 gm. was transferred from boiling water at 99·8° C. to the water in the calorimeter, and the temperature of the water rose from 14·3° C. to 29·8° C. Calculate the specific heat of iron. [Specific heat of copper = 0·10.]

6. The calorimeter used in the previous experiment weighed 149·1 gm. when two-thirds full of paraffin at 16·3° C. Calculate the final temperature which will be reached by the paraffin if the same block of iron is transferred from boiling water to the calorimeter. [Specific heat of paraffin = 0·49.]

School Certificate Questions

7. Explain what is meant by the *specific heat* and by the *water equivalent* of a body.

An aluminium calorimeter weighs 28·40 gm. empty, and 80·70 gm. after some water has been poured into it. An aluminium cylinder weighing 79·60 gm. is heated to 98·8° C. and dropped into the water. The temperature of the water rises from 15·2° C. to 34·0° C. Calculate the specific heat of the aluminium and the water equivalent of the calorimeter. (C)

8. Explain what is meant by the terms *unit quantity of heat, thermal capacity, specific heat*. A liquid of specific heat 0·5 and temperature 30° C. is mixed with another liquid of specific heat 0·4 and temperature 15° C. and the final temperature is found to be 20° C. In what proportions by weight were the liquids mixed ? (C)

9. Explain what you understand by the terms (*a*) calorie, and (*b*) specific heat. Describe fully how you would find the specific heat of copper ; point out possible sources of error in your method, and explain the precautions you would take to obtain an accurate result. Make a table showing the quantities you would enter in your practical note-book, and show how you would work out the result. (O)

10. Distinguish between *specific heat, capacity for heat*, and *water equivalent*.

Heat is supplied at 50 calories per second to 500 gm. of water in a vessel of water equivalent 40 gm. The temperature rises from 20° C. to 80° C. in 20 minutes and then remains steady. At what average rate is heat being lost, (*a*) while the temperature is rising, (*b*) after the temperature becomes steady ? State whether you would expect the two rates to agree and give your reason. (J)

11. Explain what is meant by the *specific heat* of a substance. Show how the specific heat of glycerine can be found by the method of mixtures.

A copper ball weighing 500 gm. is placed in a furnace and left until it has attained the furnace temperature. It is then placed in a copper calorimeter of weight 200 gm. containing 1980 gm. of water at 15° C. If the temperature of the water rises to 35° C., what was the temperature of the furnace ? [Take the specific heat of copper as 0·1.]   (J)

12. Describe some method for the determination of the specific heat of a block of copper, giving in detail all the necessary measurements. What precautions would you take to ensure an accurate result ?

A block of copper weighing 200 gm. is heated to 100° C. and then placed in a copper calorimeter, weighing 25 gm., containing 100 gm. of a liquid at a temperature of 10° C. If the specific heat of copper is 0·1, and that of the liquid is 0·64, to what temperature will the liquid rise ?   (B)

13. A silver teapot weighs 300 gm. Tea is made in it from 20 gm. of tea leaves and 600 gm. of water at 100° C. If the temperature of the room is 15° C., what difference will it make to the initial temperature of the tea if the pot is first heated to 80° C. ? [Specific heat of silver = 0·056 ; specific heat of tea leaves = 0·5.] (O.C)

CHAPTER 6

CONDUCTION OF HEAT—CONVECTION

6.01. When one end of a poker is placed in a fire, the end distant from the fire is warmed by heat which passes through the material of which the poker is made. This heat is said to be transferred by **conduction,** and the material is said to act as a conductor of heat. The portion in the fire becomes hot, and transfers heat to the next portion; some of this heat is passed on to the next part, and so on.

Some materials are better conductors of heat than others. If a piece of wood is placed with one end in a fire, only those parts near the fire become hot. Wood, therefore, is a bad conductor of heat.

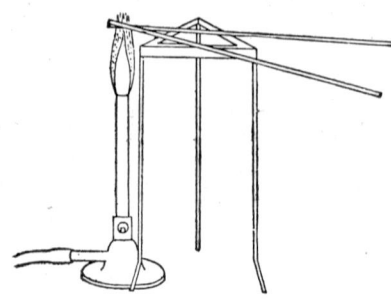

FIG. 6.01.

To compare two substances as conductors, we may use the apparatus shown in figure 6.01. Two rods of similar shapes and sizes, but made of different materials, are heated equally by a Bunsen flame. As heating proceeds, the temperature at each point in the rods increases, but finally becomes constant when as much heat is being lost at the surfaces of the rods as is gained from the flame. When this is the case the ends distant from the flame are felt with the hand. If one rod is of copper and the other is of iron, the copper feels hot, the iron cold. The copper conducts heat better than the iron. Incidentally it will be seen that the portion of the iron rod in the flame is hotter than the corresponding part of the copper rod, because the heat which passes into the iron escapes comparatively slowly along the rod.

It is necessary in this experiment to use rods of the same size. If the diameter of one rod is twice that of a second rod of the same material, the area of cross-section of the first is four times the area of cross-section of the second, and under similar conditions *four* times as much heat will pass along the first rod as along the second. Hence, although the area of the curved surface of the first rod is double that of the other, and thus the rod can lose heat *twice* as rapidly, it is nevertheless heated over a greater length. Experiments confirm this prediction.

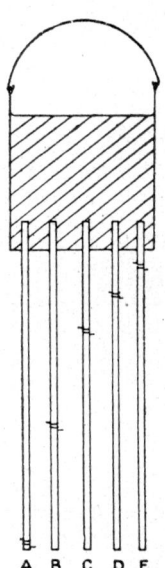

The same principle is applied in the apparatus of Ingenhousz (1730–1799) ; see figure 6.02. A number of similar bars of different metals pass through the bottom of a metal vessel. Each bar carries a small slider, which, at the beginning of the experiment, is close to the vessel, and these sliders are prevented from moving by a thin coat of wax on the bars. Boiling water is poured into the vessel, and kept boiling by an electric heater, thus keeping one end of each bar at a temperature of about 100° C. The heat conducted down the bars melts the wax, allowing the sliders to descend.

The rate at which any slider moves will depend upon the quantity of heat required to heat the bar, so *the rates at which the sliders move do not necessarily indicate which metals are the best conductors.* After some time, however, the temperature at each point in the bars will become steady, and since, when this happens, no further temperature changes occur, no heat is used in heating the bars, but as much heat is lost from their sides and lower ends as is gained at their upper ends. The greater

A B   C D E

FIG. 6.02. — THE COMPARISON OF D I F F E R E N T SUBSTANCES AS CONDUCTORS OF HEAT.

A, copper ; B, aluminium ; C, brass ; D, iron ; E, German silver.

the length of bar above the slider when this occurs, the greater is its heat loss, and hence the greater also is the quantity of heat conducted down the bar. Thus the distances the sliders have descended *when the steady state is reached,* indicate which bars are the better conductors.

Silver is the best conductor of heat, and is followed by copper and aluminium. All metals are comparatively good conductors. Glass, wood, rubber, and air are bad conductors. It is often possible to judge whether a substance is a good or a bad conductor, merely by feeling a piece of it. In a cold room a piece of iron feels cold because the heat from the hand is conducted to all parts of the iron, leaving the hand cold. On the other hand, a piece of wood at the same temperature does not feel so cold, because heat is conducted only to those parts of the wood in contact with the hand. In cold climates frost-bite may be caused by holding cold metal objects in the bare hands.

6.02. Boilers for locomotives and steam-generating plants are usually made of steel, which, being a metal, allows a rapid flow of heat from the furnace to the water in the boiler. Sometimes the portions of a boiler through which the heat must pass are made of copper. Copper conducts the heat more readily than steel, but steel is better able to resist the strains imposed by the pressure inside the boiler, and in boilers which work at very high pressures, steel only is used. Kettles are made of metal for a similar reason.

The quantity of heat which flows through a sheet of material in a given time depends upon the area of the sheet. Many boilers contain numbers of parallel tubes through which the boiler water flows. The gases from the furnace pass over these tubes, and heat is rapidly transferred to the water, owing to the large surface area of the tubes exposed to the furnace gases.

Since metals are all good conductors of heat, the temperature at the inside surface of a metal vessel exposed to a flame is seldom very different from the temperature of the outside surface. Consequently, when a metal vessel is heated, the whole of the vessel expands at the same time, and little strain is caused by excessive expansion at particular points. On the other hand, when a glass vessel is heated the portions in contact with the flame become much hotter than other parts, and the strains set up may cause fracture of the vessel. In the laboratory glass vessels are placed on a piece of wire gauze for heating. The heat from the flame is conducted by the gauze to the whole of the bottom of the glass vessel, and strains in the glass are reduced.

After manufacture, glass vessels are annealed to remove the strains set up when they are moulded. Annealing consists in maintaining the glass at a temperature of several hundred degrees centigrade. At the annealing temperature, which depends upon the type of glass, the glass is solid, but is sufficiently soft to " give " slightly, and the strains are removed. Ordinary glass vessels are annealed for a period of a week or two, the temperature being slowly reduced to room temperature. To enable the glass disc of a large telescope mirror or lens to contract as a whole, however, and to maintain the outside always at the same temperature as the inside, the annealing and cooling must be much slower. The 18-ton glass disc of the latest big telescope was annealed for 50 days at 500° C., and then cooled at less than 1° C. per day, the cooling thus requiring many months. This is in spite of the fact that the disc is made of a special glass with a small coefficient of expansion, and has a ribbed structure to allow it to take up the temperature of its surroundings more readily (see figures 7.02 and 7.03).

Although fused silica is, like glass, a bad conductor of heat, silica vessels are not easily cracked by heating, and a piece of silica may be heated red hot and plunged into water without cracking. The coefficient of expansion of silica is so small that, although strains are set up when a vessel made of it is hotter at some parts than at others, these strains are not severe enough to cause fracture.

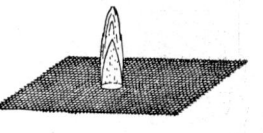

6.03. When a piece of wire gauze is placed over a Bunsen flame, the gas continues to burn below the gauze, but not above it. The gauze does not prevent gas from passing through it, for the gas burns above the gauze if a lighted match is applied to it. Indeed, the gas may be lit above the gauze while that below is not burning (figure 6.03). Gas burns only if its temperature is greater than a certain minimum temperature. When the gas below the

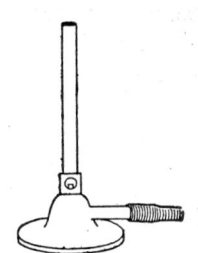

Fig. 6.03.

gauze is burning, that which passes through the gauze is cooled by the good conducting metal strands of the latter, and its temperature is too low for combustion to occur.

In coal mines, quantities of gas are sometimes present, suffi-

cient to cause an explosion if a naked flame is used in the mine.
The safety lamp, invented by Sir Humphry Davy (1778–1829)
in 1816, and independently about the same time by George
Stephenson (1781–1848), minimizes the danger by enclosing the
flame of the lamp in a cover of gauze (figure 6.04).   Air can

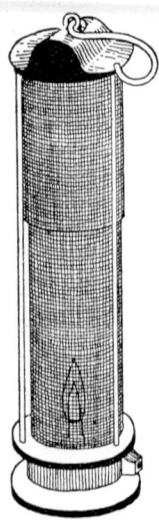

pass through the gauze to keep the flame burning, but any gas which passes into the lamp with
this air is burned inside the gauze, and the
latter prevents the flame spreading to the gas
outside.   Air and gases can only pass through
the gauze slowly, however, and contrary to the
general belief, the chief function of the gauze
appears to be to maintain a sufficiently high
percentage of carbon dioxide round the flame.
It has been shown that if a few per cent. of
carbon dioxide are present, a mixture of gas
and air does not explode, and since carbon
dioxide from the flame is always present inside
the gauze, the gas there is quietly burned,
and no explosion occurs.

The miner can also use the lamp to test for
the presence of dangerous quantities of gas, for
on turning the flame low, he sees, when gas
is present, a light blue cap of flame upon the
ordinary flame.

Fig. 6.04.—Davy
Safety Lamp.

6.04.   The barrel of a machine-gun is surrounded by a number of metal fins.   The heat
generated by continuous firing is conducted
through the fins, and since these expose a large area to
the air, the heat is quickly dissipated.   The heat from the
cylinders of air-cooled aeroplane engines is also removed in this
way by fins surrounding the cylinders (see figure 12.05).

An interesting modern application of the high thermal conductivity of copper is found in the manufacture of strong-room
doors intended to resist the attack of burglars.   A huge block
of copper, a foot or more in thickness, forms the main portion
of the door.   Copper is too soft to be fractured by explosives.
It might be expected to be readily cut by an oxy-acetylene
torch, however, because the melting-point of copper is much
lower than that of steel.   Nevertheless, such a torch can cut
a large block of copper only slowly, because the heat from the

torch is rapidly conducted away from those parts where the flame is applied.

6.05. Air is an extremely bad conductor of heat, and porous materials containing much air are also bad conductors. Clothes, particularly those made of wool, are bad conductors, and hinder the loss of heat from the body. A piece of flannel wrapped round a block of ice prevents the ice melting rapidly, the flannel in this case hindering the flow of heat to the ice. The hair of animals and the feathers of birds serve a similar purpose to that of the clothes we wear.

Straw also contains air and is a bad conductor. In places where fuel is scarce, use is sometimes made of this fact by placing a saucepan of partly cooked food in a large box, where it is surrounded by straw. Heat escapes so slowly that the saucepan remains hot for a long time, and the cooking is completed without the addition of more heat. Modern stoves are surrounded by a thick layer of porous, badly conducting material, to economize in fuel, and steam and hot-water pipes are heavily " lagged " with porous materials to minimize heat losses.

6.06. Rocks and soils are bad conductors of heat, and the heating of the surface soil by the sun's rays on a hot day cannot be detected with a thermometer buried as little as 3 ft. below the ground. Since the heat from the sun is retained in the layers of soil within a few inches of the surface, the rise of temperature of these layers is comparatively large. The water near the surface of the ocean, on the other hand, is mixed by wave motion, and the heat from the sun is distributed throughout a large quantity of water. In some cases daily changes of temperature have been observed at depths 300 ft. below the surface, and since large quantities of water are heated, the rise of temperature is small. Hence, large changes of temperature occur daily over the surface of the land. Over the sea, such changes are small, and places situated near the sea enjoy a more temperate climate than those situated in the heart of a continent. " Insular " and " continental " climates are sometimes explained as due to the fact that the specific heats of rocks and soil are small compared with that of water, but while this fact must also play a part, the principal cause is that explained above.

6.07. The only liquid which is a good conductor of heat is the liquid metal mercury. The following experiment shows that water is a bad conductor. A small piece of ice is weighted with copper wire, and sunk to the bottom of a test-tube. The water near the *top* of the test-tube is heated, and finally boils without melting the ice at the bottom, so little is the heat conducted downwards through the water.

You may wonder why it is necessary to go to the trouble of sinking the ice, and heating the water at the *top* of the test-tube. Heat is conducted along a metal bar equally well whether the bar is heated at the top or the bottom. If some ice is floated at the top of a test-tube, however, and the water is heated at the bottom, the ice quickly melts, showing that heat is transferred rapidly from the bottom to the top of the test-tube.

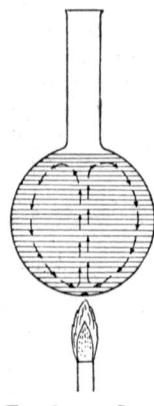

FIG. 6.05.—CON-VECTION CUR-RENTS IN A LIQUID.

A further experiment enables us to understand why this is so. A large flask is filled with water, and a small crystal of potassium permanganate is dropped into the water. As the potassium permanganate dissolves, it produces a coloured solution, and any movement of the water is shown by coloured streaks extending from the crystal. The water near the crystal is gently heated by means of a Bunsen burner. (No wire gauze is used in this experiment to distribute the heat to the whole of the bottom of the flask, since the object is to heat the water near the crystal only.) Streaks of colour show that the water in the flask is now in motion as shown by the arrows in figure 6.05. As the water at the bottom of the flask is heated, it expands and is displaced by the colder, dense water at the top of the flask.

By the time the water which was first heated reaches the top of the flask that at the bottom has been heated still hotter, and is displaced in its turn by the water above. In this way, steady currents are set up in the liquid, and heat is transferred with the moving liquid. Each portion of the latter, on reaching the bottom of the flask, receives heat, which it then carries to other parts of the vessel. Heat is said to be transferred in this case by **convection** and the currents set up in the liquid are called convection currents.

Convection currents are not readily set up in a liquid which is heated at the top, since they are caused by the expansion of the liquid. If the layers near the surface are hotter than those below, the less dense liquid on top is unable to displace the denser liquid near the bottom. In a solid, each particle has a fixed position and there can be no convection.

6.08. Convection of heat is used to cool the cylinders of motor-car engines. Figure 6.06 illustrates the method used. Heat is conducted through the cylinder walls to the water in the jacket A surrounding the cylinder. The radiator B contains water which is kept cool by means of a fan which draws a current of air through

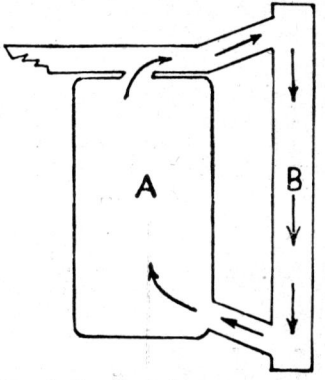

FIG. 6.06.—THE ACTION OF THE RADIATOR OF A MOTOR-CAR.

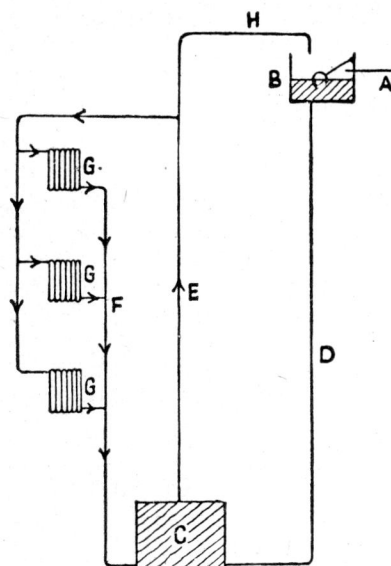

FIG. 6.07.—HEATING SYSTEM OF A HOUSE.
A, inlet from mains; B, feed tank; C, boiler; G, G, G, radiators; H, open vent.

tubes passing through the radiator. The cold, dense water in the radiator is thus able to force the hot water in the jacket out through the upper tube to the radiator, where it is cooled in turn. A continuous circulation is set up as shown by the arrows.

6.09. Figure 6.07 shows an arrangement for heating a house by means of convection currents. Cold water enters the heating system by the pipe A at the top of the house, where it flows into the tank B. An automatic valve ensures that the level of the water in B is kept constant, and allows small quantities of water to enter B whenever the level falls owing to evaporation of water from the system. Water reaches the boiler C, situated in the basement, by means of the pipe D, which enters the boiler at the bottom. As the water in the boiler is heated, it is forced up the pipe E by cold water returning along F from the radiators G. When the hot water enters these, it gives up some of its heat to the air near the radiators, is cooled, and forces its way back to the boiler, displacing more hot water, and causing a steady circulation of water as shown by the arrows. The pipe H allows air which was dissolved in the cold water to escape, and at the same time serves as a safety-valve by allowing steam to escape if the water in the boiler becomes too hot. The temperature of the water leaving the boiler is usually about 80° C. It should be noticed that the pipes D and F enter the boiler at the bottom ; E leaves from the top of the boiler ; the hot water enters the top of the radiators, and, after being cooled, leaves at the bottom. Why are these arrangements necessary ?

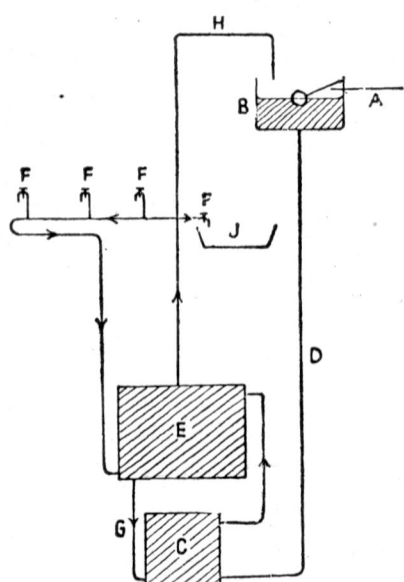

Fig. 6.08.—Domestic Hot-water System.

A, inlet from mains ; B, feed and expansion tank ; C, boiler ; E, storage tank ; F, F, F, F taps ; H, open vent ; J, bath.

The hot-water supply system of a house is shown in figure 6.08. A valve regulates the entry of water into the system through the pipe A. From the feed tank B the water flows to the boiler C. Hot water from the top of the boiler passes to the storage tank E, which serves as a hot-water reservoir, so that large quantities of hot water are available when required. A steady circulation of hot water past the taps is maintained by convection currents, the water which is cooled by heat losses from the pipes returning to the bottom of the storage tank. The colder water at the bottom of the tank is returned by the pipe G to the bottom of the boiler. Any air or steam produced escapes through the pipe H, and when the water in the boiler and storage tank is heated and expands, the excess water flows into the tank B.

6.10. Convection currents occur in gases as well as in liquids. It is possible to hold a finger within a millimetre of the *side* of a Bunsen flame without experiencing any sensation of hotness, for the hot gases from the flame are driven upwards in the convection currents. It is, however, impossible to hold the hand 10 cm. above the flame.

Convection currents in gases may be shown by using the smoke from burning blotting-paper. The blotting-paper is first soaked in a solution of nitre, and allowed to dry. When it is ignited it continues to smoulder, and gives off smoke which follows the direction of the currents in the surrounding air.

In the experiment shown in figure 6.09, a lighted candle stands in a box, the front of which is closed by a sheet of glass. The box is fitted with two glass tubes A and B. Cold air sinks through the tube B and forces out the less dense, warm air through

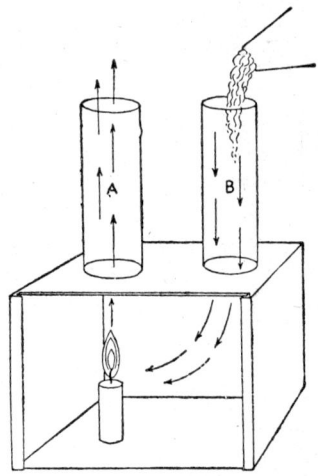

Fig. 6.09.—Convection Currents in Air.

the tube A. The air which escapes through A contains carbon dioxide produced by the combustion, and would therefore be heavier, volume for volume, than the air which enters at B, if the temperatures of both of these quantities of air were equal. The air above the flame is so much hotter than the rest of the air in the room, however, that, in spite of the admixture with carbon dioxide, it is less dense.

Two tubes are necessary for this experiment if convection currents are to be set up. If a lighted candle is placed at the bottom of a lamp glass the candle is extinguished as carbon dioxide accumulates at the bottom. A **T**-piece of cardboard, placed as shown in figure 6.10, however, allows a regular flow to be set up, the cold air sinking down one side of the **T**, and driving out the warm air from the candle on the other.

Convection currents were at one time used in the ventilation of mines. Two shafts were sunk, and connected at the bottom by a horizontal shaft. A fire was kept burning at the bottom of one of the vertical shafts, and a current of heavy, cold air from the surface descended the other, displacing the heated air

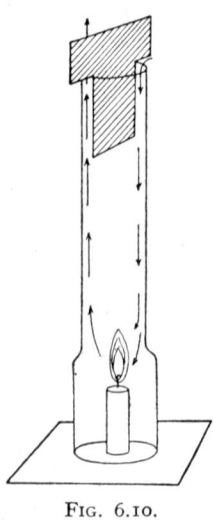

FIG. 6.10.

above the fire, and providing a stream of fresh air through the workings. Nowadays large fans are used for mine ventilation.

The ventilation of most buildings, however, is still performed by convection. A fire in a room continually replenishes the air in the room, cold, dense air driving out the warm air through the chimney. Even if no fire is burning, however, the cold, heavy air from outside displaces the warm air we breathe out. The latter contains a larger percentage of carbon dioxide than fresh air does, and when the temperature of the air exhaled reaches the same temperature as the surrounding air, it is denser than fresh air, and begins to sink again. Hence, the air breathed out should be removed before it becomes cooled, and the upper ventilators in a room should never be more than about 12 ft. above floor level. Other ventilators near the floor allow fresh air to enter.

The ventilation of draught cupboards in the chemistry laboratory is sometimes performed by means of a burner at the bottom of a flue leading out of the building.

6.11. Convection currents occur in nature upon a large scale. The surface of the land is more rapidly heated during the daytime than are neighbouring lakes and oceans. At night it cools more rapidly. During the day the air above the land is warmed by contact with the ground, and is hotter than the air over the sea; at night the air over the sea is warmer than that over the land. Hence, convection currents are set up as shown in figures 6.11 and 6.12, and a breeze blows from the sea to the land in the daytime, and from the land to the sea at night.

Such land and sea breezes render the climate of islands in the tropics much more temperate than that of continental regions in the same latitudes.

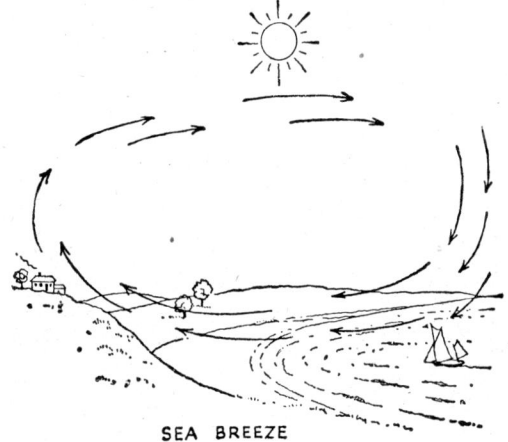

SEA BREEZE

Fig. 6.11.—A Sea Breeze.

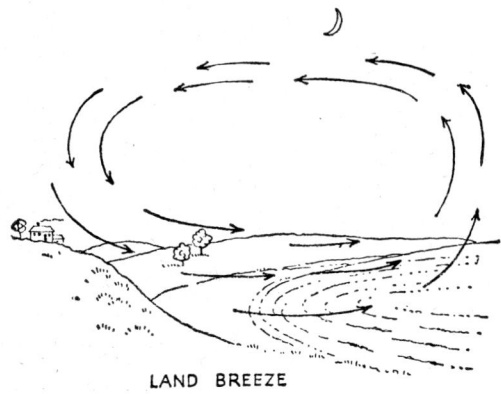

LAND BREEZE

Fig. 6.12.—A Land Breeze.

Land and sea breezes, formed in this way, are only experienced within a few miles of the seashore. Seasonal winds of a similar type, however, occur with great regularity in certain parts of the world, and influence the climate of large areas of the earth's surface.

During the summer, the huge land mass of the continent of Asia is heated more rapidly than the water of the Indian Ocean, although the latter lies nearer to the equator. About mid-summer, the monsoon sets in, carrying warm, moist air from above the Indian Ocean across south-eastern Asia, as shown in figure 6.13. The monsoon is a large convection current of air, caused by the fact that the air above central Asia is at a higher temperature than that above the oceans. The monsoonal winds

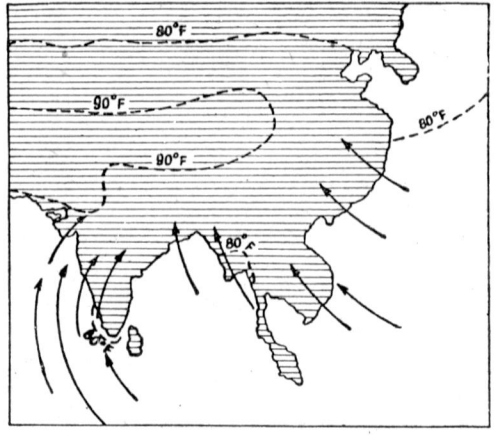

FIG. 6.13.

are cooled as they are raised to high altitudes in passing over mountain ranges, and produce the heavy summer rainfall of India, China, and the Malay peninsula. During the winter, the air above the continent is cooled to a lower temperature than that over the surrounding oceans, and flows outwards from the land. In consequence, the winter season is a comparatively dry one in the lands mentioned. The dotted lines in figure 6.13 connect places where the mean temperature during July is the same.

Other seasonal winds of the monsoon type occur in East Africa, the south-east of the United States, and in north-west Australia.

Near the equator, where the land and ocean are most strongly heated, the air is correspondingly hot, so winds might be expected to blow towards the equator from both north and south, to displace the warmer air in the torrid zone. Although regular winds of this kind occur, their direction is not due north and south. In the northern hemisphere the trade winds, as they are called, blow from the north-east, and in the southern hemisphere they blow from the south-east. The earth is rotating, and its motion is greatest at the equator. Consequently the air approaching the equator lags behind the moving earth, thus causing the easterly direction of the trade winds.

EXAMPLES 6

1. Explain what is meant by conduction of heat. How would you show (a) that copper is a better conductor of heat than brass, (b) that glass is a better conductor than wood ?

2. Explain why a thick piece of glass cracks if it is heated rapidly. Why does not a vessel crack on heating if it is made of (a) silica, (b) iron ?

3. Which is more likely to crack when boiling water is poured into it, a thick tumbler or a thin one ? Why is a piece of wire gauze placed under a glass vessel which is to be heated ?

4. Three kettles of similar shapes, sizes, and thicknesses are made of copper, aluminium, and iron respectively. They are filled with water and placed over a gas burner in turn. In which will the water boil most quickly ? Copper is about eight times as good a conductor as iron. Will the water in the copper kettle be heated eight times as quickly as that in the iron kettle ? Give reasons.

5. Explain the following facts :

(a) If a piece of wood and a piece of iron are placed in an oven the iron feels much hotter than the wood, although both are at the same temperature.

(b) In cold climates double windows are used with an air space between the sheets of glass.

(c) Bricks are often constructed with hollow spaces inside.

(d) Blocks of ice in the laboratory are wrapped in flannel.

6. On a hot day the dry sand on the seashore may be too hot to stand on with bare feet, the moist sand feels comparatively cool, the water in shallow pools feels warm, and the sea feels cold. Explain these facts.

7. Explain land and sea breezes. To what factors do you attribute the fact that the land is warmer than the sea on a hot day ?

8. Describe the hot-water system of a house, paying attention

to those factors which cause flow of the water in the system. Why is water a suitable liquid for the purpose ?

9. The windows of a room can be opened (a) at the top, (b) at the bottom, (c) at the top and the bottom. Assuming that the area through which air can enter and leave is the same in each case, which method will cause most efficient, and which least efficient ventilation ? Give reasons.

10. Would you expect (a) the air, (b) the water at a distance of 100 yards from an iceberg to be colder than the air or water farther away ? Give reasons.

School Certificate Questions

11. Explain what is meant by the *conduction* of heat. Describe (a) an experiment which shows that copper is a better conductor than iron, and (b) another which shows that water is a poor conductor.

Describe the Davy safety lamp and explain how the principle of its action can be illustrated by experiment. (J)

12. What are the physical properties of water which make it suitable for use in a house heating apparatus ? Draw a diagram of such a hot-water system and explain how the heat produced by the fuel reaches an object in the room being heated. (O.C)

13. Describe an experiment to show that copper is a better conductor of heat than iron. State and explain *two* natural phenomena which are dependent on the bad thermal conductivity of water. (O.C)

CHAPTER 7

RADIATION

7.01. By placing a metal fire screen in front of a hot fire, **the** heat from the fire is cut off. The metal screen is a good conductor of heat, and if the heat from the fire were carried to the room by conduction, the screen would assist, rather than hinder, the conduction. The heat from the fire does not reach the room by convection, because the smoke of the fire shows that the convection currents flow from the room to the fire, and thence up the chimney. Hence, objects in the room receive their heat neither by conduction nor by convection. There must therefore be a third method by which heat is transferred, and this is called **radiation.**

To cut off the heat of the fire from a given object, the screen must be placed directly between the object and the fire. Evidently radiation of heat occurs along straight lines extending outwards from the hot object. It is transferred by rays similar to rays of light. Obviously it travels extremely rapidly, because the radiation is shut off instantly, when the screen is placed in front of the fire. Conduction, on the other hand, takes place only slowly. The heat conducted along a short copper rod takes several seconds to traverse the rod. Convection also takes place slowly, and the slow motion of convection currents will have been noticed in the experiments described in the previous chapter.

The heat from the sun reaches the earth by radiation, and during most of its journey from the sun, the radiation travels through empty space. During the last few miles of its path the radiation passes through air, but it heats this air so little that air temperatures at high altitudes are much lower than those near the surface of the earth, where the air is heated by contact with the earth. Some of the radiation which reaches the earth's surface is absorbed, and the heat produced maintains the temperature of the earth. Since the radiation does not alter the temperature of the air through which it passes, it is evidently not heat, but heat is produced whenever radiation is absorbed.

During an eclipse of the sun, when the light from the sun is cut off by the moon, the heat radiation is cut off at the same time. Hence, light and heat radiation take the same time to travel from the moon to the earth, and therefore travel at the same speed. This is not a mere coincidence, for light and heat radiation are similar in many other respects. Both travel in straight lines at the same speed; both can be reflected at a mirror; both are emitted by a hot body; both can pass through some substances, and are absorbed by others; and both can be brought to a focus by a lens, as in the experiment where the sun's rays are concentrated by a magnifying-glass, and made to burn paper. The nature of the relationship between radiation and light will be better understood when light has been studied, and we shall not further discuss the matter here.

We may summarize the chief differences between the transference of heat by radiation and the transference of heat by conduction and convection by saying that:

(a) radiation occurs along straight lines only; convection and conduction take place in various directions;

(b) radiation travels extremely rapidly; convection and conduction transfer the heat slowly;

(c) radiation can travel through a vacuum, but some medium is necessary for conduction and convection;

(d) if radiation passes through a medium, the medium is only heated when radiation is absorbed, but the medium is always heated when convection or conduction occurs.

7.02. If the inner vessel of a calorimeter is covered with a thin coat of lampblack, filled with hot water, and allowed to cool, it might be expected to lose heat less rapidly than a similar calorimeter which is not so coated, since the lampblack reduces the rate at which heat is conducted to the outside of the vessel. In practice, however, it is found that the polished calorimeter loses heat more slowly than the other. The blackened surface radiates heat more rapidly than a polished one at the same temperature.

The radiation from a hot object may be detected by means of a thermopile. The principle of this instrument does not concern us here, and it is only necessary to state that, when radiation falls upon a thermopile, an electric current is produced, and this can be used to move the pointer of a galvanometer. The galvanometer is deflected, for example, if the hand is held in front of the thermopile, because the hand is warm, and radiates to the instrument. The thermopile A (figure 7.01) is placed in front of a cubical metal vessel B, one side of which is blackened, one covered with white paper, and the others brightly polished. Steam from the boiler C is passed through the cube, and maintains its temperature at 100° C. The screen D shields the thermopile from radiation from the boiler and the flame. On turning the cube so that each side faces the thermopile in turn, it is found that the galvanometer deflection is least when the

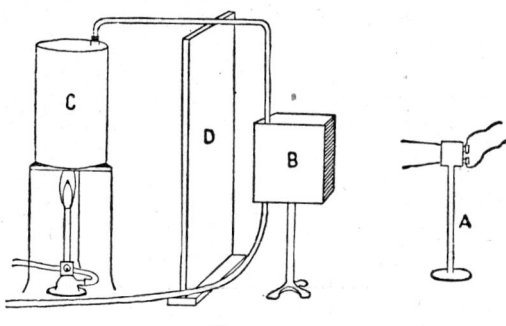

Fig. 7.01.

polished faces are radiating towards the thermopile, and is greatest for the radiation from the blackened surface. Hence, *a blackened surface is the best radiator, and a polished surface the worst.*

Silver teapots and copper hot-water urns must be kept highly polished if they are to retain their heat as long as possible. The radiators for heating a house should not be polished if they are to emit the maximum amount of heat. In the case of such radiators, however, about four-fifths of the heat they supply to a room is transferred by convection and conduction, so little advantage is gained by painting them black.

7.03. The radiation which falls upon a body may be (*a*) reflected, (*b*) absorbed, or (*c*) transmitted through the body. Radiation is reflected well at any brightly polished surface. It may be reflected to a thermopile by means of a bright sheet of galvanized iron, for example. Electric radiators are fitted with a polished copper or silver reflector, which directs a beam of radiation across the room.

If a body reflects a large fraction of the heat radiation falling on it, only a small fraction can be absorbed. In other words, **a good reflector is a bad absorber of radiation.** The polished helmets worn by firemen are good reflectors, and therefore absorb little radiation.

7.04. Good radiators are good absorbers. We have seen that a blackened calorimeter is a better radiator than a polished one. If a blackened and a polished calorimeter, both full of water, are placed in front of an electric radiator, the blackened calorimeter is heated by the radiation more quickly than the other.

That this must be so is shown as follows. The objects which surround a body cannot influence the amount of radiation it gives out. (They may, of course, reflect some of it back again, or may themselves radiate to it, but that is another matter.) If a body at room temperature is placed near a block of ice, some of the ice is melted by radiation from the body. Even if the body is cooled to 0° C., however, it does not cease to radiate, since a block of solid carbon dioxide is caused to evaporate if it is suspended inside an enclosure at 0° C. It seems, therefore, that even cold bodies are continually radiating. If this is the case, why does not every body gradually become colder and colder? The obvious answer is that bodies would do so if they were not themselves receiving radiation from other objects. **A body continues to cool until it is radiating just as much radiation as it is receiving.**

Imagine now two bodies placed side by side, one body being blackened and the other polished, but both at the same temperature. The blackened body is a good radiator, the polished body a bad one. Hence, more radiation streams towards the polished body than in the reverse direction, and if the polished body is also a good absorber, it will absorb more radiation than it loses, and its temperature will rise. Similarly, if the blackened body is a bad absorber, it will lose more radiation than it receives, and its temperature will fall. When two bodies at the same temperature are placed side by side, however, it is not found that the temperature of one rises while that of the other falls, but both bodies remain at their initial temperature. Hence, if a body is a good radiator it must also be a good absorber and if it is a bad radiator it must also be a bad absorber.

We saw earlier that a white surface is intermediate between a blackened and a polished surface as a radiator. It is also intermediate between these as an absorber. If part of a sheet of paper is blackened, part left white, and part is converted into a polished surface by painting it with aluminium paint, and the sheet is held in front of an electric radiator, the blackened

By courtesy of The Corning Glass Works

FIG. 7.02.—THE 120-IN. DIAMETER GLASS DISC FOR A LARGE TELESCOPE.

portion is heated most strongly, and the polished portion least. This may be shown by means of a piece of heat-sensitive paper attached to the back of the other piece. The sensitive paper turns green when heated, and the hottest portions become darkest.

Figure 7.02 shows the glass disc for a large telescope mirror. The disc is made with a ribbed structure, and less light is reflected from the thick ribs than from the porcelain supports beneath. Hence, the ribs appear as dark lines on the disc.

Figure 7.03 shows the same disc in the furnace before it was allowed to cool. The thick ribs are good absorbers, both of light and radiation, and they are therefore good radiators. In the furnace the disc is seen by means of the light which it itself radiates, so the ribs now appear as white lines and circles on a dark background.

A body which is a bad radiator can be heated in a Bunsen

[*By courtesy of The Corning Glass Works.*

FIG. 7.03.

The same disc as that shown in the previous figure. The disc is in a furnace, and is here seen by means of the radiation it is itself emitting.

flame to a higher temperature than a similar body which is a good radiator. Gas mantles are made of thoria and ceria, two materials which are bad radiators, and which can therefore be heated to a high temperature. Generally speaking, if a substance is a bad radiator of heat radiation, it is also a bad radiator of light rays, but these particular substances are chosen because they happen to emit light almost as well as a blackened surface, although they are otherwise bad radiators.

7.05. Dry air transmits nearly all the radiation which falls upon it. If this were not so, moving the cube B of figure 7.01 still nearer to the thermopile would cause a larger deflection of the galvanometer, but this does not happen. By placing screens of wood, cardboard, and metal between a thermopile and a source of radiation, it may be shown that none of these substances transmits radiation. These facts are expressed by saying that dry air is *diathermanous*, but wood, cardboard, and metal are *adiathermanous*.

Some solids are diathermanous. A plate of rock salt, for example, held in front of a thermopile allows more than 90% of the radiation to pass through. Rock salt is transparent, and since radiation is similar to light, we might suspect that all transparent substances are diathermanous also. Glass, for example, transmits light. Will it also transmit radiation?

By placing a glass screen in front of the radiating cube of figure 7.01, it may be shown that nearly all the radiation is shut off by the glass. Glass is apparently adiathermanous. Glass does, however, transmit radiation in certain cases, for we receive warmth from the radiation of the sun after it has passed through glass windows.

The following experiments will assist us to find the explanation of this apparent paradox. The radiating cube, whose temperature is 100° C., is replaced by an electric heater, whose temperature is about 800° C. About one-third of the radiation from this is able to pass through the glass. When a gas-filled electric-light bulb is used as radiator, a larger fraction of the radiation passes through the glass sheet. The temperature of the radiating filament is in this case about 2300° C., so we see that radiation from a very hot source is partly transmitted by glass, while radiation from a source at a lower temperature is completely stopped by it. It is obvious, therefore, that *heat radiation is not all of the same type, and that the type of heat radiation depends to some extent upon the temperature of the body emitting it.*

Fire screens are occasionally made of glass, and such screens transmit the cheerful light of the fire, while cutting off the heat radiation. The glass buildings used for growing sensitive plants make use of the same property of glass. The walls and roof of the building transmit the radiation from the sun, which is a source at 6000° C., and this radiation is absorbed and converted into heat in the interior of the building. The radiation from the interior, however, is that of a source at a low temperature, and is unable to escape. The interior is thus kept several degrees above the temperature of objects outside.

Water, like glass, is adiathermanous to radiation from cool bodies, and diathermanous to that from a hot source. This has an interesting application to the measurement of the temperature of the surface of the moon. Its temperature can be calculated if the amount of radiation emitted by it is known. The moon, however, reflects the sun's radiation, as well as emitting its own. The two different types of radiation have been separated by passing the radiation into water, when the radiation from the sun is transmitted, while that from the moon is absorbed.

7.06. We may now explain more fully the construction of the **calorimeter** (figure 5.01). The inner vessel is made of copper, because copper is a good conductor of heat. Hence, the whole vessel—not merely those parts in contact with the liquid —reaches the same temperature as the liquid in the calorimeter, as is assumed in the calculations.

Heat losses from the calorimeter must be reduced to a minimum. Conduction is prevented, as far as possible, by mounting the inner vessel upon three blocks of wood. Wood is a bad conductor, and three is the smallest number of supports which will hold the calorimeter firmly. Convection currents are not easily set up in the narrow space between the two vessels, and draughts in the room do not reach the inner vessel. Since air is a bad conductor, little heat is conducted across the air gap. To reduce radiation from it, the calorimeter is polished ; and if the temperature of the room is above that of the calorimeter, the polished surface again prevents the transfer of heat by radiation, since it is a good reflector.

The heat losses from a Dewar vacuum flask (thermos flask) are even smaller than those from a calorimeter. Two forms of vacuum flask are shown in figure 7.04. The flask is made of glass. (The outer metal container sold with it merely prevents damage to the flask.) Glass is a bad conductor, so little heat is conducted up the sides of the inner vessel to reach the air. Convection currents are completely absent in the space between the inner and outer vessels, for the space between them is evacuated. Convection currents between the inside of the flask and the air are prevented by a cork or a rubber stopper in the neck of the flask. Both cork and rubber are bad conductors. The outer surface of the inner vessel is silvered to reduce radiation, but since some radiation always occurs, the inside surface of the outer flask is also silvered. This silver coating reflects back much of the radiation which is emitted from the inner vessel.

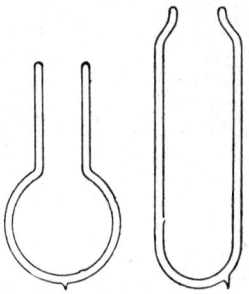

Such a flask is equally effective for storing hot or cold liquids, since the transfer of heat in either direction is reduced to a minimum. Indeed, the vacuum flask was originally designed by Sir James Dewar (1842–1923) for storing liquid air, and serves its purpose so well that liquid air can be stored in it for days. The same quantity of liquid air

FIG. 7.04.—DEWAR FLASKS.

would evaporate in a few minutes from an ordinary vessel.

EXAMPLES 7

1. A good reflector is a bad absorber of radiation. Explain why this must be so. Give an account of an experiment which illustrates the above statement.

2. Explain why a good absorber must also be a good radiator.

3. A piece of porcelain, crossed by a pattern of dark lines, is heated in a Bunsen flame in a dark room. What would you expect to observe when it became hot ? Give reasons for your answer.

4. Explain the use of incandescent gas mantles for producing light. Why do they emit more light than (a) a gas flame without a mantle, (b) a piece of platinum heated in the same flame, (c) a piece of charcoal in the flame ?

5. A thin piece of platinum foil is held in a Bunsen flame in a dark room. If some ink marks have been made on the platinum, what would you expect to observe when the foil is viewed, (a) from the side on which the marks are made, (b) from the other side ? Give reasons.

6. Explain why the temperature at the top of a mountain is lower than that at its foot. What evidence can you give, apart from that of measurements of its absorption, to show that air must be a bad absorber of radiation ?

7. Give an account of the construction of a calorimeter, pointing out the reasons for its design, and the particular materials used.

8. Explain how the use of glass houses protects sensitive plants from damage by frost.

9. A flask of hot water stands on a table. Give a concise account of the various ways in which it loses heat. In what way would the rate of loss be affected if a large sheet of copper were placed under the flask and a glass beaker inverted over it so as to enclose it completely ?   (B)

10. A red-hot metal ball is held at the end of an iron rod in the middle of a room. Describe and discuss the various ways in which the ball is losing heat. Give a cooling curve of temperature against time, showing how you think the ball will fall in temperature, and give your reason for the shape of the graph.   (O)

11. What is meant by *radiant heat* ? Describe *two* experiments to illustrate different properties of radiant heat. A red-hot ball of iron is suspended in air by a wire. In what ways does the ball lose heat ? How would you confirm your answer experimentally ? (O)

12. Describe an experiment to show that the rate at which a hot body gives out heat depends upon the nature of its surface. State clearly (a) the observations you would make, and (b) the conclusions which may be drawn from the observations.

Discuss (a) the highly polished steam pipes in an engine-room, and (b) the appearance of the outside of the cylinder of an air-cooled motor-cycle engine.   (O)

13. State the processes by which heat passes to or from a body. Describe the construction of a vacuum flask, explaining the action of its devices in keeping a cold substance at a low temperature.
                                                                                                        (L)

14. Describe *convection* and *radiation*. Discuss the relative importance of these two processes in the transfer of heat into a room from (a) a brightly burning coal fire, (b) a radiator of a hot-water system. How would you compare the amounts of heat radiated from these two sources ?   (L)

15. Explain with the help of two examples what is meant by the *radiation of heat*. State briefly how this process differs from conduction and convection respectively. Two hot bodies at the same temperature, both of good conducting material, are placed some distance apart in the same room, and supported on non-conductors. What considerations determine the relative rates of (a) loss of heat, (b) fall of temperature ?   (J)

16. How would you show experimentally (a) that the quantity of heat radiated from a surface depends upon the nature of the surface, (b) that good radiating surfaces are good absorbers ? What are the grounds for considering that the quantities of heat radiated and absorbed by the surface of a body in a room at uniform temperature are equal when the body is at the same temperature as the room ?   (J)

CHAPTER 8

THE MECHANICAL EQUIVALENT OF HEAT

8.01. The word "*work*" in everyday life is applied to any occupation which causes fatigue. In physics, however, it is used in a special sense, and work is said to be done if a force is applied to a body, and the force causes the body to move. **The work done is defined to be the product of the force and the distance the body is moved in the direction of the force.** Hence, in the language of physics, a crane which holds a heavy weight in position for several minutes is doing no work, because, although the crane is exerting a force, the distance moved is zero, so the product of force and distance moved is also zero. If the crane raises the block, however, even by so little as $\frac{1}{1000}$th of an inch, some work is done.

Work may be done by a man using his muscular strength, by such machines as cranes or electric motors, or by forces such as the weight of a body. Thus, if a body whose weight is 100 lb. falls a distance of 10 ft., work has been done by the pull exerted by the earth on the body (*i.e.* its weight), and the amount of this work is:

$$\begin{aligned} \text{Work} &= \text{force} \times \text{distance moved} \\ &= 100 \text{ lb.} \times 10 \text{ ft.} \\ &= 1000 \text{ foot-pounds (ft.-lb.).} \end{aligned}$$

In the metric system, work may be measured in *gram-centimetres*. One gm.-cm. is the work done by a force of 1 gm.-wt. moving a body 1 cm. Since forces are often measured in the metric system in dynes, work may also be measured in terms of the work done when a force of 1 dyne moves a body 1 cm. This unit of work is called 1 *erg*. One gm.-wt. is equal to 981 dynes, so 1 gm.-cm. is equal to 981 ergs. The erg is a very small unit of work, and to avoid using very large numbers, a larger unit called the *joule* is often used. One joule is equal to 10,000,000 ergs.

EXAMPLE : *A body weighing 1 ton is raised 50 ft. by a crane. Find the work done on the body (a) in ft.-lb., (b) in gm.-cm., (c) in ergs, (d) in joules.*

The work done is the product of the force applied and the distance moved.

$$\therefore \text{Work} = 2240 \times 50 = 112{,}000 \text{ ft.-lb.}$$

1 ft. = 12 in., and 100 cm. = 39·37 in., so $1 \text{ ft.} = \dfrac{12 \times 100}{39\cdot37}$ cm.

1 lb. = 454 gm.

$$\therefore \text{Work done} = \left[2240 \times 50 \times \frac{12 \times 100}{39\cdot37} \times 454\right] \text{ gm.-cm.}$$

$$= 1\cdot55 \times 10^9 \text{ gm.-cm.}$$

1 gm.-wt. = 981 dynes

$$\therefore \text{Work done} = (1\cdot55 \times 10^9 \times 981) \text{ ergs}$$

$$= 1\cdot52 \times 10^{12} \text{ ergs}$$

$$\therefore \text{Work done} = 1\cdot52 \times 10^5 \text{ joules.}$$

A body which is able to perform work is said to possess energy. If a stone at the top of a cliff is attached to a rope passing over a pulley, the stone is able to exert a force on the rope, and could do work (*e.g.* by raising another stone) as it descended to the bottom of the cliff. It would then no longer be able to do work, and therefore has less energy than before. The energy possessed by the stone was due to its position at the top of the cliff, and energy which a body possesses because of its position is called *potential energy*.

A moving body always possesses energy because of its motion. The head of a hammer, which strikes a nail and drives it into a block of wood, possesses energy of this kind. The energy possessed by a body because of its motion is called *kinetic energy*. In books on mechanics, it is shown that the kinetic energy of a body can be found by taking half the product of the mass and the square of the velocity of the moving body.

8.02. In the previous chapters of this book we have seen how heat is measured, and how it is transferred, but we have not learned what heat is. If you have thought of heat as some kind of invisible material which can flow from one body to another as water can flow from one layer of sand to another, you will have formed a picture very like that formed by scientists up to the end of the eighteenth century. Physicists believed that this invisible material, which they called *caloric*, could be absorbed in different amounts by different materials. Water, for example, has a high specific heat, and could obviously absorb large quantities of caloric. Caloric was also believed to combine with some substances to form new chemical compounds. Thus when caloric was added to ice, a new substance, water, was formed, and if water combined with more caloric, steam was produced.

If two objects, such as two pieces of wood, are rubbed together, both become hot. Similarly, when a piece of metal is bored in the workshop, the bit becomes heated, and must be cooled by applying oil. These facts were known to scientists, and could also be explained by the caloric theory. When a piece of wood or metal was rubbed or hammered, caloric was said to be squeezed out of the material, like water out of a sponge, and since the material could now contain only a smaller quantity of caloric, the surplus caloric caused a rise of temperature. Nevertheless, the investigation of the heat produced by friction was finally to show that the caloric theory was false.

8.03. It is to be noticed that, if heat is a material which is squeezed out of a solid by boring or rubbing, the solid must then possess less of this caloric than before, and if boring is carried on for a sufficiently long time, *all* the caloric should finally be squeezed out of the body. Further boring would then produce no more caloric.

About the year 1800, Count Rumford (1753–1814), a British scientist and soldier, who was at this time engaged in work at the arsenal at Munich, was struck by the very large quantities of heat which were produced by boring cannon. Among other experiments which he performed, he carried out several in which a blunt borer was deliberately chosen for boring a block of gun-metal. The block of metal having been wrapped in flannel to prevent heat losses, it was filled with water, and the borer was turned by a horse for half an hour. At the end of this time, the temperature of the block was measured, and it was found that more than 4000 calories of heat had been produced for each gram of gun-metal rubbed away by the borer. In later experiments, when the boring was continued for longer periods, still larger quantities of heat were produced.

In his account of these experiments, Rumford emphasized that it was unlikely that these large quantities of heat could be rubbed out of so little metal, and—more important still—*there seemed to be no limit to the quantity of heat which could be produced.* Rumford came to the conclusion, therefore, that heat was not a material, and he preferred to regard it as a form of energy. When the borer was turned, work was done by the horse, which thus supplied energy to the block of metal. Apparently this energy there appeared in a new form as heat.

8.04. Most scientists remained unconvinced, however, and continued to regard heat as a material. It was always possible to argue that even the large quantities of heat produced by the borer *might* have come from the abraded metal, and Rumford was of course unable to prove that the heat which could be produced was entirely without limit. These arguments do not hold, however, in the case of the following experiments, which were performed by Sir Humphry Davy a few years later.

Since water is formed by heating ice, it is obvious that, if heat is a material, water contains more of it than ice. Davy caused two pieces of ice to rub over one another, and found that water was formed. Hence, more caloric was present at the end of the experiment than at the beginning. Where did this extra caloric come from? It did not come from that part of the ice which remained unmelted, for this was in the same condition at the end of the experiment as at the beginning. Davy believed that it came neither from the iron bars which held the blocks of ice, nor from the air, and he was therefore led to conclude that heat was *produced* by the rubbing. Accordingly, **heat should be regarded as a form of energy, and not as a substance** which can be rubbed out of bodies.

Although Davy later became a skilled worker in chemistry and physics, these experiments were performed when he was a very young man, with little experience of the precautions necessary in such experiments, and there can be no doubt that he was wrong when he assumed that *all* the heat was produced by rubbing. Most of it was undoubtedly conducted to the ice from bodies outside. Although, as we now know, he was correct in his conclusion that heat is a form of energy, his experiments were not sufficiently accurate to prove that this is the case.

8.05. It was not, therefore, until a long series of experiments were performed by Joule (1818–1889) between 1840 and 1850, that the caloric theory was finally abandoned. It had long been known that energy of one type could be converted into energy of other types. A stone at the top of a cliff possesses potential energy, and if the stone rolls off the edge, its potential energy decreases. Its kinetic energy increases as it falls, however, and when its potential energy is thus converted into kinetic energy, the stone gains just as much energy of the latter type as it loses potential energy. **Whenever energy of one type disappears an equal quantity of energy of another type appears, so the total quantity of energy always remains the same.** This fact is known as the **principle of the conservation of energy.** If, therefore, heat is a form of energy, the same quantity of heat will be produced whenever a given

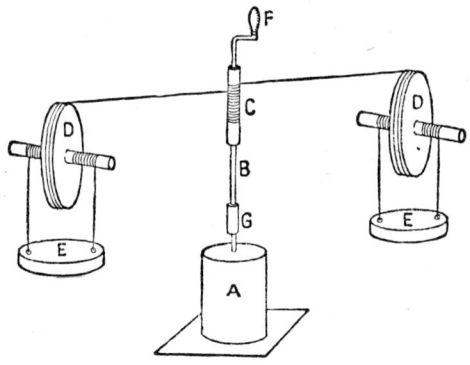

FIG. 8.01.—JOULE'S APPARATUS FOR DETERMINING THE MECHANICAL EQUIVALENT OF HEAT.

quantity of energy of another type is used to produce heat, no matter how the change takes place. It was this relation between heat and other forms of energy which Joule sought to establish by his experiments.

Joule produced heat in various ways—by forcing water through narrow tubes, by rubbing two iron rings together, by compressing air, by an electric current, by the friction between iron paddle-wheels and mercury, and by the friction of brass paddle-wheels in water. In every case, however, it was found that, to produce one British Thermal Unit of heat 778 ft.-lb. of work had to be done. Evidently 778 ft.-lb. of energy are equivalent to a quantity of heat energy of one B.Th.U. In other words, **the mechanical equivalent of heat** is 778 ft.-lb. per B.Th.U.

We shall describe only the most accurate of Joule's experiments —those in which heat was produced by the friction of brass paddles in water. A copper vessel A (figure 8.01, page 101) served as the calorimeter, and contained 10 lb. of water. This water was stirred by a brass paddle-wheel attached to the axle B, but the water was prevented from rotating freely with the paddle

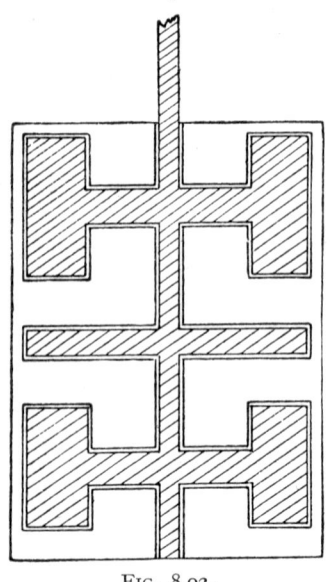

FIG. 8.02.

by vanes projecting inwards from the side of the calorimeter (see figure 8.02). The axle was attached to a cylinder C, around which were wound two cords, the other ends of which passed over, and were attached to, the pulleys DD. Two heavy lead blocks EE were supported from the axles of the pulleys, and when these blocks were released they turned the pulleys and rotated the paddle-wheel. These blocks were allowed to fall a number of times, and since the work which they did on the paddle-wheel was to be measured, the paddle-wheel was disconnected at a clutch G whenever the weights were being wound up by means of the handle F.

If w is the weight of each block, and the blocks fall n times through a distance h, the work done by the blocks is $2\,w.h.n.$ This work was used in driving the paddle in opposition to the frictional forces exerted by the water, and this caused a rise of temperature of the water in the calorimeter, the rise of temperature being measured by a sensitive thermometer. If m_1 is the mass of water in the calorimeter, and m_2 is the water equivalent of the calorimeter, paddles, etc., the heat produced is $(m_1 + m_2)t$, where t is the rise of temperature. Hence if J is the mechanical equivalent of heat (that is, the number of foot-pounds of energy which are equivalent to one British Thermal Unit)

$$J = \frac{2w.h.n}{(m_1 + m_2)t}.$$

During the experiments, the following precautions were taken to reduce heat losses to a minimum. (a) The calorimeter was placed upon a wooden stand, wood being a bad conductor. (b) The temperature was never raised more than a few degrees above that of the room. (c) A large quantity of water was used so that as little as possible of the heat produced was lost. (d) the whole experiment was performed as rapidly as possible. Joule applied a correction for the heat lost. Another correction was necessary because the blocks reaching the floor possessed kinetic energy, so that not all their potential energy was converted into heat in the calorimeter.

8.06. The mechanical equivalent of heat is 778 ft.-lb. per B.Th.U. Let us calculate its value in c.g.s. units.

$$1 \text{ ft.-lb.} = \frac{12 \times 100 \times 454}{39 \cdot 37} \text{ gm.-cm.}$$

Hence, 1 B.Th.U. is equivalent to

$$\frac{778 \times 12 \times 100 \times 454}{39 \cdot 37} \text{ gm.-cm.}$$

But 1 B.Th.U. $= \dfrac{454 \times 100}{180}$ calories,

$$\therefore 1 \text{ calorie} = \left(\frac{778 \times 12 \times 100 \times 454}{39 \cdot 37} \div \frac{454 \times 100}{180} \right) \text{ gm.-cm.}$$
$$= 42{,}700 \text{ gm.-cm.}$$

Hence, 1 calorie is equivalent to 42,700 gm.-cm., to (42,700 × 981) or 4·19 × 10⁷ ergs, or to 4·19 joules.

8.07. The mechanical equivalent of heat is usually measured in the laboratory by means of a piece of apparatus designed by Professor Callendar (1863-1930). A simple type is shown in figure 8.03. A hollow brass drum A can be rotated by an electric motor by means of the wheel B. A silk belt C passes round the drum and is attached at its upper end to the dynamometer D. When the drum rotates, the silk belt slips over the surface of the drum, and heat is produced by friction. Metal blocks E, supported at the lower end of the belt, oppose the rotation of the drum, while the pull of the dynamometer assists rotation. The net force opposing the drum is therefore $(W - w)$, where W is the weight of the blocks E, and w the pull of the dynamometer. If the drum is rotated, work is done against this force, and the quantity of heat produced is calculated by measuring the temperatures of a known mass of water in the drum by means of the specially shaped thermometer F. The bulb of this thermometer dips into the water. A revolution counter measures the number of revolutions of the drum during the experiment.

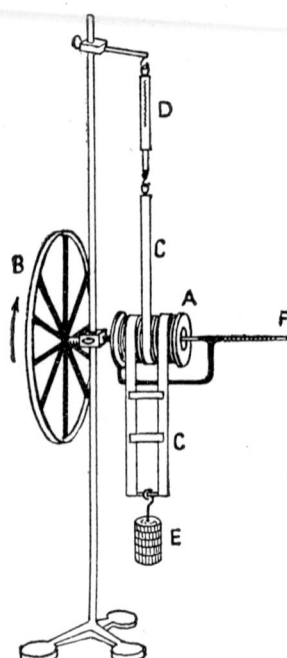

If n is the number of revolutions, and d is the diameter of the drum, the total distance moved by a point on the drum is $\pi.d.n$. The force exerted on the drum by the belt is $(W - w)$, so the work done is, $\pi.d.n(W - w)$. If m_1 is the mass of the water in the drum, and m_2 is the water equivalent of the drum and thermometer, the heat produced is $m_1 t + m_2 t$, where t is the increase of temperature.

$$\therefore J = \frac{\pi.d.n(W - w)}{(m_1 + m_2).t}.$$

The pull of the dynamometer must be measured while the drum is rotating, since the drum turns backwards after the electric motor is stopped, and the pulls on the two ends of the belt become equal. Heat losses cannot be entirely avoided, but are reduced by supporting the drum from a bad conductor (ebonite), by using a weight of about 2 kg. to produce friction, thus enabling the whole experiment to be finished in about 2 minutes, and by working at temperatures near the temperature of the room. It is advisable to start the experiment with the water in the drum a few degrees below room temperature, and to allow the drum to revolve until the temperature is about the same number of degrees above that of the room. Heat is then absorbed from the surroundings during the first half of the

FIG. 8.03.—CALLENDAR'S APPARATUS FOR DETERMINING THE MECHANICAL EQUIVALENT OF HEAT.

experiment, and a similar quantity of heat is given up during the latter half. In accurate work, a correction for the heat losses is also made.

8.08. We have seen that potential and kinetic energy can be converted into heat energy. This is, however, only one of the many different transformations energy may undergo. Energy has a number of other forms—chemical energy, light, sound, electrical, magnetic, and radioactive energy, etc.—and although energy may be changed from any one of these forms to any other, it is nevertheless true that **the total quantity of energy always remains unchanged.**

In Great Britain the chief source of the energy which we use for driving machines is the chemical energy of coal. When the coal is burned, its chemical energy is transformed into heat energy. Some of this heat energy is then changed into the pressure energy of the steam in a steam boiler. This pressure energy is converted into the kinetic energy of the piston and moving parts of the steam engine. It may then be transformed into electrical energy in a generator, and thence into light and heat energy in lamps and electric radiators. Other countries possess supplies of energy in the form of the potential energy of water in lakes high up in the mountains, and this potential energy may be converted into kinetic energy of turbines and electric generators, and thence as before into electrical, light, and heat energy.

When energy of one kind is converted into energy of another kind some of the energy is always converted into heat energy, and this energy is often lost *to our use*. Thus, when coal is burned, much of the chemical energy which is converted into heat passes out of the chimney with the escaping gases ; in the steam engine some of the kinetic energy is converted by friction at the moving parts into heat energy, which escapes to the surroundings and is wasted ; and so on. Hence, although the total quantity of energy always remains unchanged, it is unfortunately also true that the amount of energy which is *available* for use is continually diminishing. All other forms of energy are being gradually converted into heat, and this heat merely raises the temperature of the surroundings, and cannot again be used to work a machine.

8.09. The following examples illustrate the conversion of mechanical energy into heat energy.

(1) *Niagara Falls are* 50 *metres high.   Find the increase of temperature of the water when it falls from the top to the bottom.*

The work done on each gm. of water falling 50 metres is

$$1 \times 50 \times 100 \text{ gm.-cm.}$$
$$= 1 \times 50 \times 100 \times 981 \text{ ergs.}$$

But 4.19×10^7 ergs $= 1$ calorie,

∴ each gm. of water in falling produces

$$\frac{1 \times 50 \times 100 \times 981}{4.19 \times 10^7} \text{ calories}$$

∴ rise of temperature $= \dfrac{1 \times 50 \times 100 \times 981}{4.19 \times 10^7}$ ° C.

$$= 0.12° \text{ C.}$$

(2) *A squash ball is thrown* 50 *times against a wall with a velocity of* 30 *metres per second, and returns each time with a velocity of* 20 *metres per second.   Assuming that all the heat produced at the collisions with the wall remains in the ball, find the increase of temperature of the ball.   The specific heat of rubber is* 0.35.

It is shown in books on mechanics that the kinetic energy of a moving body is $\frac{1}{2}mv^2$, where m is the mass of the body, and v is its velocity.

∴ kinetic energy of the ball before it strikes the wall is $\frac{1}{2}m.(3000)^2$ ergs, since its velocity is 3000 cm. per second.

Its kinetic energy after impact $= \frac{1}{2}m.(2000)^2$ ergs

∴ loss of kinetic energy $= 50 \times \{\frac{1}{2}m(3000)^2 - \frac{1}{2}m(2000)^2\}$ ergs.

But 4.19×10^7 ergs $= 1$ calorie,

∴ heat produced $= \dfrac{50 \times \frac{1}{2}m\{(3000)^2 - (2000)^2\}}{4.19 \times 10^7}$ calories.

Heat required to raise the temperature of the ball 1° C.

$$= m \times 0.35 \text{ calories,}$$

∴ its increase of temperature

$$= \frac{50 \times \frac{1}{2}m\{(3000)^2 - (2000)^2\}}{4.19 \times 10^7 \times m \times 0.35}$$
$$= 8.5° \text{ C.}$$

EXAMPLES 8

1. Give an account of the caloric theory of heat. Describe the experiments of Rumford on this subject. Why do you consider that they render the caloric theory improbable ?

2. Describe the experiment of Sir Humphry Davy to show that heat is not a material substance.

3. Find the work done when a motor-car weighing 30 cwt. is raised to the top of a hill 100 ft. high. Express your result (a) in ft.-lb., (b) in joules.

4. Give an account of Joule's experiments, and show what bearing they have on the question whether heat is a form of energy.

5. The following readings were taken with Callendar's apparatus for determining the mechanical equivalent of heat :

Weight of water in the drum	= 60 gm.
Weight of brass drum	= 150·5 gm.
Diameter of drum	= 7·60 cm.
Weight on the free end of the belt	= 1115 gm.
Reading of dynamometer	= 125 gm.
Reading of revolution counter before the experiment	= 58,967
,, ,, ,, ,, after ,, ,,	= 60,261
Initial temperature	= 12·82° C.
Final temperature	= 22·42° C.

Calculate the mechanical equivalent of heat. [The specific heat of brass = 0·089.]

6. A bullet travelling at 200 metres per second strikes an unyielding target. Assuming all the heat produced remains in the bullet, calculate its rise of temperature. [Specific heat of lead = 0·030.]

School Certificate Questions

7. Give an account of the experiments performed by Rumford, Davy, and Joule, which prove that heat is a form of energy and not a material substance.   (O.C)

8. Explain what is meant by the mechanical equivalent of heat, and describe how it has been determined. Assuming the equivalent to be $4 \cdot 2 \times 10^7$ ergs per calorie, how much warmer would you expect to find the water at the foot of a waterfall 100 metres high than at the top ?   (O.C)

9. Energy has a number of different forms. Name three of these and describe carefully two cases of the transformation of energy from one form to another. (Either practical examples or laboratory experiments may be described.)   (B)

10. Give a full explanation of the meaning of the statement $J = 4 \cdot 2 \times 10^7$ ergs per calorie. A 2-kg. weight is arranged so that as it falls it turns a paddle which stirs 200 gm. of water in a vessel whose water equivalent is 10 gm. How far will the weight have to fall to raise the temperature of the water 2° C. ? Describe some method of making the experiment practicable. (L)

11. What is meant by the statement that heat is a form of energy ? Describe a simple quantitative experiment on the conversion of heat into work, and give an example of the reverse transformation. (L)

12. A penny can be made hot either by putting it in a fire or by rubbing it on another solid body. From what source is the heat obtained in the latter case ? Discuss another instance in which heat is produced without the application of fire or flame. Describe any scientific work which has been done on the connection between heat and energy, and state the conclusions which are drawn from the experiments. (O)

13. What is meant by the statement that the mechanical equivalent of heat is 778 ft.-lb. per British Thermal Unit ?

A cardboard tube 5 ft. long and closed at both ends contains a quantity of small shot. It is rapidly inverted 100 times. What would be the greatest possible rise of temperature of the shot if their specific heat is 0·032 ? State, with your reasons, whether you would expect actually to observe so great a rise of temperature. (C)

14. Explain fully what is meant by the mechanical equivalent of heat. For how long should a motor-cycle working at 4 horse-power be able to run on one gallon of petrol, if $\frac{1}{5}$ of the energy of the fuel is converted into useful work ? [A gallon of petrol in burning yields 120,000 B.Th.U. ; 1 horse-power is 33,000 ft.-lb. per minute ; the mechanical equivalent of heat is 770 ft.-lb. per B.Th.U.] (C)

CHAPTER 9

LIQUEFACTION AND SOLIDIFICATION

9.01. The cooling curve for a calorimeter containing water is a smooth curve, whose slope gradually decreases as the temperature of the water approaches that of the room (see figure 5.03). The slope of the graph represents the rate of cooling, and the curve is horizontal at those times when the temperature remains constant. Figure 9.01 is the cooling curve of some naphthalene contained in a test-tube. What does the horizontal portion of the curve mean? Why did the naphthalene cool in the ordinary way to 79·0° C., remain at that temperature for 3½ minutes, and then proceed to decrease again?

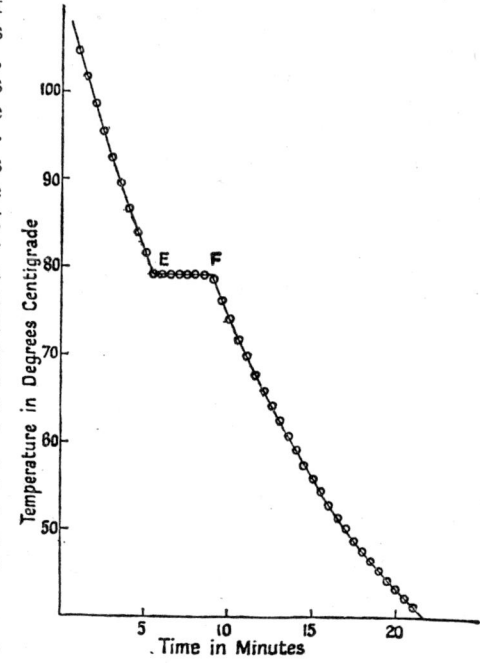

FIG. 9.01.—COOLING CURVE FOR NAPHTHALENE.

Many students, when they perform this experiment, decide that their thermometers are not working properly, but the more observant see that there is another change taking place when the thermometer readings cease to decrease. All the naphthalene is molten when the temperature is above 79° C., and it is solid when the temperature is below 79° C. Evidently the fact that the temperature is constant at 79° C. is connected with the solidification of the solid. Does the test-tube cease to lose heat while the naphthalene is solidifying? This seems unlikely, to say the least. Let us see what information is to be gained by studying the melting of a solid.

For this purpose we may use a beaker full of ice. Having confirmed with a thermometer the fact that the temperature of the ice is 0° C., we heat the beaker over a Bunsen for half a minute, stir the mixture of ice and water thoroughly and take its temperature. It is still 0° C.! Repeating the heating, we find that the temperature remains at 0° C. until *all* the ice has melted, when the temperature increases in the ordinary way. In this experiment, there can be no doubt that heat is added to the ice without increasing its temperature. Heat must be added to a solid to change its state from solid to liquid, but this heat is not shown by an increase of temperature. The heat has apparently disappeared, and it is called the *latent* (*i.e.* hidden) *heat* of fusion.

The latent heat of fusion of a substance is the heat required to melt 1 gm. of it, without raising the temperature of the liquid formed.

It is now clear that, in the experiment with the naphthalene, the temperature remained constant, not because the test-tube had ceased to give up heat, but because the heat lost was supplied by the latent heat of fusion of the naphthalene. Since the temperature at which any given substance solidifies is the same as that at which it melts, a cooling curve forms a convenient means of determining the melting-point of a substance. The melting-point is the temperature shown by the horizontal portion of the graph.

9.02. The latent heat of fusion of ice may be found as follows. A calorimeter is weighed empty, and again two-thirds full of warm water. The temperature of the water is measured, and pieces of ice, carefully dried with blotting-paper, are added piece by piece, the water being stirred until each disappears. When the temperature has been decreased a few degrees below that of the room, and the last piece of ice has melted, the thermometer is again read, and the calorimeter and water are weighed.

Dried ice must be used in this experiment, because any water clinging to the ice will have already given up its latent heat before entering the calorimeter. Since the last pieces of ice take longest to melt, it is best to begin the experiment with the water several degrees above room temperature, and to stop soon after room temperature has been passed, so that the loss of heat to the surroundings at the beginning shall be approximately equal to the gain of heat near the end. By using warm water, more ice can be melted, and greater accuracy obtained.

The following are the results of such an experiment :

Weight of calorimeter (empty)	=	55·3 gm.
Weight of calorimeter + warm water	=	152·8 gm.
∴ weight of warm water	=	97·5 gm.
Weight of calorimeter + water + melted ice	=	176·7 gm.
∴ weight of ice	=	23·9 gm.
Temperature of water before adding ice	=	35·3° C.
Temperature ,, ,, after ,, ,,	=	13·6° C.
∴ decrease of temperature	=	21·7° C.

Let x calories per gram be the latent heat of fusion of ice.

Heat taken up in melting 23·9 gm. of ice = $23·9x$ calories.

The water formed by adding these $23·9x$ calories would be at 0° C., so more heat must have been added to raise this water to its final temperature.

Heat taken up in raising 23·9 gm of water from 0° C. to 13·6° C.
= (23·9 × 13·6) calories.

∴ total heat taken up = $23·9x$ + (23·9 × 13·6) calories.

Heat given out by the water in the calorimeter at the beginning of the experiment = (97·5 × 21·7) calories.

Heat given out by the calorimeter = (55·3 × 0·1 × 21·7) calories.

∴ total heat given out
= (97·5 × 21·7) + (55·3 × 0·1 × 21·7) calories.

If we assume that no heat has been gained from, or lost to, the surroundings, the heat given out + the heat taken up.

∴ $23·9x$ + (23·9 × 13·6) = (97·5 × 21·7) + (55·3 × 0·1 × 21·7)
∴ $x = 79·8$.

Hence the latent heat of fusion of ice is 79·8 calories per gram.

9.03. The result obtained in this experiment is worth noting. Nearly as much heat is required to melt a given weight of ice as is required to heat the water formed to its boiling-point ! This remarkable fact explains why, even during very cold winters, only the surface water of ponds and rivers is frozen. Ice is a bad conductor of heat, and the large quantities of heat which must be conducted upwards to enable the water below to freeze escape so slowly that the thickness of the ice seldom exceeds a few feet. Even in the regions near the North Pole, the ice formed on the ocean reaches a thickness of only 4 or 5 metres, and its thickness changes by only a metre or two in the course of a year.

On the other hand, when ice has formed, it is melted only slowly by the sun's rays, which have to supply the latent heat required for melting. . Snow, which is merely a mass of minute ice crystals, falls in large quantities in mountainous regions, and many large rivers draw their supplies of water from such regions. If the latent heat of fusion had not to be added to the melting snow, disastrous floods would be caused when the snow began to melt.

9.04. The Ice Calorimeter.—A knowledge of the latent heat of fusion of ice may be used in the following manner, to determine specific heats. The method is interesting, because a thermometer is not required for the experiment.

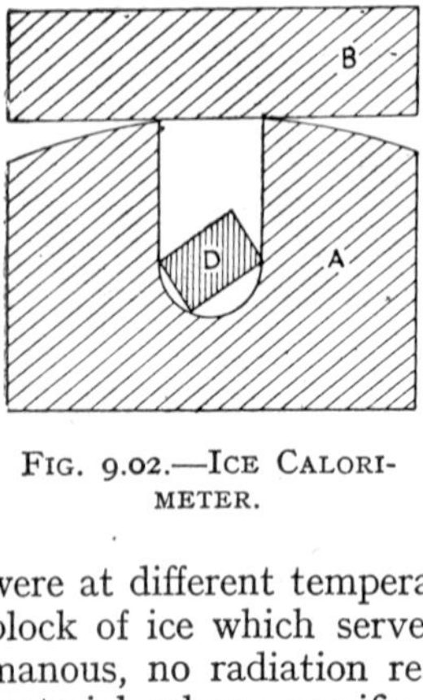

FIG. 9.02.—ICE CALORI-
METER.

The upper surface of a block of ice is rounded off, as shown in figure 9.02, so that any water formed as the ice melts will run off at the sides. A hole is formed in the top of the block, carefully dried with blotting-paper, and closed with a second block B. No heat can now reach the hole in the block. Both the inside and the outside of the block are at 0° C., and conduction could only occur if they were at different temperatures. Convection is prevented by the block of ice which serves as a lid, and since ice is adiathermanous, no radiation reaches the interior. A piece D of the material whose specific heat is required is heated in boiling water, and its temperature is calculated from the barometer reading. It is now quickly transferred to the hole in the ice, and the block B is replaced. As D cools, it gives up heat to the ice, and when D has reached 0° C., the water formed is removed with a pipette and a weighed piece of blotting-paper, and the mass of water formed is determined.

The method is somewhat clumsy, but possesses the following advantages over the ordinary methods :

(a) It is not necessary to determine the water equivalent of a calorimeter.

(b) The experiment need not be finished quickly to avoid heat losses. The block D can be left in the ice for 10 minutes if necessary, so the method is useful for finding the specific heat of a bad conductor, which gives up its heat slowly.

(c) Heat losses are negligible.

The following calculation illustrates the method of deriving the specific heat from the measurements. *200 gm. of rubber at 100° C. are added to the ice calorimeter, and 87·5 gm. of water are formed. Find the specific heat of rubber.*

Let x be the specific heat of rubber.

Heat given out by 200 gm. of rubber cooling from
$$100° \text{ C. to } 0° \text{ C.} = (200 \times x \times 100) \text{ calories.}$$

The heat required to melt 87·5 gm. of ice $= (87·5 \times 80)$ calories.

If we assume that no heat has been lost to, or gained from, the surroundings, these quantities of heat are equal.

$$\therefore 200 \times x \times 100 = 87·5 \times 80.$$
$$\therefore x = 0·35.$$

i.e. the specific heat of rubber $= 0·35$.

9.05. Although most substances behave in the same way as ice and naphthalene, and melt and freeze at definite temperatures, some substances do not do so, but change gradually from solid to liquid as the temperature is raised. A piece of glass tubing, for example, when heated in a blowpipe flame, begins to soften at a temperature of about 400° C., but has not become completely liquid at a temperature of 800° C. It is this property of glass, the property of melting gradually over a range of temperature of several hundred degrees, which enables flasks and bottles to be blown from it.

9.06. When a substance changes from the liquid to the solid state, its volume usually alters at the same time. Sometimes the volume of the solid is greater than that of the liquid ; sometimes the reverse is the case. If a substance expands on solidifying, it can be used to form castings, since the expansion forces those parts which are still liquid into the corners and depressions of the mould. Thus iron and bronze, which expand on solidifying, can be used for casting ; gold and silver contract, and cannot usefully be cast. One reason for the use of antimony in the alloy used for printers' type is that this substance causes the alloy to expand as it solidifies. The contraction of paraffin wax as it solidifies is easily shown by allowing the molten wax to cool in a test-tube.

Water expands on freezing by about $\frac{1}{11}$ of its volume, so ice floats in water with about $\frac{1}{12}$ of its volume above the surface. Enormous forces are required to prevent the expansion occurring, and water pipes are certain to burst if the water in them freezes during a frost. The damage may not be noticed until the ice again melts, but the pipes are broken during the frost, and not during the thaw.

The production of soil from rock is partly due to the expansion of water which is frozen in cracks in the rocks. During each frost the crack containing water is widened, and when the ice again melts, the water penetrates deeper to repeat the process.

The same fact has been put to use in the destruction of icebergs, which become a danger to shipping in the North Atlantic at certain seasons. Charges of thermit were placed in holes bored several feet into the icebergs. When thermit is ignited, enormous quantities of heat are produced, and the ice near the charge is melted in this way. If a crack filled with water reaches to the surface, the water there solidifies first, since it is far from the hot charge, and enormous forces are developed as the water below freezes. The explosion of the thermit has at first no apparent effect on the iceberg, but within 24 hours cracks appear in it and it breaks up and disappears by melting.

9.07. When water freezes it expands, so if it is prevented from expanding, it is to be expected that freezing will also be prevented. This is found to be the case, and water may be cooled several degrees below 0° C. without freezing, if the pressure on it is sufficiently large. In other words, the freezing-point is lowered by an increase of pressure. The lowering of the freezing-point is, however, too small to be worth taking into account in our definition of the lower fixed point of the temperature scales. An extra atmosphere pressure lowers the freezing-point less than $\frac{1}{100}$th of a centigrade degree, and the changes caused by variations of barometric pressure are negligible.

If a heavy weight is supported from a copper wire passing over a block of ice, as in figure 9.03, it is found that in an hour or so the wire passes right through the block of ice. The block is not left in two pieces, however, but still forms one solid lump. The explanation is as follows. The wire, being thin, exerts a large pressure on the ice below it, and causes some of it to melt. The water formed is squeezed out, and passes to the top of the wire, where it is under a lower pressure, and resolidifies. More ice is melted from below, the water flows to the top of the wire and solidifies, and so on. Since latent heat is required to melt the ice, and latent heat must be removed from the water which is freezing, it is advisable to use a copper wire, which can conduct the heat from above to the ice below.

This process of *regelation* (*i.e.* re-freezing) also occurs when snowballs are made. The ice crystals in the snow are in contact at only a few points, so large pressures are developed at these points when the snow is pressed together in the hands. The ice crystals therefore melt where they are in contact, and the water formed freezes again when the pressure is re-moved, leaving the ice crystals bound together. If the temperature is much below the freezing-point, the pressure may not be sufficient to cause melt-ing, and snowballs cannot be made.

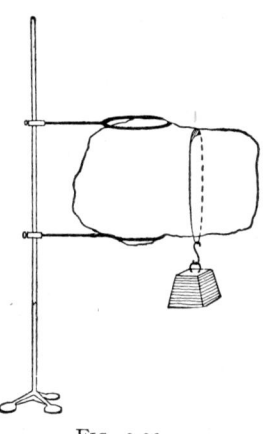

FIG. 9.03.

Ice under a pair of skates is melted by the pressure caused by the weight of the person skating. When you skate, there-fore, you do so on a thin film of water. If the ice is too cold, the pressure of the skates is insufficient to cause melting, and the skates do not " bite."

Glaciers are formed from snow, which is compressed by the weight of the layers above it. The snow is melted by the pressure, and the water formed freezes again afterwards, leaving a solid mass of ice. The glacier so formed moves slowly down the valley, changing its shape as it goes, to conform to the shape of the valley. Where an obstacle is met, the pressure of the ice behind causes the ice near the obstacle to melt, and the water formed freezes again when the obstacle is passed. Icebergs are formed by the breaking off of the end of such a glacier where it meets the ocean.

9.08. The molecules of a solid are held in position by the forces exerted by neighbouring molecules. When a solid melts, therefore, work has to be done in moving the molecules in opposition to these forces. The necessary energy to perform this work is the heat energy which is called the latent heat of fusion.

When a solid dissolves in a liquid the molecules have to be separated in opposition to the forces exerted by neighbouring molecules, so heat energy must be added to keep the temperature the same. Thus, if ammonium nitrate is dissolved in water, the temperature falls temporarily as much as 27° C. below the initial temperature of the water. In many cases, however, chemical action takes place when substances are dissolved in water, and in such cases the release of chemical energy produces an increase of temperature, instead of the decrease which would otherwise occur. Familiar examples are the rise of temperature which occurs when phosphoric oxide or sulphuric acid is added to water.

The freezing-point of water containing dissolved salts is lower than the freezing-point of pure water. If some common salt (sodium chloride) is mixed with powdered ice, some of the salt dissolves in the water on the surface of the ice, to produce a concentrated solution. Ice, however, cannot remain in contact with a strong salt solution at 0° C. without beginning to melt. As more ice melts, more of the salt is dissolved in the water formed, and the solution remains concentrated. The ice which melts absorbs its latent heat from the mixture, so the temperature falls. With common salt and water, a temperature of − 22° C. may be produced *temporarily* in this way.

EXAMPLES 9

1. What is meant by the latent heat of fusion ? Give an account of some of the consequences of the large latent heat of fusion of ice.

2. A large crucible of negligible heat capacity contains molten aluminium. It is allowed to cool, and its temperatures in degrees centigrade, measured at intervals of 1 minute, are found to be : 818, 735, 658, 658, 658, 658, 658, 620, and 553° C. Draw a cooling curve for the aluminium, and from the curve deduce (a) the melting-point of aluminium, (b) its rate of cooling near 658° C., (c) its rate of loss of heat at this temperature, assuming that the aluminium weighs 1000 gm. and that the specific heat of solid aluminium is

0·22. Calculate also from your graph how long the aluminium remained at 658° C., and its latent heat of fusion.

3. Discuss the importance of the change of volume which occurs when various substances are melted.

4. What is meant by regelation ? Give examples where regelation occurs.

SCHOOL CERTIFICATE QUESTIONS

5. A block of ice has a large hole scooped out of it. The hole is dried with a sponge, and immediately afterwards a piece of copper of mass 500 gm. is taken from an air oven at 110° C. and dropped quickly into the cavity. When the copper has finished cooling, the water formed in the cavity is absorbed in a dry sponge and weighed. This water is found to weigh 70 gm. Given that the specific heat of copper is 0·095, calculate the latent heat of fusion of ice. Criticize this method. (J)

6. Explain what you understand by the term *latent heat of fusion*. A piece of metal of specific heat 0·1, weighing 50 gm., is made hot in an oven and is then placed in a hole in a block of ice at 0° C. It is found that 12·5 gm. of ice are melted by the hot metal. The latent heat of fusion of ice is 80 calories per gram. Find the temperature of the metal when it was put into the hole in the ice. Discuss the practical difficulties involved in measuring temperatures by this method. (O)

7. What is meant by the *latent heat* of a change of state ? Describe how you would measure the latent heat of fusion of ice, mentioning the precautions you would take to minimize the sources of error and showing how you would calculate your result. A quantity of ice at 0° C. is mixed with 5 times its weight of water at 94° C. What is the maximum temperature attained by the mixture ? [Latent heat of fusion of ice = 80 calories per gram.] (O)

8. Define the *latent heat of fusion* of a substance. Pieces of dry ice were dropped into a copper calorimeter weighing 120 gm. and containing 225 gm. of water at 21° C. After the ice had melted the temperature was found to be 6° C. How much ice was used ? [Specific heat of copper = 0·1. Latent heat of fusion of ice = 80 calories per gram.] (L)

9. What do you understand by the terms specific heat, and latent heat ? What explanation can you offer for the latter phenomenon ? Into a mass of water at 0° C. 100 gm. of ice at − 10° C. are introduced ; 6·3 gm. of the water are frozen, and the temperature of the ice rises to 0° C. If the specific heat of ice be 0·5, find its latent heat of fusion. (L)

10. Define *specific heat, water equivalent, latent heat of fusion.*

A piece of dry ice at 0° C. is dropped into 250 gm. of water at 25° C. contained in a vessel of water equivalent 12 gm. When the ice has melted, the final temperature is found to be 8° C. By weighing, the amount of ice added is found to have been 50 gm. Calculate from these data the latent heat of fusion of ice. (L)

11. What do you understand by the statement that the mechanical equivalent of heat is 1400 ft.-lb. per lb. ° C. ? How may the value be determined experimentally ? At what speed should a piece of ice move so that the heat produced by stopping it suddenly should be just sufficient to melt it ? [Latent heat of ice = 80 lb. ° C. per lb.] (B)

12. Heat is applied at a constant rate to solid paraffin wax, contained in a vessel, until its temperature is a few degrees above melting-point. Describe and explain, with the aid of a rough graph, how the temperature of the wax changes as the heating proceeds. 60 gm. of ice at 0° C. are put into a calorimeter containing 60 gm. of water at 60° C. Determine whether or not all the ice will melt. (Assume the water equivalent of the calorimeter to be 10 gm.) (B)

13. Define *specific heat* and *latent heat*.

A piece of ice at a temperature of − 20° C. is dropped into a calorimeter containing 100 gm. of water at 35° C. The mass of the ice is 30 gm., the water equivalent of the calorimeter is 5 gm., and the resulting temperature corrected for heat losses is 7·2° C. Calculate the specific heat of ice. [Latent heat of fusion of ice = 80 calories per gram.] (O.C)

14. Give a short account of the method you would use to find the specific heat of a liquid. A piece of iron, of mass 20 gm. and specific heat 0·089, is cooled to the temperature of liquid air, and is then placed in a beaker of ice-cold water. 4·08 gm. of ice are formed round the iron. Calculate the temperature of the liquid air. [Latent heat of fusion of ice = 80 calories per gm.] (O.C)

15. Explain the following observations : (a) When a thaw comes after a severe frost it is sometimes found that the water pipes have burst. (b) Very cold snow is powdery and does not cake together, whereas snow which is only slightly below 0° C. sticks to the feet. (O.C)

CHAPTER 10

EVAPORATION AND CONDENSATION

10.01. When a dish containing a little water is exposed to the atmosphere in a warm room for a few days, the water disappears, and the dish is left dry. The water is said to have *evaporated*. It has been converted into an invisible form called water vapour, and the water vapour has mixed with the atmosphere. Some of the water which evaporates from a vessel containing hot water can be recovered by holding a cold sheet of glass over the hot water. The drops of water formed on the glass are formed by the *condensation* of the water vapour.

Other liquids behave in a similar way, but the rate of evaporation of any given liquid may be faster or slower than that of water. A little ether evaporates from a dish in a few minutes, whereas the same quantity of mercury could be left for years without any appreciable loss of mercury.

Vapours are merely gases at temperatures not far above their condensation points, and, like the more " permanent " gases, they exert pressure. The following experiment shows that this is the case. A tube about 80 cm. long, open at one end, and closed at the other with a specially designed tap, is filled with mercury and inverted in a bowl of mercury to form a barometer (figure 10.01(a)). A few cubic centimetres of ether are poured into the tube above the tap. The tap is so constructed that, each time it is turned, a single drop of ether is transferred to the space above the mercury. As the first drop is introduced it evaporates, and the pressure of the ether vapour depresses the mercury in the tube. Each subsequent drop forces the mercury down farther, until the mercury is about 35 cm. below its initial level. The addition of more ether now has no further effect upon the pressure, but drops of ether can be seen upon the walls of the tube, and floating on the mercury. Hence, ether vapour at the temperature of the room can exert a pressure up to 35 cm. of mercury, the actual pressure exerted depending upon the mass of ether vapour in any given volume, *but it cannot exert a pressure greater than* 35 *cm. of mercury, however much ether is present.* The space is said to be *saturated* with ether vapour when the vapour is exerting this maximum pressure, and the vapour is said to be exerting its *saturation vapour pressure*. If, on the other hand, more ether vapour can be introduced into a given space without condensation occurring, the space is said to be unsaturated.

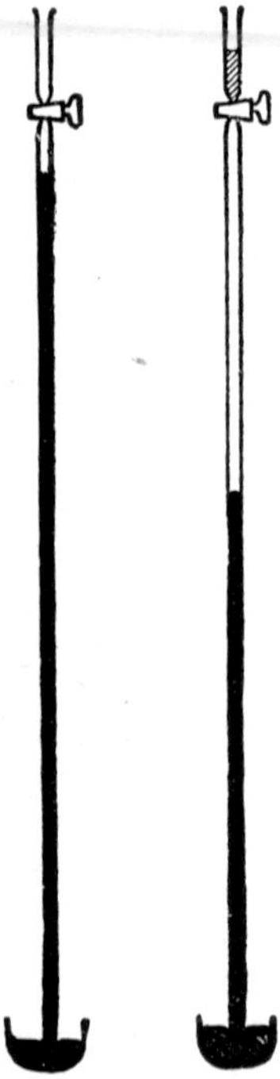

Other liquids behave in a similar way, but the saturation vapour pressures at room temperature are often so low that they are not suitable for demonstrating the properties of vapours. The saturation vapour pressure of mercury, for example, is less than $\frac{1}{1000}$th of a millimetre. This fact renders mercury suitable for use in barometers, for although the space above the mercury in a barometer is not a perfect vacuum, it is very nearly so.

Figure 10.02 shows the graph obtained by plotting the pressure of a given mass of ether vapour against its volume. The readings were obtained with a Boyle's Law apparatus, in which ether vapour was used in the closed limb instead of air. The curve consists of two parts, the straight line AB, and the curved portion BC. If the volume of the given mass of ether vapour is large, the space is unsaturated, and the vapour behaves like a gas—its pressure varies inversely as its volume, and the curve BC is obtained, similar to the p,v curve obtained earlier for air. But when the ether vapour is compressed until the pressure reaches 35 cm. of mercury, the vapour becomes saturated, and further compression merely causes some of the vapour to condense, the pressure remaining at 35 cm., as shown by the portion AB of the graph.

(a)   (b)

FIG. 10.01.

10.02. If some liquid is introduced into a vessel which contains air or some other gas, the vapour of the liquid is found to exert very nearly the same pressure that it would exert in a vacuum, so the total pressure inside the vessel is equal to the sum of the pressures which would be exerted by the gas and vapour acting **separately.** This fact was discovered by Dalton (1766–1844) and its statement is known as **Dalton's Law.**

The law is *sometimes* true of a mixture of two vapours and a gas, the resulting pressure being equal to the sum of those which

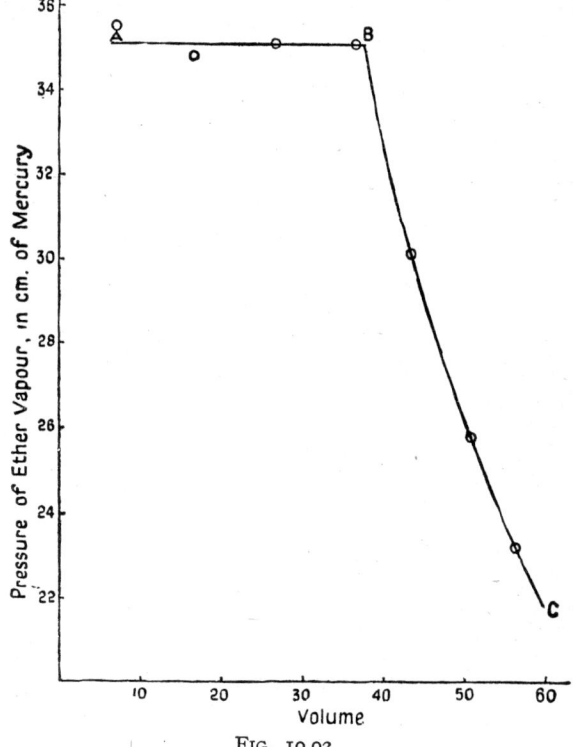

FIG. 10.02.

would be exerted by the gas and the vapours if each occupied the vessel alone. If a chemical reaction occurs between the two vapours, however, the pressure may be much lower. Thus, water vapour does *not* exert its own saturation vapour pressure when sulphuric acid is present.

10.03. The saturation vapour pressure of every liquid increases rapidly when its temperature is increased. Figure 10.03 shows a piece of apparatus for measuring the saturation vapour pressure of water at various temperatures up to about 75° C. Two barometer tubes stand side by side in a bottle of mercury open to the atmosphere. The space above the mercury in one tube is a vacuum; a little water occupies part of the space above the mercury in the other. If the vapour pressure of water were zero, the mercury would stand at the same height in each tube (except for the small difference caused by the pressure of the liquid water, and this is negligible for our purpose). Hence, the difference between the two levels is equal to the pressure of the water vapour. The water bath surrounding the upper portions of the tubes can be heated by passing steam from a boiler through the inverted brass U-tube, until any required temperature is reached. The Bunsen is then removed from the steam boiler, the water around the barometer tubes is thoroughly stirred, and the measurements of temperature and the height of the mercury in each tube are taken.

Figure 10.04 shows the graph obtained by plotting the saturation vapour pressures of water against the corresponding temperatures. As the temperature increases, the slope of the curve increases, showing that the vapour pressure increases most rapidly at high temperatures.

10.04. If a vessel containing water is heated over a Bunsen flame, water vapour escapes from the surface of the water into the air, and the rate of evaporation increases as the temperature rises. When the temperature reaches 50 or 60° C., bubbles of dissolved air begin to escape from the water, and these bubbles contain water vapour as well as air. By the time the temperature reaches 70 or 80° C. a steady stream of bubbles escapes. The bubbles rise through the water from the bottom of the vessel, where the water is hottest, and the water vapour in the bubbles is condensed as they reach the colder water above, causing the bubbles to collapse with the

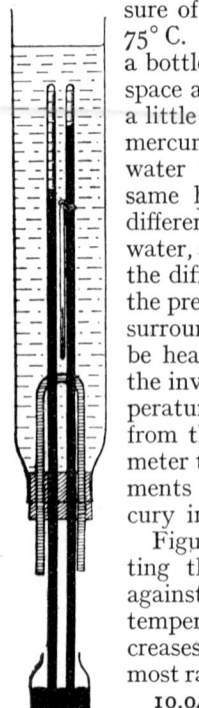

Fig. 10.03.— Apparatus for Measuring the Saturation Vapour Pressure of Water at Various Temperatures.

" singing " sound of a liquid about to boil. When the temperature reaches 100° C., bubbles of water vapour or steam (steam is
merely another name for hot water vapour) can pass right through
the liquid and escape at the surface, and the liquid is said to boil.
Since the bubbles of steam do not collapse, although acted upon
by the pressure of the atmosphere, the pressure of the water
vapour of a boiling liquid must be equal to atmospheric pressure.

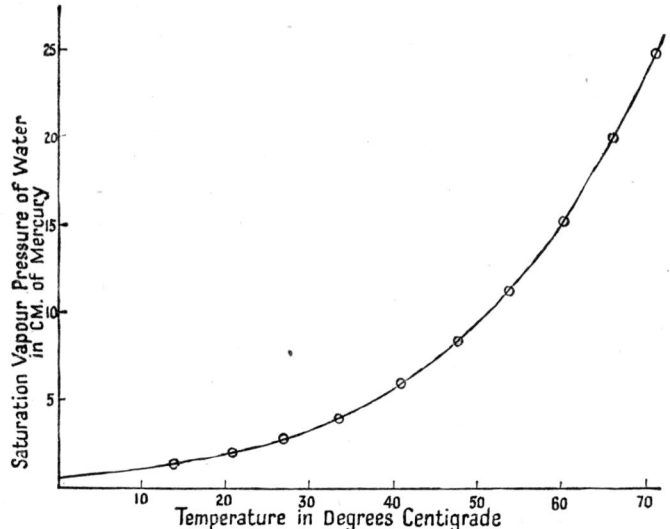

FIG. 10.04.—GRAPH SHOWING THE RELATION BETWEEN THE SATURATION
VAPOUR PRESSURE OF WATER AND THE TEMPERATURE.

The following experiment shows that a liquid boils when its
vapour pressure is equal to atmospheric pressure. A U-tube
closed at one end, open at the other to the atmosphere, is filled
with mercury, and a drop of water is placed in the open end,
and transferred to the closed limb. Mercury is then removed
until the mercury in the closed limb stands at a higher level
than that on the open side (figure 10.05). The U-tube is now
surrounded by a jacket through which steam from boiling water
is passed. The steam heats the water in the U-tube to its
boiling-point, and it is then found that the levels of the mer-

cury in the two limbs are the same. In other words, the pressure of the water vapour is equal to atmospheric pressure.

Since this is the case, the boiling-point of any liquid depends
upon the barometric pressure. Hence, it is necessary to specify
the pressure when defining the upper fixed point of the scale
of temperature. At high altitudes water boils at temperatures
lower than 100° C., because the atmospheric pressure is lower
there. Near sea-level the boiling-point of water decreases by
about 0·9° C. for each thousand feet above sea-
level, and this fact may be used for estimating
altitudes.

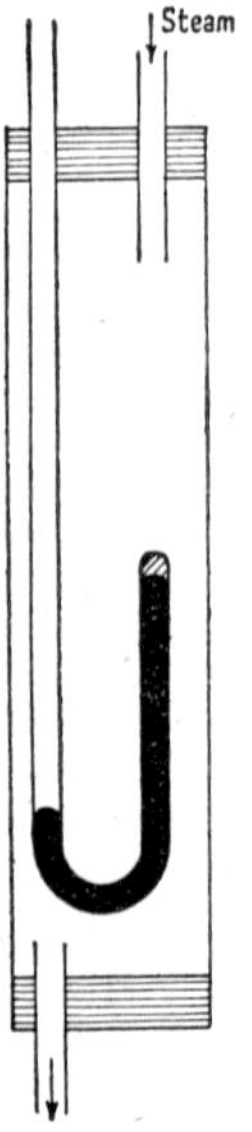

In the process of sugar refining, the sugar is recovered from a syrupy solution by evaporating the
water. The sugar would be damaged if the solution were boiled at atmospheric pressure, but if the
pressure on the liquid is decreased by means of air
pumps, the liquid boils at a lower temperature
and the sugar is not damaged.

The intermittent action of geysers in volcanic
regions is probably caused by changes of pressure
affecting the boiling-point. The water in the
fissure from which the jet of water emerges is heated
by contact with the hot volcanic rock. The pressure at the bottom of such a fissure is high, because
the water there is at a considerable depth below
the water surface. The boiling-point of the water
at the bottom will therefore be much above 100° C.,
and steam will not form until the boiling-point is
reached. When steam does form, however, some
of the water overflows at the top, reducing the
pressure on the whole column of water below, and
causing it to boil violently. A jet of water is thus
forced high into the air.

FIG. 10.05.

In modern locomotive boilers, where the steam pressure is
about 250 lb. per square inch, the water boils at 200° C.

Water may be caused to boil at room temperatures or lower,
if the pressure on its surface is decreased sufficiently. By means
of a fast air-pump and the apparatus shown in figure 10.06,
water may be made to boil and freeze at the same time ! The
water is contained in the double-walled vacuum flask A to
reduce heat exchanges between the water and the room, but

the flask is left unsilvered, so that the water can be seen.   The
air is removed by the pump as shown, the vessel B, half-full of
strong sulphuric acid, serving to absorb water vapour.   As the
pressure is decreased, the water suddenly commences to boil,
and after it has boiled for about a minute the temperature of
the water is reduced to 0° C.,
and a layer of ice forms on the
surface.

10.05. In the experiment just
described, the water in the flask
cooled as it boiled, and finally
ice was formed.   What has
happened to the heat which was
removed from the water to cool
and freeze it ?   We shall see
that heat is required to convert
a liquid into vapour, and in
this experiment this heat was
obtained at the expense of the
water which remained behind.

When a beaker of water is
heated over a Bunsen burner,
the temperature of the water
rises to about 100° C., and boiling commences.   After this,
further heating does not raise
the temperature of the water.
The extra heat supplied is used
to convert the liquid into water vapour, or steam.   This heat
is called the latent heat of vaporization.

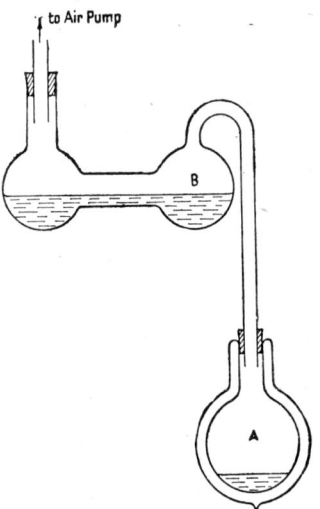

FIG. 10.06.—WATER BOILING AND
FREEZING AT THE SAME TIME.

**The latent heat of vaporization of a liquid is the quantity of
heat required to change 1 gm. of the liquid to vapour, without
increasing its temperature.**

If a test-tube containing water is stood in a beaker of water
which is kept boiling (figure 10.07), the water in the test-tube
does not boil, however long it is kept there.   To convert the
water in the test-tube to steam, heat would have to be transferred from the water in the beaker.   This water is at its boiling-
point, and if the water in the test-tube reached the same temperature, no heat would be conducted through the test-tube.
As a matter of fact, the water in the test-tube does not even

reach its boiling-point, because evaporation occurs at its surface, and the latent heat required to produce this evaporation can only be conducted through from the water outside if the latter is at a higher temperature than the water in the test-tube.

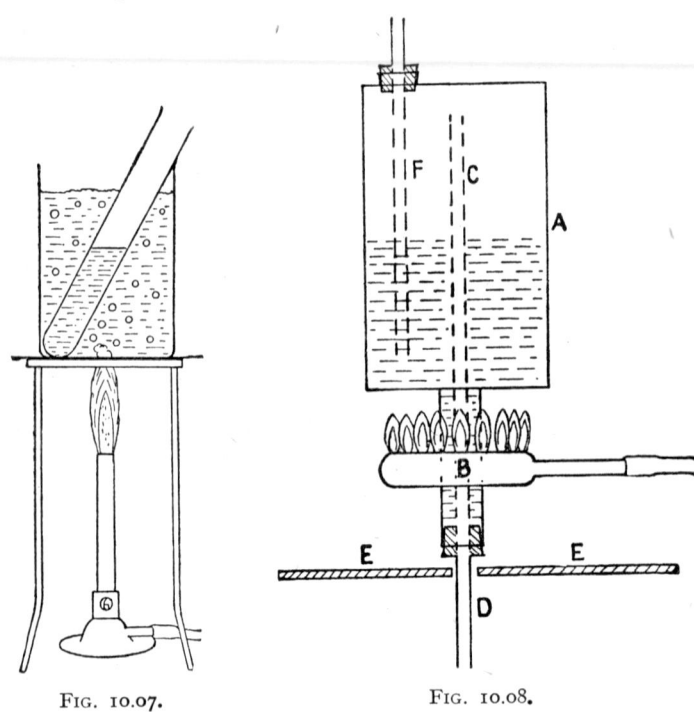

FIG. 10.07. FIG. 10.08.

10.06. The latent heat of vaporization of water may be determined, using the apparatus shown in figure 10.08. Water contained in the copper vessel A is kept boiling vigorously by means of the gas-ring burner B, and the steam formed escapes through the glass tube CD. This tube is made as short as possible, and is surrounded for most of its length by boiling water, so the steam escaping does not condense until it leaves the tube. A sheet of asbestos E prevents radiation from the burner to a calorimeter below the tube. The second tube F merely serves as a safety device to show when the water level in the boiler falls too low; steam then escapes through this tube.

A calorimeter is weighed empty, then two-thirds full of cold water. The temperature of the water is measured, and the calorimeter is placed for 30 seconds under the tube D, so that the jet of steam plays on the surface of the water. The water is stirred meanwhile, and when the temperature has risen about as much above room temperature as it was initially below it, the calorimeter is removed, the water is stirred thoroughly, and its temperature is measured. The calorimeter and the water are now weighed as quickly as possible. The weight of steam condensed is small, and it is essential to weigh the calorimeter as soon as its temperature has been taken, to avoid errors caused by evaporation. The second and third weighings are to the nearest hundredth of a gram, because the small weight of steam condensed is determined from these.

The calculation is performed as follows :

Weight of calorimeter (empty)	= 70·6	gm.
Weight of calorimeter + cold water	= 196·46	gm.
∴ weight of cold water	= 125·9	gm.
Weight of calorimeter + water + condensed steam	= 201·06	gm.
∴ weight of steam condensed	= 4·60	gm.
Temperature of water at the beginning	= 9·0° C.	
Temperature of water at the end	= 30·2° C.	
Temperature of boiling water	= 100·7° C.	

Let x calories per gram be the latent heat of vaporization.

4·60 gm. of steam condensing give out $4·60x$ calories. The 4·60 gm. of water formed are cooled from 100·7° C. to 30·2° C., and give out 4·60(100·7 − 30·2) calories.

∴ total heat given out = $4·60x$ + 4·60(100·7 − 30·2) calories.

The heat taken up by the cold water is 125·9(30·2 − 9·0) calories. That taken up by the calorimeter is 70·6 × 0·1 × (30·2 − 9·0) calories.

∴ total heat taken up

= 125·9(30·2 − 9·0) + 70·6 × 0·1 × (30·2 − 9·0) calories.

If we assume that no heat has been gained from, or lost to, the surroundings, the heat given out is equal to that taken up.

$$∴ 4·60x + (4·60 × 70·5) = (125·9 × 21·2) + (70·6 × 0·1 × 21·2)$$
$$∴ x = 542.$$

The latent heat of vaporization of water is 542 calories per gram.

More than five times as much heat is required to change

water at 100° C. into steam, as is required to heat the same quantity of water from 0° C. to 100° C. ! When steam condenses, it gives up its latent heat, and this heat causes the bad burns which occur when a jet of steam meets the hand. If steam is superheated (*i.e.* further heated after it has taken the form of steam) it does not scald, for the cooling of the steam which comes into contact with the hand is not sufficient to reduce it to the boiling-point, and the steam retains its latent heat. Steam at 100° C. causes severe burns ; steam at 200° C. does not.

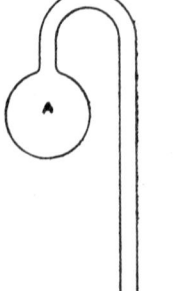

FIG. 10.09.
CRYOPHORUS.

10.07. Latent heat is required to convert liquid into vapour, whether or not the liquid is boiled. If a little water is spilled on a desk, and a shallow dish containing ether is placed in the water, the ether can be caused to evaporate rapidly in a current of air, and as it evaporates the ether absorbs latent heat from its surroundings and cools them ; the water freezes, and the dish is stuck to the desk. Similarly, a few drops of ether sprinkled on the hand produce a sensation of intense cold, for the latent heat of evaporation of the ether is taken from the hand.

Although water evaporates much more slowly than ether, the cooling produced by wet clothes often results in a chill. In hot climates it is the custom to place drinking water in canvas bags, which are hung in the shade. Evaporation of the water through the pores of the canvas lowers the temperature of the remainder, making it pleasanter to drink. Perspiration from the bodies of man and animals evaporates, and maintains the body at a uniform temperature, even when the air temperature is higher than that of the body.

The cooling of water by evaporation is illustrated by the *cryophorus* (figure 10.09). The apparatus contains only water and water vapour. When the bulb A is surrounded by a freezing mixture of ice and salt, the water vapour in the bulb is condensed, and water vapour passes from the other bulb B into A, lowering the pressure on the water in B. Water therefore evaporates in this bulb, absorbing latent heat as it does so, and cooling the water which remains. The process continues until a sheet of ice forms in the lower bulb.

10.08. Many **refrigerators** make use of the fact that latent heat is absorbed by a liquid when it is changed to vapour. The substances commonly used in refrigerators are ammonia, sulphur dioxide, and carbon dioxide. These substances are in the vapour state at ordinary temperatures and pressures, but an increase of pressure raises the boiling-points of all liquids, and high pressures cause these vapours to condense.

The vapour chosen, ammonia say, is compressed by means of the pump A (figure 10.10). During this compression the vapour does not condense, because work is done on it when it is compressed, and the extra energy added to it causes its temperature to increase. The ammonia vapour passes from the pump, through a valve B to long tubes C, over which cold water runs. Here the ammonia is cooled and condenses, its latent heat being carried away by the water. The liquid ammonia now passes through a valve D to the tubes E, where the pressure is kept low by means of the pump, and the ammonia evaporates and

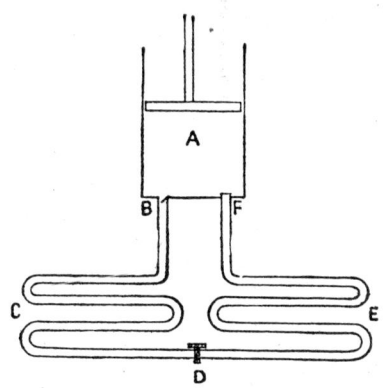

FIG. 10.10.—THE PRINCIPLE OF THE REFRIGERATOR.

absorbs its latent heat from the tubes and their surroundings. A strong solution of calcium chloride (technically called " brine ") passes over these tubes, and is cooled by the ammonia to temperatures below 0° C. The ammonia is then returned to the pump to be used again. The brine is not frozen at the temperatures reached, but is led away through pipes near the ceilings of the cold store-rooms. Convection currents in the air convey the heat from these rooms to the brine in the pipes, and the rooms are cooled. If ice is required, the brine is pumped into tanks in which cubical tins containing water stand.

10.09. When a solid is dissolved in a liquid the vapour pressure of the solution is lower than that of the liquid, so its boiling-

F

point is higher than that of the pure solvent. The boiling-point is only slightly raised by the presence of the dissolved solid. Thus more than 60 gm. of cane sugar have to be added to 100 gm. of water to produce a solution whose boiling-point is 1° C. higher than that of pure water. Nevertheless, the elevation of the boiling-point is of importance for the chemist. It is found that when a given substance is dissolved in a liquid, the boiling-point is raised by an amount which varies directly as the mass of the substance dissolved in a given mass of liquid. Moreover, the mass of a substance required to cause a given elevation of the boiling-point varies directly as the molecular weight of the substance dissolved, and this fact is used in the determination of molecular weights.

10.10. The molecules of a liquid are closely packed together, but in a gas or vapour their distance apart is greater. Thus the molecules of water which occupy 1 c.c. in the liquid state, occupy 1700 c.c. when converted into steam. The molecules attract one another, so when a liquid is converted into vapour work must be done in separating them in opposition to the forces of attraction. The energy necessary to do this work is supplied in the form of latent heat.

Molecules are constantly in motion, and we may think of evaporation as occurring whenever a fast-moving molecule escapes from the surface in opposition to the attraction of its neighbours. Molecules in the vapour state, however, may also collide with the liquid surface and return to the liquid state, and during evaporation there is a continual exchange of molecules between the liquid and the vapour. If more molecules are leaving the liquid per second than are returning to it, the quantity of liquid will continually decrease, and the vapour is said to be unsaturated. If, however, molecules are returning to the liquid from the vapour in numbers equal to those leaving it, the quantities of liquid and vapour remain unchanged, and the vapour is saturated.

A liquid will evaporate most rapidly if the vapour is carried away from its surface by means of a pump or a current of air. The current of air does not cause more molecules to leave the liquid, but it prevents molecules returning to the liquid, and in this way causes the quantity of liquid to decrease rapidly. If the gas above the surface of a liquid contains many molecules in the vapour state, evaporation will be slow, although the vapour does not prevent molecules leaving the liquid. What it does do, however, is to replace some of the molecules which escape from the liquid surface by others which were previously in the form of vapour, so the *net* loss of molecules from the liquid is slower. Hence, rapid evaporation from a pool of water will occur if a wind containing little water vapour blows over its surface.

Raising the temperature of a liquid increases the velocity of the molecules, allows greater numbers to escape from the surface, and causes the liquid to evaporate rapidly.

To sum up, a liquid evaporates rapidly if :

(*a*) a large surface is exposed to the air,

(*b*) the air contains little of the vapour,

(*c*) a current of air sweeps the vapour away as it is formed,

(*d*) the temperature is high, and

(*e*) the liquid is volatile ; *i.e.* possesses a high vapour pressure.

EXAMPLES 10

School Certificate Questions

1. Explain what is meant by a *saturated vapour*. What are the chief properties of such vapours ? Plot a vapour pressure curve for water from the following data :

Pressure of saturated water vapour in mm.	720	746	773	802
Temperature in ° C.	98·5	99·5	100·5	101·5

Use your curve to find the error in a thermometer which reads 99·7° C. when placed in steam on a day when the barometer stands at 767 mm. (O.C)

2. Explain what is meant by *vapour pressure*. Describe one experiment in each case to show (*a*) that the vapours of different liquids exert different pressures at the same temperature, (*b*) that the vapour pressure of a liquid increases as the temperature is raised. How is the boiling-point of water affected by a reduction in pressure ? Describe an experiment in support of your statement. (J)

3. Distinguish clearly between a *saturated* and an *unsaturated* vapour. Moist air is confined over mercury in a barometer tube. What experiments would you make to discover whether the air is saturated with water vapour or not ? How could you show that water evaporates to the same ultimate pressure in air as it does into a vacuum ? (O)

4. Explain the terms " specific heat " and " latent heat." A vessel of water equivalent 50 gm contains 400 gm. of water, and is supplied with heat steadily at the rate of 50 calories per second. The temperature rises from 20° C. (which is also the temperature of the surrounding air) to 100° C. in 15 minutes. At what average rate has heat been lost meanwhile ? What will be the approximate rate subsequently ? If 60 minutes more are required to boil away half the water, find a value for the latent heat of evaporation. (B)

5. Define two units in which quantities of heat are measured. If the calorific value of coke is 8500 B.Th.U. per lb. and a coke-fired boiler produces 5 lb. of steam at atmospheric pressure per lb. of coke used, what is the efficiency of the boiler ? Assume the temperature of the water supply to be 62° F. and the latent heat of evaporation of water to be 540 calories per gram. (L)

6. Define *latent heat of steam*. Steam at normal atmospheric pressure is blown into 300 lb. of water contained in a vessel of water equivalent 20 lb. When the temperature has risen from 40° F. to 104° F. the steam supply is removed and the increase in weight is found to be 19 lb. Calculate the latent heat of steam. (L)

7. Explain the term *latent heat of vaporization*, and describe one method of measuring it for water. Vapour from a liquid boiling at 80° C. and of latent heat 200 calories per gram, is led into 100 gm. of this liquid at 15° C. contained in a calorimeter weighing 40 gm. and of specific heat 0·1. If 4 gm. of vapour bring the final temperature to 30° C., find the specific heat of the liquid. (J)

8. Define *latent heat* and *specific heat*.
An ice machine produces ice by the vaporization of liquid ammonia. How much ammonia at 0° C. must be vaporized to convert a kilogram of water at 10° C. into ice at 0° C., assuming that all the heat lost by the water is communicated to the ammonia ? The latent heat of vaporization of ammonia is 340 calories per gram, and the latent heat of fusion of ice is 80 calories per gram. (O.C)

9. Distinguish clearly between *capacity for heat, specific heat,* and *latent heat*. A piece of metal weighing 5 gm. is hung inside a chamber containing steam at 100° C. The original temperature of the metal was 20° C. It is found that 0·2 gm. of steam condenses on to the metal. What is the specific heat of the metal ? [Latent heat of steam = 540 calories per gram.] (O.C)

10. Explain the statement that *the latent heat of vaporization of alcohol is 371 B.Th.U. per lb.*, and define the heat unit used. A copper kettle weighing 2 lb. and containing 3 lb. of water at 52° F., is placed over a burner, and the water starts to boil after 10 minutes. Neglecting losses of heat to the surroundings, find what fraction of the heat supplied has been absorbed by the kettle itself. What further time will elapse before ½ lb. of water has boiled away ? [Take the specific heat of copper as 0·1, and the latent heat of steam as 972 B.Th.U. per lb.] (J)

11. Distinguish between *evaporation* and *boiling*, and discuss the conditions which determine the boiling-point of a liquid.   Describe an experiment which shows that a liquid may be cooled by evaporation, and explain why this cooling takes place.   (O)

12. Distinguish between *boiling* and *evaporation*.   What conditions affect the boiling-point of water, and in what way ?   Describe experiments which support your statements.   (B)

13. Heat is supplied at a regular rate to a quantity of ice at 0° C., finally changing it to steam at 100° C.   Illustrate by graphs, pointing out briefly their distinguishing features, (*a*) how the temperature varies with time, (*b*) how the volume of the water in its different physical states varies with temperature.   (L)

14. How would you find the boiling-point (*a*) of a pure liquid, (*b*) of a salt solution ?   Explain any differences of procedure.   Describe and explain an experiment to show the effect of pressure on the boiling-point of a liquid.   (O.C)

15. Explain the following observations :   (*a*) Water boils at a lower temperature at high altitudes ;   (*b*) The temperature at the top of a mountain is less than at the foot.   (O.C)

CHAPTER 11

MOISTURE IN THE ATMOSPHERE

11.01. Water vapour, unlike water, is completely invisible. When a flask containing water is heated as shown in figure 11.01, the steam inside the flask cannot be seen, although a cloud is formed a short distance beyond the delivery tube. Although this cloud is often referred to as a cloud of steam, it does not really consist of steam at all, but is a mass of very tiny droplets of water formed by condensation of the water vapour as it comes in contact with the cold air. If the Bunsen is removed, the cloud disappears; the drops of water evaporate, and the water vapour mixes with the air.

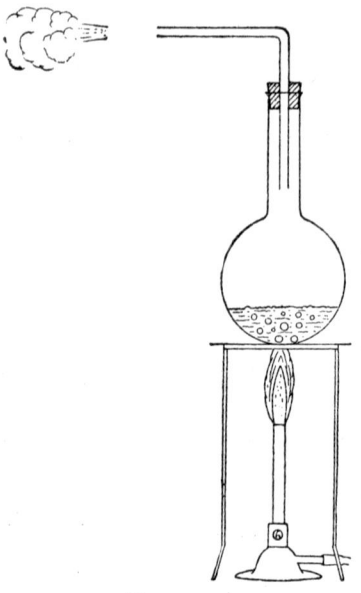

FIG. 11.01.

The atmosphere always contains water vapour. A little phosphoric oxide exposed to the air rapidly absorbs water vapour and becomes damp; and by cooling air, some of the moisture may be condensed. Thus, if a jug of iced water is stood in a warm room, the outside of the jug quickly becomes coated with a film of moisture condensed from the air. The water, which is condensed in this way by the cooling of the air in contact with the jug, is called *dew*, and the temperature to which the air must be cooled to cause dew to form is called the *dew-point*. The greater the quantity of water vapour present in the atmosphere, the less cooling will be required to form dew, and the higher will be the dew-point.

The ventilation of buildings is necessary for two reasons—to remove the carbon dioxide exhaled by persons in the buildings, and to remove the water vapour evaporated from their lungs and bodies. If the atmosphere is nearly saturated with moisture, evaporation can occur only slowly, the air feels close and oppressive, and the conditions may cause people to feel ill or faint. This is particularly the case if the temperature of the air is also high, for the body depends upon evaporation to prevent its temperature rising above its normal value. Hence, the weather in India during the wet season is more oppressive than temperatures 10 to 20° F. higher in lands where the atmosphere is drier.

At low temperatures the air is able to take up only small quantities of water vapour, whereas at higher temperatures much larger quantities of vapour may be present without the vapour pressure approaching the saturation vapour pressure. Consequently, warm air may feel dry although it actually contains sufficient water vapour to render the same air damp and muggy at lower temperatures. The important factor is not the quantity of water vapour present, but the relation between the amount actually present and the amount required to produce saturation, and this is measured by the relative humidity.

The relative humidity is :

$$\frac{\text{the mass of water vapour in a given volume of air}}{\text{the mass of water vapour required to saturate this volume at the same temperature}}$$

A knowledge of the relative humidity is required in certain industries as well as for ventilation purposes. Thus cotton-spinning can only be performed if the relative humidity exceeds a certain minimum value, and the importance of the cotton industry in Lancashire is partly due to the fact that the relative humidity there is usually high. Nowadays, the relative humidity is maintained artificially at the correct value in cotton mills. It must not be so low that the cotton breaks easily, and must not become so high as to cause distress to the workers in the mill. The artificial seasoning of timber is also carried out under special conditions of temperature and of relative humidity.

11.02. The relative humidity is measured by instruments

called *hygrometers*, and the most direct of these is the chemical hygrometer (figure 11.02). Two **U**-tubes, A and B, are filled with pieces of pumice-stone soaked in strong sulphuric acid, are weighed, and connected to the bottles C and D as shown. D is initially full of water, and as this water runs out through the tap, air passes through the tubes. The volume of this air is equal to that of the water which escapes, and as the air passes through the **U**-tubes, its moisture is removed by the sulphuric acid. The increase of weight of the **U**-tubes at the end of the experiment gives the weight of water present in the given sample of air. The function of the strong sulphuric acid in the bottle C is merely to prevent water vapour passing back from D into the **U**-tubes.

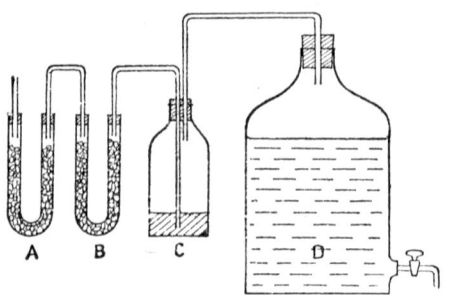

FIG. 11.02.—CHEMICAL HYGROMETER.

The mass of water vapour in the sample of air having been thus determined, it remains to find the mass of vapour which would saturate the same volume of air at the same temperature. This might be determined by drawing through the same apparatus saturated air from a bottle containing some water. The masses required to saturate a given volume of air at various temperatures have been measured, however, and in practice the value could be determined from tables.

The chemical hygrometer gives accurate results, but is troublesome to use, for the air must be drawn very slowly through the **U**-tubes if it is to be thoroughly dried. It is usual, therefore, to use one of the types of hygrometer now to be described.

11.03. The pressure of a given mass of an unsaturated vapour varies inversely as its volume (*i.e.* the unsaturated vapour obeys Boyle's Law). If the volume occupied by a vapour is kept constant while the mass of vapour is increased to n times that which was originally present, each gram of vapour now occupies $\frac{1}{n}$th of its original volume, so its pressure—assuming the vapour to be still unsaturated—will be n times as great as before. In other words, the pressure of an unsaturated vapour varies directly as the mass of it contained in a given volume.

The relative humidity R is :

$$R = \frac{\text{the mass of vapour present in a given volume}}{\text{the mass required to saturate the volume at the same temperature}}$$

$$\therefore R = \frac{\text{the pressure of water vapour present}}{\text{the pressure required to saturate the air at the same temperature}}.$$

The denominator of this fraction is merely the saturation vapour pressure of water at the temperature of the air. The numerator can be found with sufficient accuracy by determining the dew-point. The dew-point is seldom more than 10° C. below room temperature. If the vapour and air are cooled together both are affected in the same way, and the vapour pressure remains nearly the same fraction of the whole. Hence, the pressure of the water-vapour present is nearly equal to the pressure which the same vapour would exert at the dew-point, and this is the saturation vapour pressure at the dew-point.

$$\therefore R = \frac{\text{the saturation vapour pressure at the dew-point}}{\text{the saturation vapour pressure at room temperature}}.$$

Both numerator and denominator can be found from tables of the vapour pressure of water if the dew-point and room temperature are measured, and this is the principle used in hygrometers which measure the dew-point. There are several varieties of these, but we shall describe one only.

11.04. Regnault's Hygrometer.—Two similar tubes A and B (figure 11.03) contain thermometers, and are joined by a cross-tube C. When air is drawn out of D, a stream of air enters at E, and bubbles through ether at the bottom of the tube B. Ether evaporates, and cools this tube. The stream of air is so regulated that the temperature falls only slowly, and after a time dew begins to form on B. The thermometer in this tube is then read, the stream of air stopped, and the temperature slowly rises. When the dew disappears the thermometer is again read, and the mean of the two temperatures is taken as the dew-point. The second tube serves merely as a comparison tube. The bottom of each tube is covered with a brightly-polished silver cap, since it is easier to detect the formation of dew on a

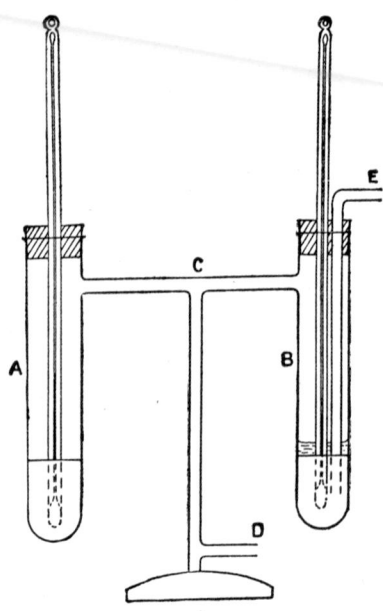

FIG. 11.03.—REGNAULT'S HYGROMETER.

polished surface. The thermometer in the tube A is used to measure the temperature of the room, and the relative humidity is calculated as described above.

In using the apparatus, a large sheet of glass is placed between the observer and the hygrometer, so that the moisture exhaled does not affect the readings of the instrument.

11.05. The Wet and Dry Bulb Hygrometer.—Two thermometers are hung side by side. Around the bulb of one of these is wound a piece of muslin, one end of which dips into a bottle of water, and keeps the muslin round the thermometer bulb moist. As water evaporates from the muslin, latent heat is absorbed, and the wet-bulb thermometer is maintained at a lower temperature than the other. In still air the rate of evaporation, and hence the difference of temperature of the thermometers depends upon the temperature of the air and upon its humidity, and varies only when these factors vary. In other words, corresponding to any given air temperature and humidity there will be a particular difference of temperature of the wet and dry bulbs. Tables have been drawn up showing the relationship between the humidity and the temperatures of the two thermometers, and these tables are used for interpreting the thermometer readings.

11.06. Clouds are formed when the cooling of steam or water vapour causes condensation to occur. In the atmosphere, air containing water vapour may be cooled to produce clouds, either (*a*) by contact with a stream of colder air, or (*b*) by expansion such as occurs when air is driven upwards to great heights in crossing mountain ranges. When a mass of air expands, it does work in forcing back the surrounding air, so its energy decreases, and this decrease of energy is shown by a fall of temperature.

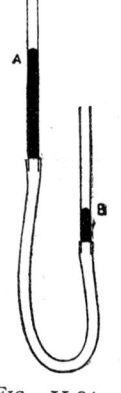

Fig. 11.04.— To show that Condensation is caused by the Rapid Expansion of a Saturated Vapour.

This second method of cooling air containing water vapour, and the consequent formation of a cloud, may be imitated with the apparatus shown in figure 11.04. A tube A, closed at the top, is connected with the open tube B by rubber tubing, and a few drops of ether, with or without air, are enclosed in the tube A by mercury. When the tube B is suddenly lowered, the pressure on the ether vapour in A is decreased, the ether expands, is cooled, and condenses as a fine mist of tiny droplets.

The droplets of water in a cloud are so small that they fall only slowly towards the earth, and may even be carried upwards by convection currents in the atmosphere. If cooling proceeds sufficiently far, however, more water vapour condenses into the droplets, until they become too heavy to be supported by rising currents of air, and the drops fall as rain. When the air temperature is below 0° C., moisture may change directly from vapour to solid, to form the tiny ice crystals which constitute snow.

Hailstones can be formed only if very rapid vertical convection currents are present, and such currents are usually associated with thunderstorms. Drops of rain, falling towards the ground, are caught up in these currents and carried to high altitudes where the drops freeze. As they again fall through the cloud they gather a further layer of water on their surfaces, and if they are again carried upwards, this water freezes in its turn. Finally, after several such layers have been deposited and frozen, the hailstones become too heavy to be transported by upward air currents, and fall to the ground. The successive layers of ice in a hailstone can be seen by cutting one in halves.

11.07. Mists and fogs are merely clouds formed near the earth's surface. The early morning mists so often found in valleys and near rivers are caused when the cold air from the hillsides comes into contact with the warm saturated air in the valley. During the night the land cools by radiation, and the air near it is cooled by contact with the land. It is then denser than the surrounding air, and sinks to the bottom of the valley, producing the mist there. The very dense fogs which occur off the coast of Newfoundland are caused by the cooling of warm saturated air over the Gulf Stream by cold currents of air from the north. Dust and smoke particles serve as nuclei, upon which drops of water readily condense, and such nuclei assist in the formation of fogs in large cities.

11.08. The atmosphere is very nearly transparent to the sun's rays, and it has been estimated that only about one-tenth of the sun's radiation is absorbed by the atmosphere. Water vapour, however, is adiathermanous to radiation from a cold body such as the earth, and the water vapour in the atmosphere absorbs about nine-tenths of the radiation from the earth. Consequently, in regions where the humidity is high, the radiation from the earth escapes less readily, and the temperature decreases slowly at night. In desert regions, on the other hand, the humidity is low, and the earth cools quickly at night by radiation. Hence, in such regions high day temperatures are often followed by extremely cold nights.

11.09. Dew is formed by the condensation of moisture on

grass, earth, roofs, etc. The following conditions favour the formation of dew :

(a) A cold night following a warm day. The air contains large quantities of water vapour in warm weather, and is more readily cooled to the dew-point.

(b) Absence of clouds, which, if present, would prevent radiation escaping from the earth into space.

(c) Absence of wind. If the air is in motion, the air near the ground is removed before it is cooled to the dew-point.

(d) Dew forms on objects near the ground. When objects above the level of the ground are cooled by radiation, and cool the air around them, this air sinks as a convection current before it has been cooled sufficiently to deposit dew.

Hoar frost is formed in a similar manner, and the crystals of ice formed on plants and on the ground are usually produced by the condensation of the water vapour in the atmosphere directly into ice. In some cases, however, the particles of water in a fog may coalesce and freeze upon plants, and if the hoar frost is produced in this way, it is not necessary that there should be no wind. The damage which a frost causes to trees and plants is *not* due to the particles of ice which form on the outside of the plants, but to the freezing of the sap in the plants themselves. Hence, just as much damage can be caused by a cold night during which no hoar frost forms, as on one in which the ground becomes covered with a white layer of ice crystals. A *black frost* is a cold period during which so little water vapour is present in the atmosphere that no ice crystals are formed, although the temperature falls below 0° C.

EXAMPLES 11

1. Explain why, after a shower of rain on a warm sunny day, the roads often appear to be " steaming."

2. Of what importance is a knowledge of the relative humidity? Show that the relative humidity can be calculated from a knowledge of the room temperature and the dew-point, pointing out what approximations are made in your argument.

3. Describe the use of the Regnault hygrometer for determining relative humidities.

4. Explain why the rainfall is usually higher near a range of mountains than over flat plains.

5. A flask, the inside of which is wet, is connected to an air-pump.

When air is pumped out of the flask a mist appears inside it, but the mist disappears when air is admitted to the flask. Explain why this is so.

6. Describe the conditions which favour the formation of dew, and explain how they affect its formation.

School Certificate Questions

7. Define *dew-point*, and *relative humidity*. Explain how the values of these quantities affect the drying power of air. Describe a method of measuring the relative humidity of the air. (C)

8. What conditions govern the condensation of a vapour and what phenomena accompany it? What are hoar frost, black frost, snow, hail, rain, fog? (L)

9. Explain the terms (a) dew-point, (b) relative humidity of the air. Describe how the dew-point may be found.

On a certain day the relative humidity was 40%. The temperature of the air was 12° C., at which temperature the pressure of saturated water vapour is 10·5 mm. of mercury. Find the pressure exerted by the water vapour in the air on the day in question. (O)

CHAPTER 12

HEAT ENGINES

12.01. The Steam Engine.—The principle of the steam engine may be understood by reference to figure 12.01. Steam from a steam boiler enters the steam chest B by means of the pipe A. A sliding valve C serves two functions. It allows steam from the steam chest to pass to the cylinder, alternately at E through

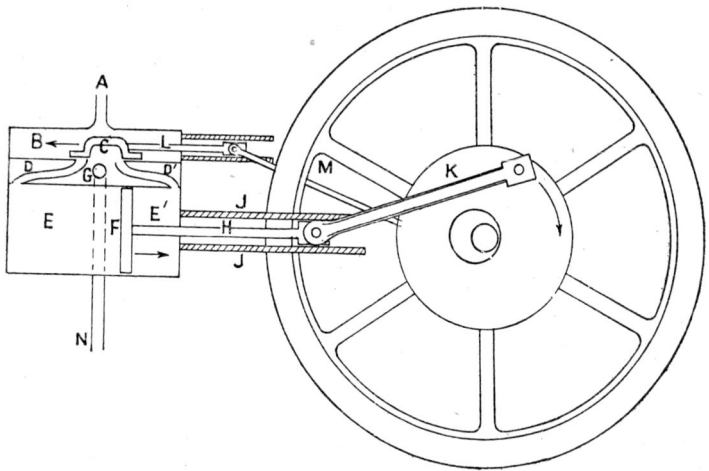

FIG. 12.01.—RECIPROCATING STEAM ENGINE.

the inlet port D, and at E′ through the port D′. It also allows the steam in the cylinder to escape after it has expanded and done work in moving the piston F. The steam escapes through D and D′ and the exhaust port GN. The valve C is worked automatically by the engine as described later.

We shall suppose that the piston is at the left-hand end of the cylinder. With the piston in this position, D is connected to the steam chest, D' to the exhaust port, and E' is full of steam which has expanded, and is therefore at a lower pressure than that of the steam entering. Steam from the steam chest therefore passes into the cylinder via D, forcing back the piston, and driving out the steam in E'. When the piston has completed about half its stroke, the port D is closed. The steam in E continues to expand, however. As the piston nears the end of its stroke, D' is first shut off from the exhaust port, and then put in communication with the steam chest B, while D is at the same time connected to the exhaust port. Steam now enters through D', forcing the piston back. During this second stroke the port D functions as D' did during the first stroke, D' meanwhile acting as D did previously. At the end of the second stroke, the whole cycle is repeated.

The piston rod H is rigidly connected to the piston, and is constrained to move backwards and forwards with it by means of the guides J. The connecting rod K is connected to the piston rod by means of a pin, and by a second pin to a point on the fly-wheel, half the length of the stroke of the piston from the centre of the wheel. The backwards and forwards motion of the piston thus causes the wheel to rotate. At two positions of the wheel during each revolution the piston rod and connecting rod are directed along the same straight line, and in these positions the forces exerted on the piston do not assist rotation. The flywheel, however, is so massive that its inertia carries it past these positions without serious loss of speed.

The valve C is moved by means of the valve rod L and an eccentric rod M, connected to a small wheel whose centre is near, but not at, the centre of the fly-wheel. As the latter rotates, this wheel rotates with it, and opens and closes the valve C at the appropriate times.

12.02. By no means all the chemical energy of the coal which is burned to drive a steam engine is converted into useful mechanical energy. In fact, by far the larger part of the energy is wasted in various ways, and only a small fraction is used in doing work. The ratio

$$\frac{\text{work done by the steam on the piston}}{\text{heat energy supplied}}$$

is called the thermal efficiency of the heat engine. The heat energy supplied is equal to the product of the weight of coal burned and the heat given out when unit weight of the coal is burned. The work done on the piston is the product of the average force on it and the distance it is moved.

The principal losses of heat energy are:

(1) Heat is carried into the air by the hot gases escaping from the furnace. These losses are reduced by leading the hot gases, after they have been used for heating the boiler, over tubes containing the cold water which is to be fed into the boiler. The feed water absorbs some of the heat which would otherwise be lost.

(2) Heat is lost by convection currents and by radiation from the boiler, from the steam pipes, and from the cylinder of the engine. These losses are reduced by covering the metal surfaces with a thick layer of asbestos, which is a bad conductor of heat.

(3) Heat is carried away by the exhaust steam.

(4) When the steam is expanded in the cylinder its temperature falls, and if water is formed, the steam which remains occupies a larger volume than it need do, exerts a smaller pressure on the piston, and does less work. Condensation in the cylinder is prevented by using superheated steam and by surrounding the cylinder with a steam jacket (*i.e.* a space kept filled with steam), which keeps the cylinder walls hot. Superheated steam is steam which has been further heated after leaving the boiler. When it is expanded and cooled in the cylinder, therefore, its temperature remains above that at which it will condense, and no water is formed.

(5) If the steam exhaust leads into the atmosphere, the pressure on the exhaust side of the piston must be at least atmospheric pressure. Hence, work has to be done in driving out the steam through the exhaust port, and the energy required to do this is no longer available. By passing the steam as it escapes into a condenser, the pressure on the exhaust side of the piston is much reduced, and this useless work is diminished.

Even when all these precautions are taken, however, the thermal efficiency of a steam engine seldom exceeds about 25% ; in other words, three-quarters of the chemical energy of the coal is wasted. Many steam engines have a thermal efficiency below 10%.

12.03. When these losses of energy have all been taken into consideration, others still remain. These are the mechanical losses due to friction of the moving parts of the engine. Thus, of the energy which is applied in doing work on the piston, a fraction is lost through its conversion into heat by friction at the bearings of the engine.

The mechanical efficiency is defined to be

$$\frac{\text{the useful work done by the engine}}{\text{the work done on the piston}}.$$

Fortunately, the mechanical efficiency of the steam engine is high, values of 85% or more being common.

12.04. A better thermal efficiency than that of the reciprocating steam engine can be obtained by means of the **steam turbine.** In this machine, the pressure energy of the steam from the boiler is first converted into kinetic energy by allowing the steam to escape through steam jets, from which it issues at a high velocity. The steam jets then play upon blades fixed to a shaft able to rotate, and the kinetic energy of the steam is transformed into kinetic energy of the blades and shaft.

If steam from a steam boiler at a pressure of 250 lb. per square inch is allowed to escape through a jet, the velocity of

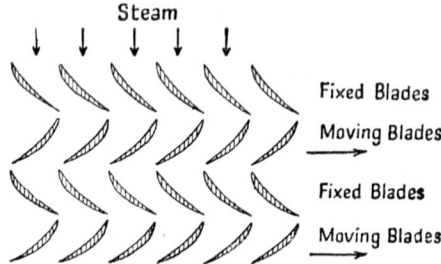

Fig. **12.02.**—The Arrangement of the Blades of a Steam Turbine.

the steam escaping is about 4000 ft. per second. In order that the steam should give up the whole of its kinetic energy, the velocity of the moving blades would have to be about one-half of this amount. Such velocities are quite impossible in practice, because any wheel built to carry the blades would fly to pieces if rotated at such a speed. It is usual, therefore, to allow the steam to expand only slightly before it reaches the blades of the rotor. In expanding, the steam loses a little of its pressure energy, and this amount of energy is converted into kinetic energy. As only a part of the pressure energy is so converted, the velocity of the steam is not large. The kinetic energy of the steam is converted into kinetic energy of the rotor in passing through the blades. The same steam is now allowed to expand further, gains kinetic energy at the expense of its pressure energy, and this kinetic energy is transferred to the

[*Planet News photo.*

FIG. 12.03.

The rotor of one of the steam turbines of the *Queen Mary.*

rotor by a second set of blades. A further such expansion is allowed to occur before the steam passes through each row of blades, the pressure of the steam gradually decreasing until the other end of the turbine is reached. Here the steam is condensed in the condenser.

In the reaction turbine, the blades are arranged as shown in figure 12.02. Every alternate set of blades is fixed to the outer casing of the turbine, and serves to direct the steam passing through them against the following set of blades, which is attached to a shaft able to rotate. This shaft and its sets of blades form the rotor of the machine (see figure 12.03). The arrows on the right of figure 12.02 show the direction of motion of the blades of the rotor.

The thermal efficiency of a well-designed turbine may be as high as 36%. The mechanical efficiency of a large turbine is usually about 85%.

12.05. The Petrol Engine.—In this type of heat engine, the fuel is vaporized at the carburettor and mixed with air. It then passes to the cylinders, where the mixture is ignited by electric sparks, and burned. The gases formed by the combustion are at a high temperature, and consequently exert a high pressure on the pistons. From two to twelve cylinders are commonly used, each cylinder receiving a charge in turn. The pistons exert forces on the crankshaft by means of connecting rods attached to the pistons, and the use of a number of cylinders ensures that a steadier thrust is obtained than could be given by a single piston.

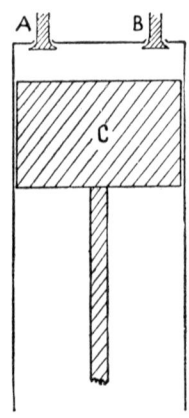

FIG. 12.04.

Most petrol engines work in what is known as the *four-stroke cycle*. Two valves, operated automatically from the engine, serve to introduce the mixture of petrol vapour and air, and to release the waste products formed by their combustion. These two valves are represented in figure 12.04 by the valves A and B.

We begin by considering the piston C at the top of the cylinder. During the first (downward) stroke, the inlet valve A is opened, and a mixture of petrol vapour and air enters the cylinder, the valve B remaining closed. During the second (upward) stroke both valves remain closed, and the mixture is compressed. When the piston has nearly reached the top of its stroke, an electric spark is passed through the mixture by means of a spark plug let into the wall of the cylinder. The electric spark causes rapid combustion of the petrol, and the pressure in the cylinder rises. Both valves remain closed during the downward stroke of the piston which follows, and it is only during this third stroke that work is done on the piston by the hot gases formed. During the fourth (upward) stroke, the exhaust valve

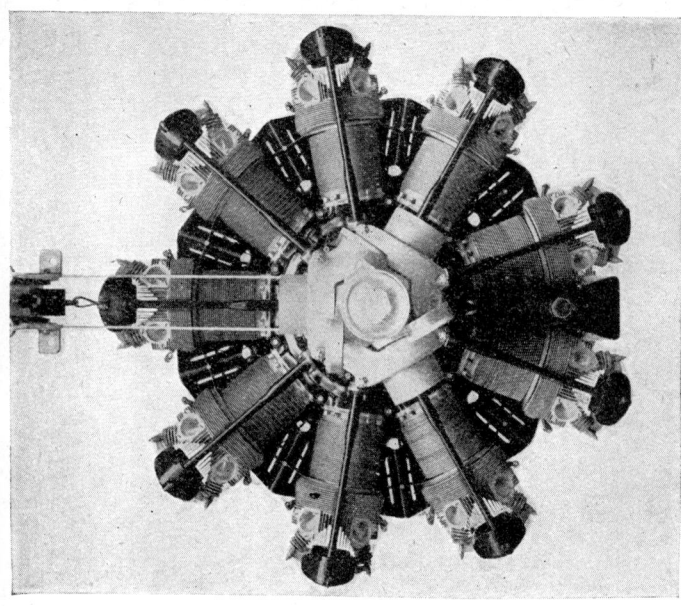

(a)

(b)

[By courtesy of the Bristol Aeroplane Co., Ltd

FIG. 12.05.

The back and front view of a Pegasus X air-cooled radial aeroplane engine. At 2600 revs. per minute the engine develops 920 horse-power. Its weight is 1005 lb. Note the fins round the cylinders and on the cylinder heads, to assist air cooling.

B is open, and the waste products escape, leaving the engine ready to repeat the cycle.

The cylinders are prevented from becoming too hot by surrounding them by a jacket through which water circulates, or by providing them with fins which expose a large surface to the air. From these fins the heat produced is dissipated to the air. Air-cooled engines are not much used in motor-cars, but are often used in aeroplanes, where the extra weight of the water, water-jacket, and radiator of the water-cooled engine is an important consideration.

EXAMPLES 12

1. Explain what is meant by the mechanical efficiency and the thermal efficiency of a heat engine. How do you account for the fact that the thermal efficiency of a reciprocating steam engine seldom exceeds 25% ? What steps are taken to make the value as high as possible ?

2. Describe the construction and use of the steam turbine, and trace the conversion of the heat energy of the coal burned into the kinetic energy of rotation of the rotor.

3. Give an account of the four-stroke-cycle petrol engine.

4. A locomotive burns 50 lb. of coal per minute and does work at the rate of 1050 H.P. in drawing a train. The feed water is at 60° F. and is converted into steam at 400° F. at the rate of 50 lb. per minute. The heating value of the coal is 14,000 lb. deg. F. units, and the latent heat of vaporization at 400° F. is 850 B.Th.U. per lb. Find the thermal efficiency and the mechanical efficiency of the locomotive. [1 H.P. = 33,000 ft.-lb. per minute ; 1 B.Th.U. = 778 ft.-lb.]

LIGHT

CHAPTER 13

13.01. Light is that which enables us to see objects. The objects in a room do not themselves affect our eyes, for if the room is darkened, and all light is excluded, we are unable to see the chairs, desks, and walls, although we know that they are still there, because they can be felt with the hands. When an electric lamp is switched on in the darkened room, the lamp becomes visible because it emits light, and some of this light passes directly from the lamp to the eyes. The other objects in the room become visible at the same time, because, although they do not themselves emit light, some of the light from the lamp passes to the objects, whence it is thrown back to the eyes.

Light travels along straight lines between objects. The path of the beam of light from the projecting lantern to the screen of a cinema can be seen, and the edges of the beam are straight. If light did not travel along straight lines to the eye it would be possible to see round corners.

Curiously enough, although light enables us to see objects, *it is not itself visible*. The rays of light falling on this book cannot be seen. When we see the path of the beam of light at the cinema, we do so, not by observing the rays of light travelling from the lantern to the screen, but by observing the dust and smoke particles which are illuminated by the beam of light. In an atmosphere perfectly free from such particles, even the path of the intense beam of light from the lantern could not be seen.

13.02. Such an object as the point of a pin is seen by means of the rays of light which travel from it to the eye. Rays of light from the point of the pin travel out in all directions in space, but only the rays which enter the eye assist in rendering the point of the pin visible. Such rays form a cone whose apex is at the point of the pin, and whose base lies on the eye (figure 13.01). Each tiny portion of the pin sends its own cone of rays to the eye, and the eye is thus able to see the whole object at once. It is obviously impossible, however, to draw all these rays in one diagram, and to avoid confusion, we shall draw the paths of rays from only one point on the object, leaving the others to be imagined.

If a cone of rays enables the eye to see an object distinctly *the apex of the cone must be at least* 25 cm. *distant from the eye.* Its distance may be as much greater than 25 cm. as we please.

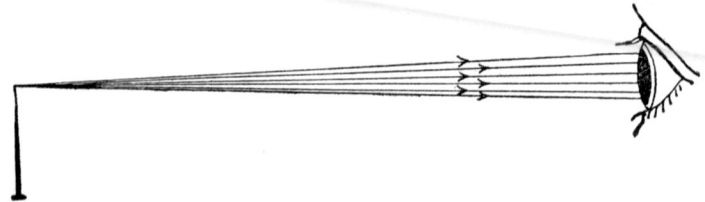

FIG. 13.01.

The apex of the cone of rays from a point on a star is many millions of miles distant, but the star is nevertheless visible as a distinct point. On the other hand, the print of this book appears blurred and indistinct if it is held close to the eyes. At a distance of 25 cm. it can be seen clearly ; at shorter distances it can be seen for a few moments by straining the eyes ; and when it is brought still closer it becomes blurred. For this reason the distance of 25 cm. is known as *the least distance of distinct vision.*

13.03. Light is able to pass through certain substances, or media, such as air, glass, and water, and these are called *transparent* media. Paper and paraffin wax stop most of the light which falls upon them, but if light falls on thin sheets of these materials, some of it passes through. Such substances are said to be *translucent.* Other materials such as wood and iron do not transmit light, and are said to be *opaque.*

When an opaque body is placed between a source of light and a screen, the opaque body prevents light from reaching some parts of the screen, and a shadow is formed. Thus when light is thrown out in all directions by the point source of light A (figure 13.02) the ball B intercepts all the light in the cone shown in the figure, and a uniform circular shadow is formed on the screen C.

Figure 13.03 illustrates the formation of shadows by the ball when the source of light is not a point, but a second sphere AB.

Straight lines can be drawn to the point J from any point on the side of AB facing the screen, so the opaque ball CD shuts off no light which is travelling towards this point, and the screen

is brightly illumin-
ated there. Light
from only the upper
portion of AB can
reach the point L,
and no light reaches
the point F. The
shadow begins at E
and becomes darker
as F is approached.
Between F and G
the shadow is dark-
est, because no light
reaches these points;
from G to H the

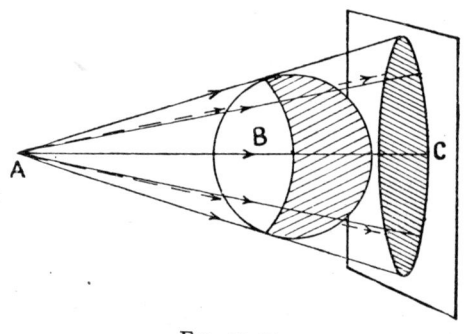

FIG. 13.02.

shadow becomes lighter, and vanishes beyond H. The appear-ance of the shadow is thus similar to the diagram at the right of the figure. The central dark region, which receives no light

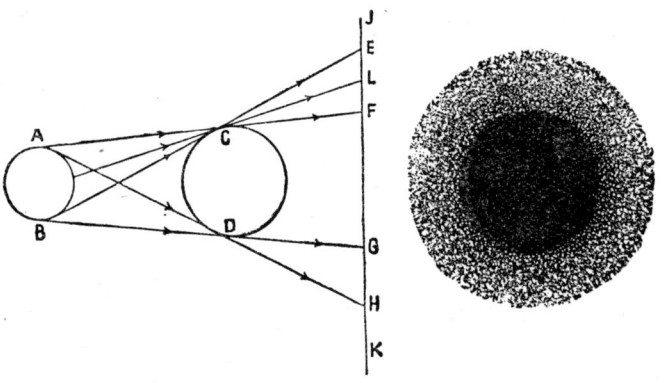

FIG. 13.03.

from the source, is called the *umbra*. The ring of shadow, which receives light from parts only of the source, is called the *penumbra*.

13.04. The ball in figure 13.02 throws part of its own surface into shadow, and parts of the surface of the moon and earth are thrown into shadow in the same way. Only those portions of the moon which are illuminated by the sun are visible from the earth, so the moon appears of some such shape as the unshaded part of the ball in the figure. The apparent shape varies from a narrow crescent to a circle, according to the position from which we view the moon. Night and day are caused by the rotation of the earth, each part of the earth passing in turn into its own shadow.

Occasionally the earth passes into the shadow cast by the

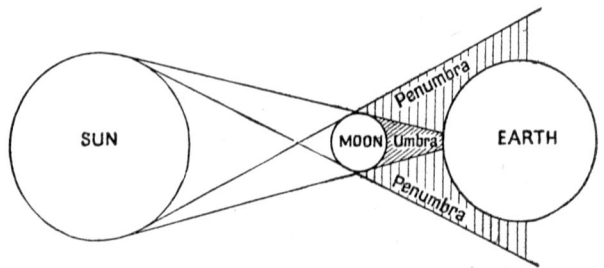

FIG. 13.04.—AN ECLIPSE OF THE SUN.

moon, and in this case an eclipse of the sun is said to take place. If the eclipse of the sun is a total one at some point on the earth's surface, the sun is completely hidden from this point, and such a point therefore lies in the umbra. Other points, at which the eclipse is only partial, pass through the penumbra. These two cases are illustrated in figure 13.04. When the relative positions of the sun, moon, and earth are those shown in figure 13.05, only the rays from the edges of the sun reach the point A, and from this point an annular eclipse is seen.

Eclipses of the moon are caused in a similar way, when the moon passes into the shadow of the earth.

EXAMPLES 13

1. What evidence can you give to show (a) that light travels along straight lines, (b) that we see objects by means of light travelling from the objects to the eye, and not from the eye to the objects ?

2. Draw diagrams showing in plan the relative positions of the

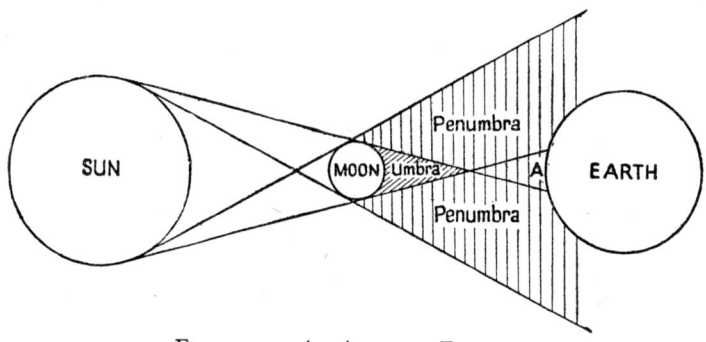

FIG. 13.05.—AN ANNULAR ECLIPSE.

sun, moon, and earth, when (a) a full moon, (b) a new moon, (c) a half-moon is visible from the earth.

3. Describe, with the aid of a diagram, the appearance of the shadow of a ball which is illuminated by light from a narrow vertical slit.

4. What will be the phase of the moon when (a) an eclipse of the sun, (b) an eclipse of the moon, occurs ? Explain your answers with the aid of suitable diagrams.

5. Describe the appearance of the earth, when viewed from the moon, when (a) a total eclipse of the sun, (b) an annular eclipse of the sun, is visible from the earth.

CHAPTER 14

REFLECTION AT PLANE SURFACES

14.01. You have doubtless heard the expression " personal magnetism." Have you ever seen an electric lamp run by " personal electricity " ? It is to be feared that you never will, but the following interesting deception almost makes it look possible.

FIG. 14.01.

Two exactly similar electric-light bulbs are placed, one in front of, and the other behind, a large sheet of glass. The bulb in front of the glass is connected to the electric-light mains in the ordinary way, but the bulb behind the glass is connected only to the hand of the demonstrator. When the electric current is switched on, however, both lamps light up. It would perhaps be better to say that the lamp behind the glass appears to light up, for if you slip round to the back of the glass you will find that this apparently cheap method of running two lamps for the price of one is only a deception. The lamp at the back is giving no light.

Doubtless you will have guessed that the sheet of glass acts like a mirror, and forms behind the glass a " reflection " of the white-hot filament of the front lamp. In scientific language this reflection is known as an " image," and the purpose of this chapter is to enable us to discover something about the images formed by a plane (*i.e.* flat) mirror.

It is first necessary to find where the image is. You may not have realized that an image has any definite position, apart from the fact that it is somewhere in or behind the mirror. Nevertheless, it has a perfectly definite position, as the last experiment shows, for on moving the lamp which is behind the glass, the whole illusion is destroyed. The lamp behind the glass appeared to give out light because its filament occupied the same position as the image of the hot filament of the lamp in front. Since it is not easy to measure accurately the position of a lamp filament we shall perform the next experiment using pins instead of lamps.

14.02. In finding the positions of images we make use of the *principle of parallax*. If you hold your arm outstretched, and observing both the hand and the wall behind it, move the head slowly from side to side, you will notice that the distant object (the wall) appears to move past the nearer one (the hand) in the same direction as the head moves. The same effect is observed from a moving train, when the distant objects appear to move with the train past the nearer ones. Two objects at equal distances from the head, however, do not move relative to one another when the head is moved, and if no apparent motion occurs the objects observed are equally distant. In this case there is said to be *no parallax* between the two objects.

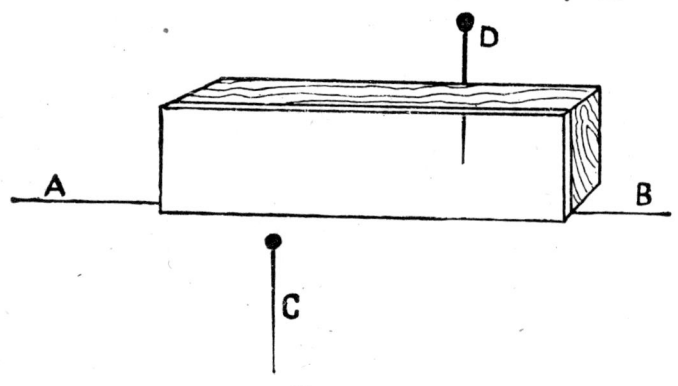

Fig. 14.02.

14.03. These facts may be used to find the position of an image. A line AB (figure 14.02) is drawn across the middle of a sheet of paper, and a narrow mirror is placed with its silvered reflecting surface along this line. A pin C, which we shall call the object pin, is placed upright in the paper about 10 cm. in front of the mirror, and a second pin D is placed vertically upright behind the mirror, and moved until a position is found such that its head is directly over the image of the first pin, and remains directly over this image from whatever point it is viewed. The pin D now occupies the same position as the image of the first pin. On removing the mirror it is found that :

    (a) **The foot of the object and of its image lie on the same perpendicular to the mirror ;**

    (b) **The image is the same distance behind the mirror as the object is in front of it.**

14.04. Having discovered rules which enable us to predict the position of an image, we may now proceed to show how an

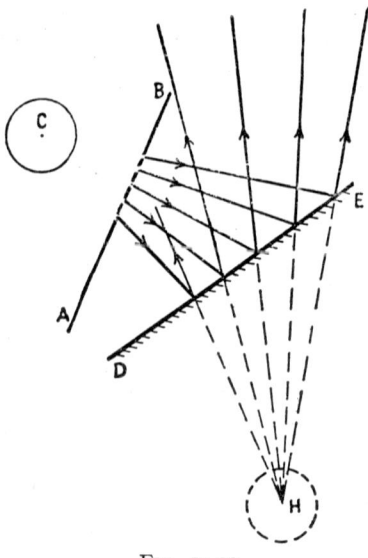

FIG. 14.03.

image is formed. For this purpose it is desirable to trace the paths of the rays from the object to the eye, and this may be done using the filament of a motor head lamp as object. The lamp C (figure 14.03) is held just above the surface of a sheet of white paper, and a metal screen AB with a number of narrow vertical slits cuts off most of the light. The rays which pass through this screen, however, form brightly illuminated streaks on the paper, and these enable the paths of the rays to be seen. When the mirror DE is placed to intercept these rays, they are reflected as shown in the diagram, and on placing the eyes in position to look back along the reflected rays, it is found that each ray is travelling in such a direction that it appears to come from the point H, where the image of the filament can be seen. *The eye sees an image at H because the rays leaving the mirror form part of a cone whose apex is at the point H,* and, as we have shown, the eye sees an object at the apex of the cone of rays entering the eye. If the rays leaving the foot of the pin in the previous experiment

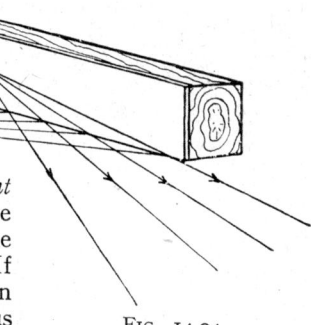

Fig. 14.04.

could be seen they would appear as in figure 14.04.

We shall in future use figures similar to figure 14.05 to show the formation of images. O is a point on the object, and CD is the mirror. To draw the path of the rays from the object to an eye placed at EF, the position I of the image is first found. The rays enter the eye as though they come from I, so AE and BF are parts of the paths of the extreme rays of the cone, IAE and IBF being straight lines. These rays reach the mirror by the paths OA and OB, so OAE and OBF are the complete paths. The lines IA and IB are dotted to show that they are merely construction lines. They show the paths along which

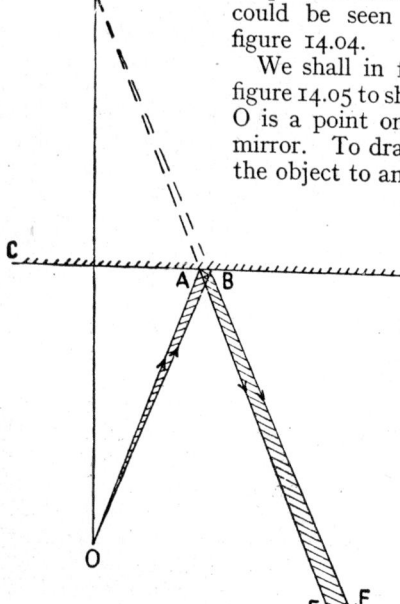

Fig. 14.05.

G

rays appear to travel, not paths of actual rays. Notice that the lines AE and BF, which are drawn first, are those parts of the ray paths along which the light travels last.

14.05. The light from a point on an object appears, after reflection at a plane mirror, to come from a particular point behind the mirror. Is it possible to find a rule which enables the *directions* of the reflected rays to be calculated? Let us suppose that O is an object in front of the plane mirror AB (figure 14.06), and that OC is any ray from O to the mirror. After reflection, this ray appears to come from I, the image of O, so its path is along the line CD, the continuation of the line IC. Let CE be the normal to the mirror at C, the point of incidence.

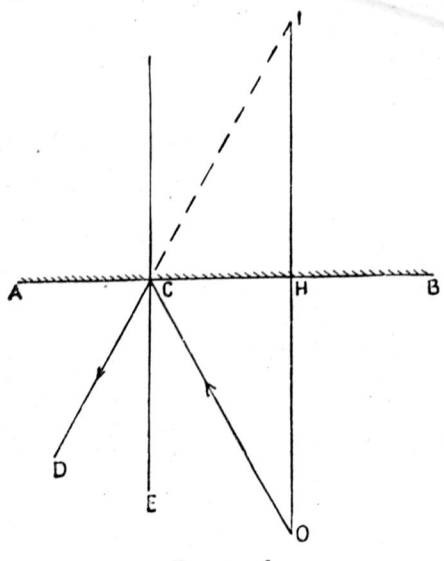

FIG. 14.06.

Since the object and image both lie on the same normal to the mirror, the mirror lies in a plane at right angles to that of the paper. C is a point in the plane of the paper, so CE, which is normal to the mirror, also lies in this plane. CD is the continuation of the line IC, since the reflected ray CD appears to come from I. Hence the ray CD lies in the same plane as I and C, and is therefore in the plane of the paper. The incident ray OC also lies in this plane, since O and C do so. Hence,

(*a*) **The reflected ray lies in the same plane as the incident ray and the normal to the mirror at the point of incidence.**

The angle OCE, between the incident ray and the *normal*, is called the **angle of incidence**; and the angle ECD between the reflected ray and the *normal* is called the **angle of reflection.**

In the triangles ICH, OCH,

CH is common,

IH = OH, (the object and image are equidistant from **the** mirror),

$\lfloor$ IHC = $\lfloor$ OHC, (object and image lie on the same normal to the mirror).

Hence, the triangles are congruent, and $\lfloor$ COH = $\lfloor$ CIH

But, since CE and IO are parallel,

$$\lfloor COH = \lfloor ECO, \text{ and } \lfloor CIH = \lfloor DCE$$
$$\therefore \ \lfloor ECO = \lfloor DCE.$$

Hence (*b*) **The angle of reflection is equal to the angle of incidence.** The two rules (*a*) and (*b*) are known as **the laws of reflection.**

14.06. Heat radiation obeys the same laws of reflection as light. To show this, an electric radiator A is set up in front of a tube B (figure 14.07), and a sheet of galvanized iron is used to reflect the radiation down a second tube C to the thermopile D. Screens F,F, shut off all the radiation except that which enters the tube B. It is then found that the deflection of the galvanometer is greatest when the

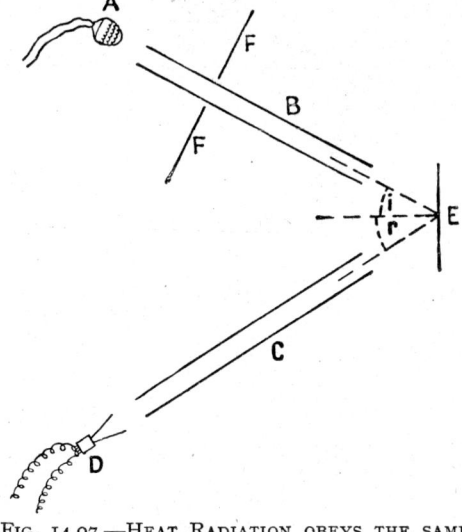

Fig. 14.07.—Heat Radiation obeys the same Laws of Reflection as Light.

" mirror " is so placed that (i) the angles of incidence and reflection are equal, and (ii) the tubes B and C lie in the same plane as the normal to the reflecting surface at E.

14.07. Since you have never been able to step out of your own body and view it from in front, you may not have realized that your appearance is not exactly the same as that of your image in a plane mirror, and if as a result of an unfortunate accident you came to possess a wooden leg (the left one, say) you might be surprised to find that your image in a mirror possessed a sound left leg, but that its right leg was the wooden one. This distortion of the true appearance of objects by the mirror is called *lateral inversion*, and is the cause of the curious appearance of writing when viewed in a mirror.

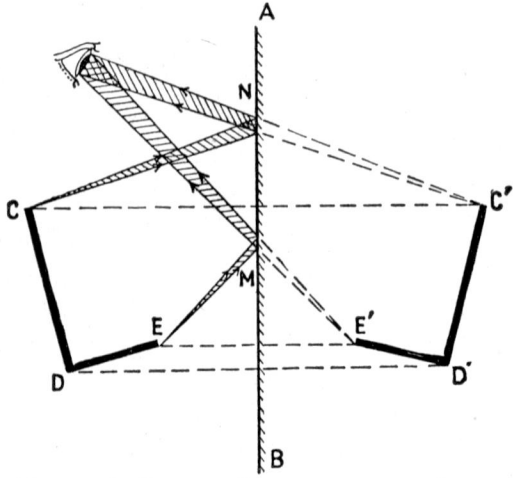

FIG. 14.08.—LATERAL INVERSION OF THE IMAGE.

Figure 14.08 shows the formation of the image of a letter L, and shows how lateral inversion occurs. The image is drawn by finding the image of each of the points CDE, and the paths of the rays from each of the extreme points C and E to an eye are shown. In order to view the image, the eye uses the part of the mirror between the points N and M. If the diagram is drawn to a suitable scale, the length of mirror required may be found by measurement of the distance NM.

One other fact about the image formed by a plane mirror is obvious from the diagram. **The image formed by a plane mirror is the same size as its object.**

14.08. When two plane mirrors are placed at right angles to one another, as are the mirrors AB and BC in figure 14.09, three images I_1, I_2, I_3, are formed in such positions that I_1, I_2, I_3, and the object O are at the corners of a rectangle.   The images I_1 and I_2 are formed in the ordinary way by the mirrors AB and BC acting separately ; I_3 is formed by light which has been reflected at both mirrors.

Light from the object O strikes the mirror AB, and forms the image I_1.   After reflection at this mirror some of the light

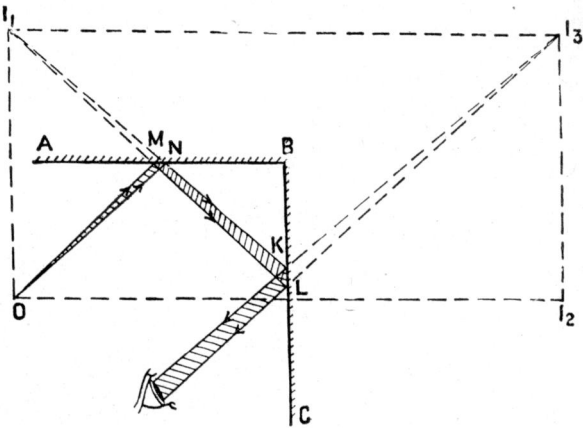

FIG. 14.09.—THE IMAGES FORMED BY TWO PLANE MIRRORS AT RIGHT ANGLES.

meets the other mirror BC. It does so, however, as though it came from I_1, and is therefore reflected from BC as though it came from I_3, the image of I_1 in the mirror BC.   In the same way, light which travels from the object to the mirror BC is reflected so that it appears to come from I_2.   Some of this light meets AB, and is then reflected as though it came from the image of I_2 in the mirror AB.   With the two mirrors at right angles this image of I_2 happens to be at I_3, so the image I_3 may be regarded as the image of I_1 in the mirror BC, or as the image of I_2 in the mirror AB. I_3 is behind both mirrors, so rays of light travelling from the direction of I_3 cannot meet the face of either mirror, and no image of I_3 is possible.

The rays by means of which an eye placed in the position shown sees the image I_3 are drawn as follows : The light entering the eye appears to come from I_3, so its paths are along the lines joining I_3 to the eye. These lines are drawn first. I_3 is, however, the image of I_1 formed by the mirror BC, so before meeting this mirror the rays came from the direction of I_1. I_1 is therefore joined to the points K and L, and the parts of the lines I_1K and I_1L between the mirrors are the actual paths of the extreme rays. I_1 is the image of O, so before the rays were reflected at the mirror AB they were travelling from O. The lines OM and ON are thus the paths of the rays at the edge of the cone which enters the eye.

14.09. Two mirrors inclined at 60° form five images as shown in figure 14.10. The object and images all lie on the circumference of a circle whose centre is A. AB and AC are the two mirrors ; O is the object. O forms an image I_1 in the mirror AB ; I_1 is in front of the mirror AC, and therefore forms a second image I_2, by reflection from AC ; I_2 is in front of the mirror AB, and forms a further image I_3 ; I_3 is behind both mirrors, and forms no further image. Similarly I_1' is the image of O in AC ; I_2' is the image of I_1' in AB ; the image of I_2' in AC coincides with I_3.

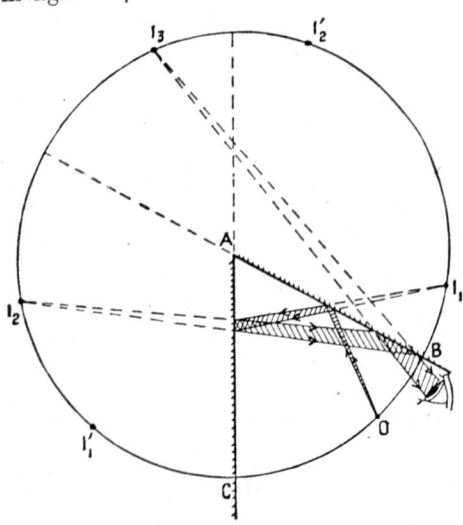

Fig. 14.10.—The Images formed in Two Plane Mirrors inclined at 60°.

The diagram shows also the paths of the rays which enable an eye, placed in the position indicated, to see the image I_3.

14.10. You may have noticed, in a room containing two

mirrors situated opposite one another, that one mirror contained an image of the second mirror, and that this image contained an image of the first mirror, which contained . . . We shall not

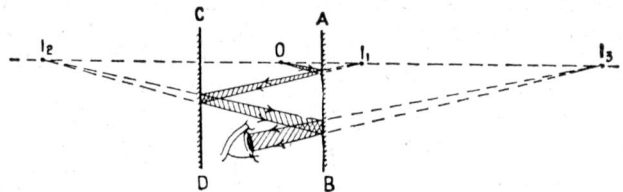

FIG. 14.11.—THE IMAGES FORMED BY TWO PARALLEL PLANE MIRRORS.

attempt to finish the sentence, because, although the head finally gets in the way, a dozen or more images of this kind are often visible.

Some of the images formed by two parallel mirrors are shown in figure 14.11. I_1 is the image of O formed by the mirror AB ; I_2 the image of I_1 formed by the mirror CD ; I_3 the image of I_2 formed by AB. We may continue drawing these images in this way as long as we please, provided our sheet of paper is large enough, and if we become tired of drawing this set of images, we may begin drawing another series, for O forms an image in CD, which forms an image in AB, and so on. Figure 14.11 shows also the rays which enable the image I_3 to be seen.

FIG. 14.12.—PATTERN FORMED BY A KALEIDOSCOPE.

The kaleidoscope is a toy which contains two or three inclined mirrors inside a tube. By dropping into the tube some curiously shaped pieces of paper, beautiful designs are formed by the objects and their images. One such design is shown in figure 14.12.

14.11. When light from a point falls on a flat surface such as a mirror, a single sharp image is formed. If the surface is not smooth, however, no sharp image is produced. Figure 14.13 illustrates the reflection of light from the surface of a pond disturbed by waves. As shown in the diagram, there are a num-

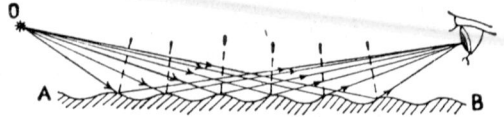

FIG. 14.13.—REFLECTION OF LIGHT FROM WATER.

ber of points from which rays are reflected to the eye, making the angle of reflection equal to the angle of incidence. The light entering the eye comes from various directions, and a patch of light is seen instead of a single image point.

14.12. A sheet of paper is a flat surface, so it might be expected to reflect light in the same way that a mirror does. When a beam of light AB (figure 14.14) is directed on to a sheet of paper,

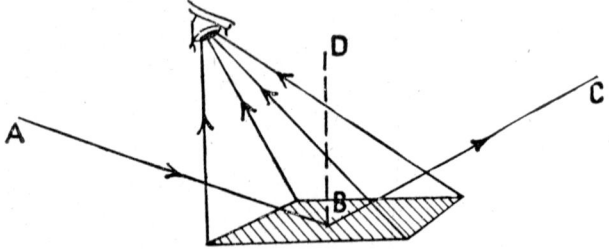

FIG. 14.14.—IRREGULAR REFLECTION FROM A MATT SURFACE.

however, it is found that only a small fraction of the incident light is reflected in the direction BC, as required by the laws of reflection. Most of the light is scattered in other directions by the paper. Such light is said to suffer *irregular reflection*.

If a beam of light shines on the surface of the paper, the eye, placed as shown, receives light from various parts of the paper, and not from one particular direction only. Hence, what is seen is not an image of the source of the beam of light, but the various parts of the paper. The paper becomes, so to speak, a new source of light. Irregular reflection takes place at all except a few surfaces, such as those of glass and polished metals.

14.13. EXAMPLE ON THE USE OF THE PLANE MIRROR.—*A man 6 ft. high views his image in a vertical plane mirror. What is the shortest length of mirror which he can use in order to see the whole of his image?*

AB (figure 14.15) represents the man, and CD the mirror, to

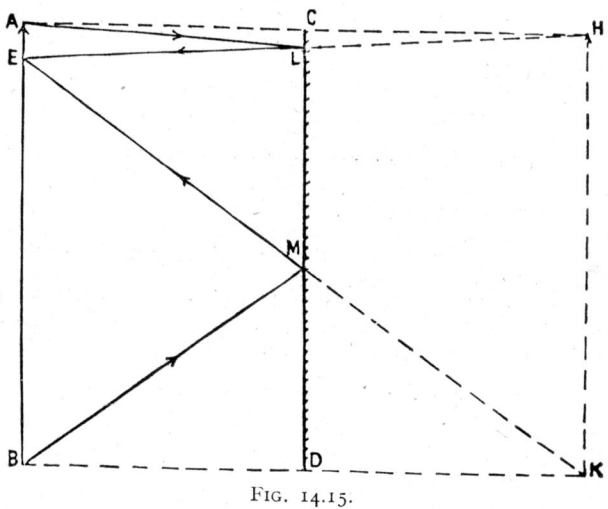

FIG. 14.15.

a suitable scale. Let E represent the position of the man's eye. The image at the top of his head is at H, the same distance behind the mirror as A is in front of it, and on the same perpendicular ACH to the mirror. Similarly K represents the position of the image of his feet. The rays from the top of the man's head enter his eye as though they come from H, so LE is their path from the mirror to his eye, and AL is the path from A to the mirror. Similarly BME represents the path of the rays from the soles of his shoes to his eye. The part of the mirror used is that between L and M, and by measurement LM is found to represent 3 ft. Hence, the smallest mirror which will serve the purpose is 3 ft. long.

EXAMPLES 14

1. Describe the use of the method of parallax for finding the position of the image formed by a plane mirror. At what point is the image formed ?

2. ABC is a triangle in which $\lfloor$ABC $= 135°$ and BC $= 3$ in. A plane mirror is placed along AB, and a pin is placed at C. Draw a diagram to scale showing the position of the image, and the paths of rays which enable the image to be seen by an eye placed in a suitable position.

3. Describe an experiment to show how an image is formed by a plane mirror.

4. State the laws of reflection and show that these can be deduced from a knowledge of the respective positions of a plane mirror, an object, and its image.

5. A ray of light meets a mirror at an angle of incidence of 50°. Draw a diagram showing the ray and the mirror, and then, without using a compass or protractor, show how the path of the reflected ray can be found.

6. Draw a diagram showing the formation by a plane mirror of the image of the letters AE.

7. With the aid of a diagram explain why the image formed by a plane mirror is laterally inverted. Why does it not appear that a man is standing upside down when his image is viewed in such a mirror ?

8. ABCD is a rectangle in which AB $= 3$ in., BC $= 2$ in. A pin is placed at C, and two plane mirrors are placed along the sides AB and AD. Draw a diagram showing the positions of the images formed, and indicate the path of the rays by means of which the eye sees an image formed by reflection from both mirrors.

9. ABCD is a parallelogram, in which AB $= 3$ in., BC $= 2$ in., and $\lfloor$BAD $= 60°$. A pin is placed at C, and two plane mirrors along AB and AD respectively. Draw a diagram showing the position of all the images formed, and show how an eye suitably placed sees the image which is behind both mirrors.

10. Draw a diagram showing the formation of the images in two mirrors inclined at 72°, and draw the rays by means of which the image behind both mirrors is seen by an eye suitably placed.

11. Two plane mirrors, each $1\frac{1}{2}$ in. long, are placed opposite one another on two parallel lines 2 in. apart, with the reflecting surfaces of the mirrors facing one another. A ray of light meets one of the mirrors at an angle of incidence of 30° at a point near the end of the mirror. Draw a diagram to show the subsequent path of the ray, using the method of images.

12. A plane mirror 3 ft. high, hangs on the wall of a room 12 ft. high and 15 ft. broad. By means of a diagram drawn to scale find the greatest distance from the mirror at which a man may place his eyes in order to see the image of the whole height of the opposite wall.

School Certificate Questions

13. State the laws of reflection of light, and describe how they may be verified experimentally. What are the characteristics of the image formed by a plane mirror ?

An electric strip-light 2 ft. in length is 2 ft. vertically above, and parallel to, a horizontal strip of plane mirror 1 ft. long. Their centres lie in the same vertical line. Find the length of (a) the image of the strip-light in the mirror, and (b) the reflected patch of light on the ceiling 2 ft. above the strip-light.   (B)

14. State the laws of reflection of light ; and say how you have proved them experimentally. A pin is placed vertically 4 cm. in front of a plane mirror, fixed vertically ; draw a pencil, of at least three rays, showing how an eye situated to the side of the object sees the image.   (L)

15. State the laws of reflection of light. Draw a rectangle ABCD to represent the plan of a laboratory table, AB = 10 ft., BC = 6 ft., scale $\frac{1}{2}$ in. = 1 ft. A plane mirror can be rotated about a vertical axis through O, the middle of BC. Show how the mirror must be placed for a person looking in the direction BO to see in it the image of a vertical rod at A. Through what angle must the mirror be turned so that the image of a vertical rod at D may be seen ? How is this angle related to the angle AOD ?   (L)

16. Explain carefully how an image is formed by a plane mirror. Two vertical plane mirrors are inclined to one another at an angle of 60°. How many images are formed, and how may their positions be found ?   **(O.C)**

CHAPTER 15

REAL IMAGES FORMED BY A LENS

15.01. Although lenses have been known for more than 2000 years they were not much used until the close of the Middle Ages, because their action was not understood. Nowadays, however, lenses form important parts of such instruments as telescopes, microscopes, cameras, and spectacles, and before it is possible to understand these instruments some knowledge of lenses is essential.

The lenses shown in figure 15.01 are all convex lenses. The important point about each of these is that it is thicker at the middle than at the edges. Such lenses are sometimes called positive, or converging lenses, and we shall in the present chapter deal with this kind of lens only.

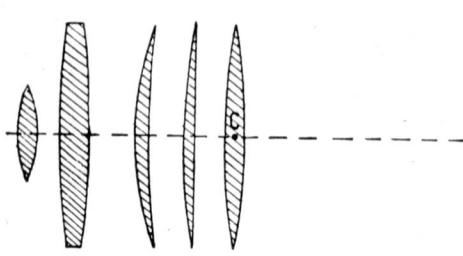

FIG. 15.01.—CONVEX LENSES.

The point C is called the *centre* of the lens, and the line (shown dotted in the figure) which passes through the centre of the lens and meets each of its faces normally is called the *principal axis* of the lens.

15.02. When a convex lens is held near the wall of a room opposite the windows, a blurred, indistinct picture of the windows is seen on the wall. By moving the lens nearer to, or farther from the wall, a position can be found such that the picture appears sharp and distinct. This sharp picture of the windows, like the picture formed by a plane mirror, is called an image.

The image formed on the wall by a lens is unlike that formed by a plane mirror in several respects. It is upside down, or inverted, whereas that formed by the mirror was the correct way up, or erect. The image formed by the lens is not the same size as its object (the windows), but the image formed by the mirror is.

How is the image formed by the lens? The following experiment will help to make this clear. For the purposes of the

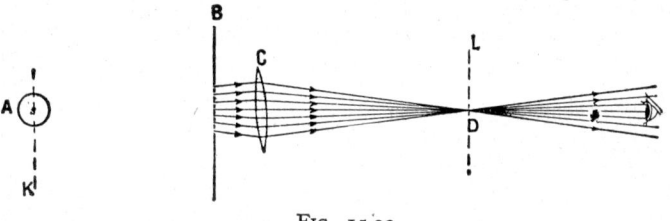

FIG. 15.02.

experiment we shall make use of a convex cylindrical lens instead of a convex spherical one, but the principle is the same for both types of lens, and the cylindrical lens enables light streaks to be used.

The light from the bulb of a motor head lamp A (figure 15.02) passes through slits cut in a screen B, and forms streaks of light on the far side of the screen. These streaks diverge from one point, since the light which forms them comes from the vertical filament of the lamp. In pass-

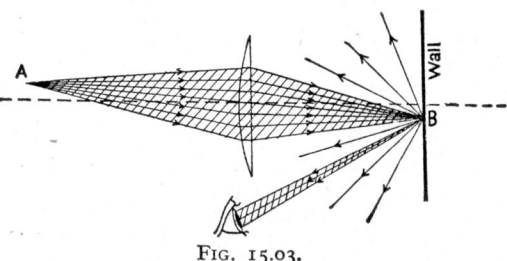

FIG. 15.03.

ing through the lens C each ray of light is bent, and the light is caused to converge to a single point D on the far side of the lens. From this point the rays diverge again, so, to an eye placed as shown, the rays appear to come from D instead of from A, and the eye sees an image of the filament at D.

When the image was formed on the wall, however, the eye was not placed in this position, but as shown in figure 15.03. The rays from one point A on the object have been drawn.

After passing through the lens, these rays are caused to converge to a single point B which is the image of A. Since the wall is a rough surface, however, the rays which meet it at B are reflected in various directions, and some of these rays pass to the eye. These rays all diverge from the point B, so an image of A is seen at B. Comparatively little of the light which reaches B is reflected in the direction of the eye, so the image formed on an opaque screen can only be seen clearly if the rays are proceeding from a bright source of light such as the windows.

When the lens forms an image of an object of finite size, instead of the image of a point, it does so in a similar way, by causing the rays from each point on the object to converge to a corresponding point on the wall, and the image observed must be thought of as made up of innumerable points of this kind. If the lamp A in figure 15.02 is moved along the line AK, the light streaks show the paths of rays from various points of an object lying along AK. This object lies in a plane perpendicular to the principal axis of the lens, and if the movement of the lamp is small, it is found that, whatever its position, the rays from it meet at some point in the line DL ; that is, at some point in a second plane at right angles to the principal axis. Hence, *a convex lens forms a sharp image of an object lying in a plane perpendicular to the principal axis, and this image also lies in a plane perpendicular to the principal axis.*

If, however, the lamp is moved to greater distances along the line AK, an important change occurs. The rays passing through the lens no longer converge to one point, and the farther the lamp is moved from the principal axis, the greater is the error caused by assuming that the rays do so. Hence, **the image formed by a lens is sharp, only if the object lies on, or near, its principal axis.**

We may note now one further difference between the images formed by a lens and those formed by a plane mirror. The rays which produce the image behind the mirror appear to come from the image, but have not in fact done so. Those which form the image on the wall do pass to the image and thence to the eye. To distinguish between the two types of image, that formed on the wall is called a *real image* ; that formed by the plane mirror is called a *virtual image*.

15.03. When the distance between an object and a lens is altered, the distance between the lens and the image alters as well. Since it is not possible to show this by altering the positions of walls and windows, we shall use the artificial " window " of a lamp tin for the next experiment, and shall use a screen to catch the image formed. The lamp tin A (figure 15.04) is merely a tin containing a lamp which illuminates a piece of glass scale covering a hole in one side of the tin. This brightly illuminated piece of scale constitutes the object. A lens is clamped in a stand, and is adjusted to the same height as the glass scale. It is then placed about 50 cm. from the tin, and the tin is moved until the hole in it is on the principal axis of the lens. An image can now be caught on the screen when the latter is placed at the correct distance on the far side of the

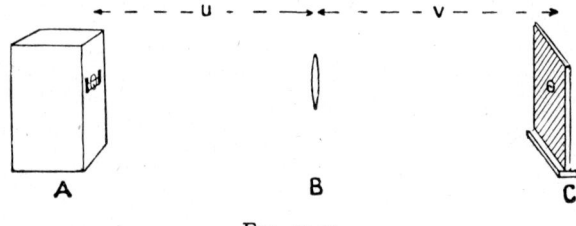

FIG. 15.04.

lens. Altering the distance of the lamp tin, we find that the screen must be placed farther away when the lamp tin is brought closer to the lens.

Is it possible to discover a rule which enables the distance of the image to be calculated, when the distance of the object from the lens is known ? We shall see that it is, but it is necessary that we should first agree on the method of stating our measurements. It is found to be most convenient to measure the distances apart of object, lens, and image, by measuring all distances from the centre of the lens. As we shall see later, the light by means of which a lens forms an image does not always pass through the image, but sometimes merely appears to do so. To enable these facts to be taken into account, we may agree to use the following conventions :

(1) **All distances are to be measured from the centre of the lens.**

(2) **Distances measured along the paths of actual rays are**

counted as positive ; distances measured along lines which appear to be paths of rays, but which are not actual ray paths, are counted as negative.

Let us suppose that in the experiment where an image of the window was formed on the wall, the wall was 20 cm. distant from the lens, and the window 500 cm. from the lens, and let us call u the distance of the object, v that of the image. The light passed from the window to the image in this experiment, so both the distance of the object and that of the image are measured along the actual paths of rays, and must therefore be counted as positive ; *i.e.* $u = +$ 500 cm., and $v = +$ 20 cm.

15.04. The following table gives the values of u, the distance of the object from a lens, and the corresponding values of v, the distance of the image.

I v in cm.	II u in cm.	III $\dfrac{1}{v}$	IV $\dfrac{1}{u}$	V $\dfrac{1}{v} + \dfrac{1}{u}$
+ 22·4	+ 99·7	+ 0·04464	+ 0·01003	+ 0·05467
+ 26·3	+ 60·1	+ 0·03802	+ 0·01664	+ 0·05466
+ 33·1	+ 41·1	+ 0·03021	+ 0·02433	+ 0·05456
+ 37·8	+ 35·5	+ 0·02646	+ 0·02817	+ 0·05463
+ 52·0	+ 28·3	+ 0·01923	+ 0·03534	+ 0·05457
+ 78·9	+ 23·8	+ 0·01267	+ 0·04202	+ 0·05469

Columns III and IV show the reciprocals of v and u respectively, and column V shows the results obtained by adding the reciprocal of u to the reciprocal of v. Allowing for slight errors of measurement, the results in column V agree in giving the same value (+ 0·0546). Hence, for any given lens,

$$\frac{1}{v} + \frac{1}{u} = F$$

where F is a constant which is called the **power** of the lens. F is different for different lenses, and a knowledge of its value for any particular lens is of importance, since it enables us to calculate the position of the image formed by the lens, if the distance of the object is known.

15.05. We have now to study the way in which particular rays are deviated (*i.e.* bent) by a lens.   Using a lamp and a screen with slits to produce light streaks, we push the lamp farther and farther from the screen.   The streaks of light, which were at first diverging at a large angle, become more and more nearly

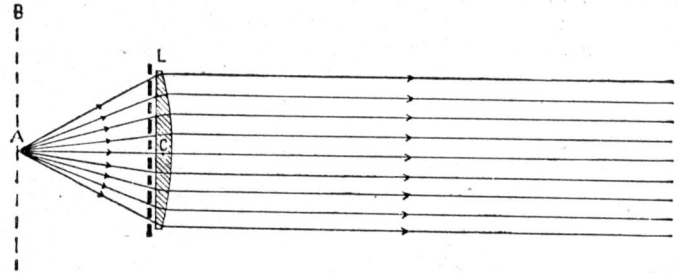

FIG. 15.05.

parallel as the lamp is moved away, and if the lamp could be moved to an infinite distance the rays from it would be accurately parallel.   The lamp cannot be placed at an infinite distance, but if a lens is placed at a suitable distance from the lamp, the streaks emerging from the lens are parallel, as shown in figure

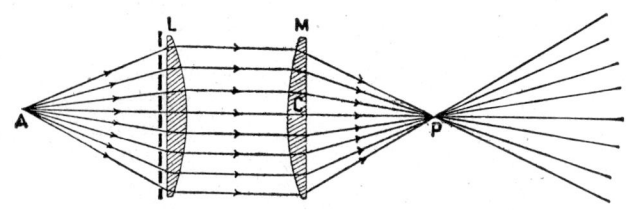

FIG. 15.06.

15.05, and the light emerging from the lens is then travelling *as though* it came from a point at infinity.

If this light is allowed to fall on a second lens, as shown in figure 15.06, all the rays travelling parallel to the principal axis of this lens are caused to converge to a point P on the axis. This point P is called the **principal focus** of the lens, and the distance CP is called its **focal length**.   When the lens M is turned through a *small* angle, the parallel rays falling on it are caused to converge to some other point on a plane through P and perpendicular to the principal axis CP. This plane is called the **focal plane** of the lens.

Rays from an object at infinity are caused to converge to the principal focus of the lens, and therefore form an image there. Hence, when $u = +\infty$, v is equal to the focal length of the lens. Let f be the focal length. The lens formula is:

$$\frac{1}{v} + \frac{1}{u} = F.$$

In this case $u = +\infty$, and $v = f$,

$$\therefore \frac{1}{f} + 0 = F$$

$$\therefore \frac{1}{f} = F, \text{ or } f = \frac{1}{F}.$$

In words, **the focal length of a lens is the reciprocal of its power.**

Since $F = \frac{1}{f}$, the lens formula may also be written,

$$\frac{1}{v} + \frac{1}{u} = \frac{1}{f}.$$

15.06. In the previous experiments, the lens L was used to produce a set of rays parallel to its principal axis. If these rays were very nearly, but not quite, parallel, they would meet to form an image at a great distance beyond the lens, and the more nearly they were parallel, the farther away this image would be. Hence, we may consider the parallel rays as meeting to form an image at an infinite distance beyond the lens. In this case $v = \infty$, and $\frac{1}{v} = 0$,

$$\frac{1}{v} + \frac{1}{u} = \frac{1}{f}$$

$$\therefore \text{ when } v = \infty, \frac{1}{u} = \frac{1}{f}, \text{ so } u = f$$

Hence, to produce a set of parallel rays, the object must be placed the focal length of the lens distant from it. CA, in figure 15.05, is thus equal to the focal length of the lens L. The point A is also a principal focus of the lens, and BA is part of its focal plane. Rays from any point in the plane AB and near the principal axis produce an image at infinity. Hence, all the rays which come from a given point in the focal plane of the lens emerge from the lens as a parallel beam.

15.07. We have seen that, provided the rays are travelling along paths close to the principal axis of a convex lens, they are deviated by the lens in such a way that:

   (*a*) **Rays parallel to the principal axis of a lens are caused by the lens to pass through its principal focus.**

   (*b*) **Rays which pass through the principal focus of a lens before meeting the lens are caused to emerge along directions parallel to the principal axis.**

To these two rules we may add a third:

   (*c*) **Any ray which passes through the centre of a lens is undeviated in passing through it.**

This fact is easily demonstrated using a single streak of light with the light streaks apparatus.

Using these facts, the lens formula may be proved as follows. Let AB (figure 15.07) represent a small object near the principal axis, and let DE be its image formed by the convex lens. BE is the undeviated ray passing through the centre C of the lens; BL is a ray parallel to the principal axis, and passes through the principal focus P' after emerging from the lens.

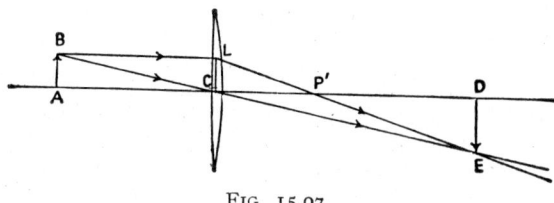

Fig. 15.07.

The triangles BAC, EDC are similar.

$$\therefore \frac{AB}{DE} = \frac{AC}{CD}.$$

But, AB = CL

$$\therefore \frac{CL}{DE} = \frac{AC}{CD}.$$

The triangles LCP′, EDP′ are similar.

$$\therefore \frac{CL}{DE} = \frac{CP'}{DP'}$$

$$\therefore \frac{AC}{CD} = \frac{CP'}{DP'}, \text{ since each is equal to } \frac{CL}{DE} \quad . \quad . \quad . \quad (1)$$

AC is the distance of the object from the lens, and since it is measured along the path of actual rays, it must be counted as positive

$$\therefore AC = + u.$$

Similarly,

$$CD = \text{the distance of the image} = + v,$$
$$CP' = \text{the focal length} = + f,$$
$$DP' = (CD - CP') = v - f.$$

Substituting these values in the above equation gives:

$$\frac{+ u}{+ v} = \frac{+ f}{v - f}$$

$$\therefore u.v - u.f = v.f$$

$$\therefore u.v = u.f + v.f.$$

Dividing throughout by $u.v.f$,

$$\frac{1}{f} = \frac{1}{v} + \frac{1}{u}$$

Since $\frac{1}{f} = F$, we have also,

$$F = \frac{1}{v} + \frac{1}{u}.$$

15.08. You cannot have failed to notice in your experiment with the lamp tin that the size of the image depends on the distance of the lamp tin from the lens. Sometimes the image on the screen is larger than its object, the glass scale; sometimes it is smaller. In *both* cases, however, the lens is said to produce a magnification of the image.

The **magnification**, *m*, produced by a lens is defined by the equation:

$$m = \frac{\text{the length of the image}}{\text{the length of its object}}.$$

The magnification is thus the ratio of the length of the image to the length of the object. The magnification may be calculated if the distances of the object and image are known, for, as we shall show, the magnification m is given by the formula, $m = \dfrac{v}{u}$. The sign of the numerical result calculated by means of this equation may be used to indicate whether the image is erect or inverted. As we shall see, the following rule is true, both for lenses and for spherical mirrors:

If the numerical value of m calculated from the formula $m = \dfrac{v}{u}$ is positive the image is inverted; if it is negative the image is erect.

Thus, in figure 15.07,

$$m = \frac{\text{the length of the image}}{\text{the length of the object}}$$

$$\therefore m = \frac{DE}{AB}.$$

The triangles BAC, EDC are similar.

$$\therefore \frac{DE}{AB} = \frac{CD}{CA}.$$

$$\therefore m = \frac{CD}{DA}$$

$$CD = +v; \quad CA = +u$$

$$\therefore m = +\frac{v}{u}.$$

This is the required equation.

The numerical values of both v and u are positive in the case illustrated in figure 15.07, since the rays actually pass from the object to the image. Hence, the numerical value of the magnification is also positive, so the image should be inverted, as the figure shows it to be.

15.09. The power of a convex lens is a positive number, and since the focal length is the reciprocal of the power, this also is positive. For this reason the convex lens is sometimes called a positive lens. It may also be called a converging lens, because it causes a parallel beam of light falling on it to converge to a point.

The power of a lens is measured in units called **dioptres**, and the numerical value of its power in these units is found by taking the reciprocal of its focal length when the latter is measured *in metres.* Thus the power of a lens whose focal length is $+ 20$ cm. (*i.e.* $+ 0.2$ metre) is $\dfrac{1}{+ 0.2} = + 5$ dioptres (5D). For the purpose of calculating powers of lenses the focal length is expressed in metres, because, by doing so, small fractions are avoided. In the laboratory lengths are usually measured in centimetres, and it is useful to remember that the power in dioptres can be found by taking the reciprocal of the focal length measured *in centimetres*, and multiplying the result by 100.

15.10. The position of the image formed by a lens, and the magnification produced by it, can be found either by drawing or by calculation. It is better to calculate the results than to measure them from a diagram drawn to scale, for, as we shall see, the scale drawing is not very reliable for accurate work. It is useful, however, because it indicates how the image is formed, and also serves as a rough check on the calculations, so in the examples which follow we shall use both methods.

EXAMPLES.—(1) *A convex lens of power 5·00D forms an image of an object, placed on, and perpendicular to, the principal axis of the lens. The object is 40 cm. from the lens and is 1 cm. long. Find the position and size of the image formed.*

We have, $F = 5.00D$, $u = + 40$ cm., or $+ 0.40$ metre. We have first to find v. The lens formula is:

$$\frac{1}{v} + \frac{1}{u} = F$$

$$\therefore \frac{1}{v} + \frac{1}{(+ 0.4)} = 5$$

$$\therefore \frac{1}{v} = 5 - 2.5 = 2.5$$

$$\therefore v = 0.40 \text{ metre} = 40 \text{ cm.}$$

Hence, the image is 40 cm. from the lens, and on the side distant from the object.

The formula for the magnification gives:

$$m = + \frac{v}{u}$$

$$\therefore m = + \frac{40}{40} = + 1.$$

Hence, the image is the same size as the object, and the positive value for the magnification indicates that it is inverted.

Figure 15.08 shows the graphical construction.   C is the centre
of the lens, and AC its principal axis.   AB is the object, distant 40 cm. from C, and the diagram shows the paths of the
rays from the point B on the object.   The ray BC passes through
the centre of the lens, and is therefore undeviated ; BL is a ray
parallel to the principal axis, and therefore is deviated to pass
through P', the principal focus of the lens.   Both these rays
meet at the point E and at no other point, and since the lens
forms an image of the point B, and hence causes the rays
from B to *appear* to come from some one point, this point must
be E.   Hence, every other ray from B must, after passing
through the lens, also pass through E, so ME and NE are the

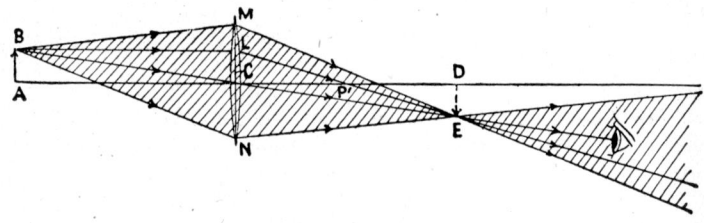

FIG. 15.08.

Horizontal scale : 1 unit represents 5 units.
Vertical scale : 1 unit represents 1 unit.

subsequent paths of the rays which reach the lens along BM
and BN respectively.   The shading shows the paths of all the
rays from B which pass through the lens.   Every other point
on the object AB gives out light which travels in a similar way,
and is caused to converge to some point in DE, which is therefore
the image of AB.

The image is seen to be inverted, and by measurement from
the figure it is found to be the same size as the object, and
40 cm. from the lens.   To see the image of the point E, the eye
must be placed where it will receive light coming from E, and
it must be at least 25 cm. from E if the image is to be clearly
seen.   A suitable position for the eye is indicated in the figure.

The construction is not reliable for accurate work because
the position of the image is found by determining where the
lines BC and LP' meet.   These lines intersect at a small angle,
so the slightest error in drawing them causes a large error in

the position of E, and hence in the size and position of the image.

(2) *A convex lens of power 5·00D forms an image 30 cm. from the lens on the side distant from the object. If the image is 1 cm. high, find the size and position of the object.*

$$F = + 5\text{·}00D$$
$$v = + 30 \text{ cm.} = + 0\text{·}3 \text{ metre}$$

$$\frac{1}{v} + \frac{1}{u} = F$$

$$\therefore \frac{1}{0\text{·}3} + \frac{1}{u} = 5$$

$$\therefore u = + 0\text{·}60 \text{ metre, or } + 60 \text{ cm.}$$

$$m = + \frac{v}{u} = + \left(\frac{+30}{+60}\right) = + \tfrac{1}{2}.$$

Hence, the object is 60 cm. from the lens, and twice as large as the image; *i.e.* it is 2 cm. high. Figure 15.09 shows the graphical construction, which is similar to the previous one. The image DE is drawn first, however, and since E is the image

Fig. 15.09.

Horizontal scale : 1 unit represents 5 units.
Vertical scale : 1 unit represents ¼ unit.

of the top of the object, the top of the object lies somewhere on the line through C and E. From the top of the object a ray parallel to the principal axis passes through both P′ and E after emerging from the lens, and therefore comes from the point L on the lens. Hence, the top of the object lies on a line through L parallel to the axis, and is thus at the point B.

15.11. The lamp tin and glass scale used in an earlier experiment are useful for verifying the formula, magnification $= \dfrac{v}{u}$.
The lamp-tin method is not an accurate one for determining focal lengths, however, because it is not easy to judge when the image formed on a screen is as sharp as it can be made,

so the values of v cannot be found accurately. The values for u and v given in the table on page 176 were found using a different method, which is much more accurate. Since this method is not a difficult one, you may want to try it for yourself. We shall use it, not to check the lens formula, but to measure the focal length of a lens as accurately as possible.

The lens chosen is first used to form an image of the windows on the opposite wall of the room. The windows form a distant object, so the image is formed near the focal plane of the lens, and by measuring the distance between the lens and wall, a *rough* value for the focal length is obtained. We shall use this rough value later, in determining the accurate value.

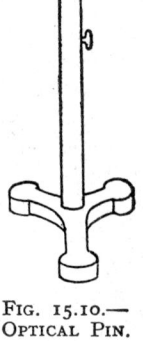

Two optical pins, each similar to that shown in figure 15.10, are now adjusted to the same height, and a lens is clamped in a stand so that its centre is the same height as the pins. The two pins are placed on opposite sides of the lens on its principal axis, each pin about twice the focal length distant from the lens. When the lens is viewed from behind one of the optical pins an inverted image of the far pin is seen near the other pin. The nearer pin is pushed sideways until it lies below the image, when the appearance becomes similar to that shown in figure 15.11. If the appearance is similar to (a) or (b) a small vertical adjustment of the lens brings the tip of the image into contact with the pin, as shown at (c).

FIG. 15.10.—
OPTICAL PIN.

Moving the head slowly from side to side, we now find that either the near pin, or the image above it, lies closer to the eye, and the near pin is pushed backwards or forwards until there is no parallax between it and the image. The near pin now marks the position of the image of the far pin, so both the distances of the image and its object can be measured. The value for F or f can then be calculated from one or more such sets of readings, as in the earlier experiment.

There are two advantages to be gained by placing the object at about twice the focal length from the lens. The image is then also at about twice the focal length from the lens, so the magnification is unity. It is easy to set the pins accurately if both the image and the pin marking its position are the same size. Moreover, if the object is not at this distance from the lens, either the object or the image is less distant than twice the focal length, and a small error in the setting of the pins makes a large percentage error in the result.

One other point may be noted in this experiment. When

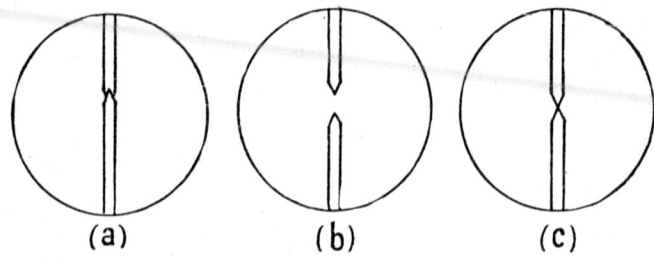

(a) (b) (c)

FIG. 15.11.

the image of pin A is over the top of pin B, the image of pin B is also over the top of pin A. Hence, each setting of the pins gives two values for u and two corresponding values for v. This is no advantage in calculating F or f from the formula, because both sets of values lead to the same result. The two sets of values are useful, however, when a graph is to be drawn, for

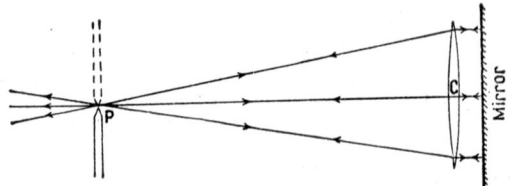

FIG. 15.12.—DETERMINATION OF THE FOCAL LENGTH OF A LENS, USING A PLANE MIRROR.

each setting of the pins gives two points for the graph. Thus, if $u = + 42.0$ cm. when $v = + 38.0$ cm., v is $+ 42.0$ cm. when u is $+ 38.0$ cm., and each of these pairs of values may be used.

15.12. One other simple method of measuring the focal length of a convex lens remains to be described. If a plane mirror is placed behind a lens as shown in figure 15.12, and a light pin

is placed in the focal plane of the lens, its image will be formed
in the focal plane. When the tip of the pin is placed at the
principal focus, the rays from the tip of the pin emerge from
the lens parallel to the principal axis. Such rays meet the

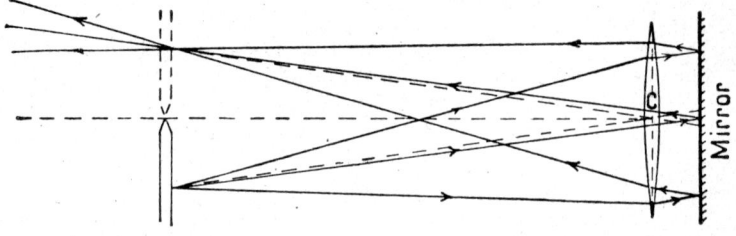

FIG. 15.13.

mirror normally, and are reflected back along their own paths.
They enter the lens again parallel to its principal axis, and
therefore converge to form an image of the pin at the principal
focus. Figure 15.13 shows the paths of rays from a point on
the pin off the principal axis.

EXAMPLES 15

1. Describe an experiment to show how an image is formed by
a convex lens.

2. State and explain the convention of signs used in dealing with
lenses.

3. What is meant by the *centre, principal axis, principal focus,
focal plane,* of a lens? Draw diagrams to illustrate your answer.

4. How would you show by experiments, (*a*) that a set of parallel
rays is brought to a focus in the focal plane of a convex lens, (*b*) that
light from a point in the focal plane of such a lens leaves the lens
as a parallel beam?

5. You are given a small source of light, such as the bulb of a
motor headlamp, and a convex lens. Describe fully how you
would arrange the apparatus to obtain a parallel beam of light,
and explain how you would test your setting.

6. A convex lens of power 5D is used to throw on the wall an
image of the opposite windows. If the windows are 10 metres
distant from the lens, what is the error in assuming that the image
is formed in the focal plane of the lens?

7. Draw diagrams to show how the image formed by a convex lens is seen by the eye, (a) when the image is formed on a screen, (b) when no screen is used. Why is it not possible to catch the image of a light pin on a screen ?

8. A convex lens of power 4D forms an image. The object is 2 cm. high, placed at right angles to its principal axis, and 50 cm. from the lens. Calculate the size of the image produced, and verify your result by means of a diagram drawn to scale.

9. The image formed by a convex lens of power 4D lies on the principal axis, 75 cm. from the lens, and is 3 cm. high. Find the position and size of the object, and illustrate your answer by a diagram drawn to scale.

10. A convex lens forms an inverted image at a distance of 50 cm. from the lens. If the magnification is 2, find the focal length of the lens.

11. A convex lens of power 5D forms an image of an object, 1 cm. long, placed perpendicular to its principal axis. The image is inverted and 2 cm. long. Find the distances of the object and image from the lens. Draw a diagram to scale to illustrate your answer.

12. A convex lens of focal length 15 cm. is placed between a lamp tin and a screen, and forms a real image of the scale of the lamp tin on the screen. The lamp tin and screen are 62·5 cm. apart. Show that there are two possible positions for the lens, and find the magnification produced in each case.

13. An object 1 cm. long lies *along* the principal axis of a lens of focal length 30 cm. The nearer point of the object is 40 cm. from the lens. Find the positions of the two ends of the image, and hence the magnification. [The formula $m = \dfrac{v}{u}$ can only be used in cases where the object is at right angles to the principal axis.]

14. You are given a light pin, a convex lens, and a plane mirror. Describe how you would use these to find the power of the lens. Explain the theory of the method you use.

SCHOOL CERTIFICATE QUESTIONS

15. Prove the formula $\dfrac{1}{v} + \dfrac{1}{u} = \dfrac{1}{f}$ as applied to lenses, where v and u are the distances of image and object respectively from the optical centre of the lens, and f is the focal length. When an object is placed 9 in. in front of a certain convex lens a real image twice as large as the object is produced. Where must the object be placed so that its real image may be three times as large as itself ? (O.C)

16. Derive an expression connecting the focal length of a thin lens with the distances of the object and image from the lens. A lantern slide $3\frac{1}{4}$ in. square is to be projected so as to give an image 8 ft. square on a screen 30 ft. away. What should be the focal length of the lens required ?   (O.C)

17. How would you find accurately the focal length of a convex lens ? What do you understand by the *magnification* produced by a convex lens ? Prove that if v and u are the distances of an image and object respectively from the lens, the magnification produced is equal to $\dfrac{v}{u}$.

An object 2 cm. high is placed 50 cm. from a convex lens of focal length 40 cm. Find the position and size of the image produced, and state, with reasons, whether it is erect or inverted.   (O)

18. State clearly what is meant by the *focal length* of a convex lens, and describe one good method of measuring it. A bright object 12 in. from such a lens gives a real image on a screen 8 in. beyond the lens. The object is moved 6 in. nearer to the lens. How must the screen now be moved so as to receive a clear image ?

           (J)

16.01. Although the image formed by a plane mirror, and the inverted image formed by a lens, are both given the same name, they are, as we have seen, by no means exactly alike. The image formed by the lens can be caught on a screen correctly placed ; the image formed by the plane mirror is behind the mirror at a point which is not reached by rays reflected from the mirror, and since the rays do not reach such points, the image cannot be caught on a screen. The rays from the lens converge and pass through the image formed by the lens ; the rays from the mirror diverge in such a way that they appear to come from the image, whereas they do not in fact do so. We distinguish between the two types of image by calling that formed by rays passing through it, a *real* image, and calling the other type a *virtual* image.

When rays of light, coming from a point, are (*a*) caused to converge to a second point, or (*b*) are made to appear to diverge from a second point, the second point is called an image of the first point. In case (*a*) the image is said to be real ; in case (*b*) it is said to be virtual.

16.02. The images discussed in Chapter 3 were the real images formed by a convex lens. Such a lens can, however, form virtual images also. Let us consider the following problem :

A convex lens of power 5·00D forms an image of a small object placed 10 cm. from it on its principal axis. Find the position of the image, and draw a diagram showing how it is formed.

$$F = 5\cdot00D$$
$$u = +\ 10\ \text{cm.} = +\ 0\cdot10\ \text{metre}$$

$$\frac{1}{v} + \frac{1}{u} = F$$

$$\therefore\ \frac{1}{v} + \frac{1}{(+\ 0\cdot10)} = 5\cdot00$$

$$\therefore\ v = -\tfrac{1}{5}\ \text{metre} = -\ 20\ \text{cm.}$$

When the numerical value of v is negative as in this case, the distance of the image is not measured along the paths of actual rays. In other words, the rays which form the image do not actually pass through it, so the image is virtual. Similarly, a positive value for v indicates that the image is real.

Figure 16.01 shows how the image is formed. As usual, only the rays from one point on the object have been drawn. AB is the object and DE its image. The ray BC passes through the centre of the lens, and is therefore undeviated. Hence, after emerging from the lens, it appears to come from some point in the line BC, or BC produced. The ray BL is parallel to the principal axis, and after emerging from the lens, passes

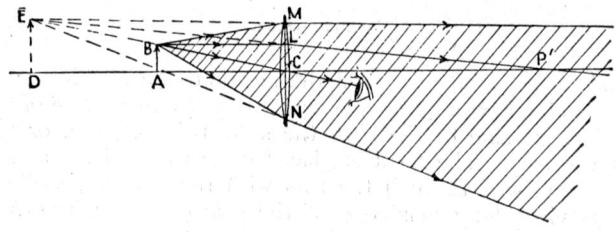

FIG. 16.01.

Horizontal scale: 1 unit represents 2 units.

through the principal focus P′. It appears, therefore, to come from some point in LP′ or LP′ produced. The lines BC and LP′, when produced backwards, meet at E, and at no other point. Hence, if an image is to be formed by the lens, all the rays which start from B and pass through the lens, must appear to come from this point E, whence the rays BLP′ and BC appear to come. Thus the paths of the rays BM and BN, after these rays emerge from the lens, are the continuations of the lines EM and EN respectively. The lines BE, LE, EM, and EN are dotted in the diagram, to show that these are not the paths along which rays actually travel, but are merely the *apparent* paths of rays.

The image DE is virtual since the rays leaving the lens merely appear to diverge from it. By measurement CD is found to be 20 cm., so the image is 20 cm. from the lens, as we discovered by the calculation. To see the image of B clearly, the eye must be placed in the space shaded, and at least 25 cm. from the image. A suitable position is that shown.

It is instructive to form a virtual image of this kind using light streaks. Streaks are caused to diverge from a point A (figure 16.02), this point serving as object. When viewed through the lens, however, these streaks appear to diverge from the point B, so B is the image of A.

It is not so easy to find by experiment the position of the

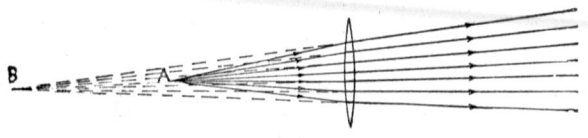

Fig. 16.02.

virtual image, as it is to find the position of a real image. It can be done, however, by placing an object and a piece of scale on the same side of the lens, the scale being 25 cm. or more from the lens. The head is placed close to the lens, and the object is viewed through the lens with the left eye, while the scale is viewed by looking past the side of the lens with the right eye. Both the scale and the image of the object can then be seen at the same time, and the head is moved from side to

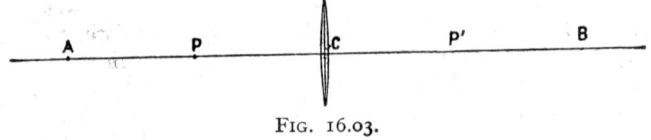

Fig. 16.03.

side to discover whether parallax exists between the two. By moving the object backwards or forwards a position is found where no parallax exists. The image then lies on the scale, and its distance from the lens can be measured.

16.03. The following table gives various details about the image formed by a convex lens, when the object is placed at various distances. It is important, and is worth learning by heart. The letters refer to figure 16.03. C is the centre of the lens, P and P' are the principal foci, and A and B are two points, each distant double the focal length of the lens from C. As shown in the final column, the image is diminished when it is formed between P' and B. It is very small at P', but is the same size as the object when it is formed at B. Its size continues to increase as it moves towards infinity, and it is finally very large. The virtual image is very large when formed at $-\infty$, but decreases in size as it approaches the lens, and its length finally becomes equal to that of the object.

Notice that the image is real if it is formed on the side of the lens opposite to that of the object. It is virtual if formed on the same side as the object.

As the object moves from	The image moves from	Character of the Image		
∞ to A	P' to B	inverted	real	diminished
A to P	B to $+\infty$	inverted	real	enlarged
P to C	$-\infty$ to C	erect	virtual	enlarged

GRAPHS

16.04. The power of a convex lens may be found by substituting measured values of u and v in the formula, $\frac{1}{v} + \frac{1}{u} = F$. It may also be found by means of various graphs. Figure 16.04 is that obtained by plotting the distances of the image against the corresponding distances of its object, the full line CBD showing the values for which the image is real, and the dotted line those for which it is virtual. The graph shows that as the distance of the object decreases, that of the real image increases. Moreover, the smaller the distance of the object, the steeper is the slope of the graph, so the distance of the image increases most rapidly for a given displacement of the object when the distance of the object is small.

The focal length is obtained from the graph by drawing a line to bisect the angle between the axes. This line AB cuts the graph at B, and B is a point on the graph equidistant from both axes. Hence, the point B represents the distances of object and image from the lens when these two distances are

H

equal. For the conditions represented by the point B, $u = v$.

$$\frac{1}{v} + \frac{1}{u} = \frac{1}{f}$$

$$\therefore \ \frac{1}{v} + \frac{1}{v} = \frac{1}{f}$$

$$\therefore \ \frac{2}{v} = \frac{1}{f}, \text{ or } f = \frac{v}{2}.$$

For the graph shown in figure 16.04, v is 0·366 metre for the point B. Hence, $f = 0·183$ metre, or 18·3 cm., and $F = \frac{1}{f}$ = 5·46D.

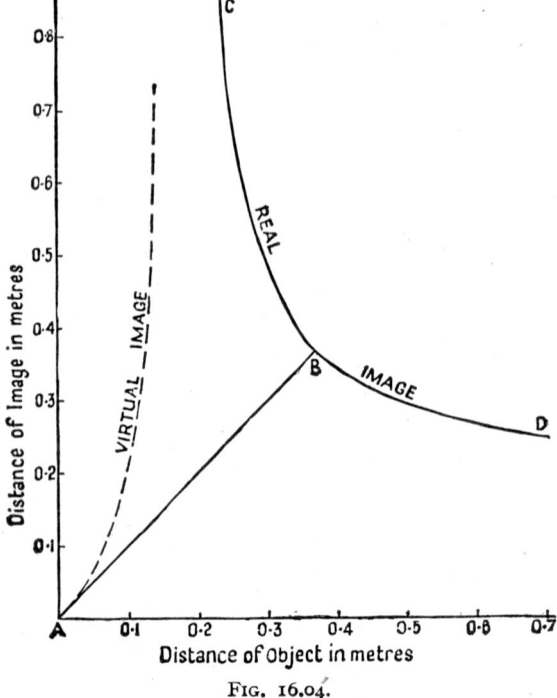

FIG. 16.04.

16.05. The graph shown in figure 16.05 is that obtained by plotting $\frac{1}{v}$ against $\frac{1}{u}$. The graph is in this case a straight line, and when $\frac{1}{v}$ is zero, $\frac{1}{u}$ is 5·46. But, $\frac{1}{v} + \frac{1}{u} = F$.

Hence, when $\frac{1}{v} = 0$, $F = \frac{1}{u}$.

Thus for the lens whose graph is shown, $F = 5\cdot46\mathrm{D}$.

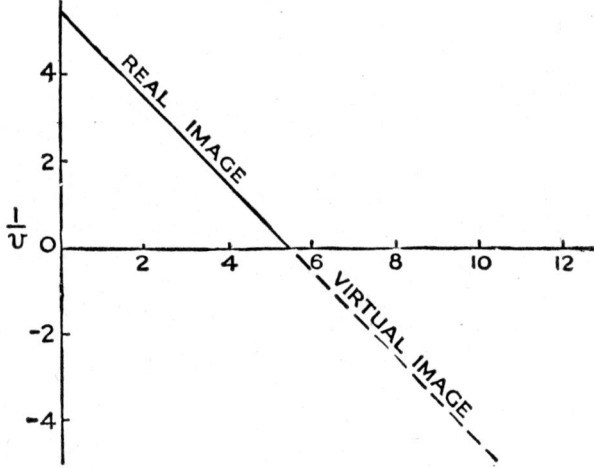

FIG. 16.05.

16.06. Figure 16.06 shows the graph obtained by plotting the distance between the object and image against the distance of the object from the lens. Only those values for which the image is real are plotted in this figure. v is the distance of the image from the lens; u is the distance of the object, so $(v + u)$ is the distance between the object and image. It is this which is plotted against the distance of the object from the lens in order to obtain the graph. The distance apart of the object and image decreases rapidly as the distance of the object increases, reaches a minimum value, and then increases again. The object and image are closest together when each is distant $2f$ from the lens, and their distance apart is then $4f$. From the graph, this minimum distance is seen to be 0·732 metre.

$$\therefore \quad 4f = 0\cdot732 \text{ metre}$$
$$\therefore \quad f = 0\cdot183 \text{ metre, and } F = 5\cdot46\text{D.}$$

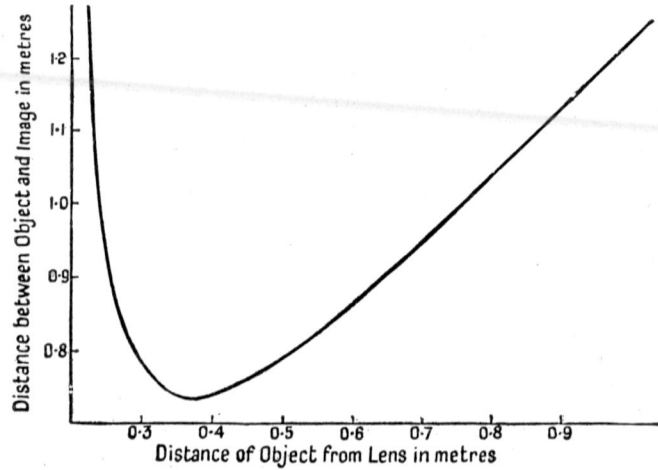

FIG. 16.06.

NEGATIVE LENSES

16.07. The three lenses shown in figure 16.07 are all of the type known as concave, diverging, or negative, lenses. Their chief properties may be demonstrated by means of the light streaks apparatus, and it may be shown that:

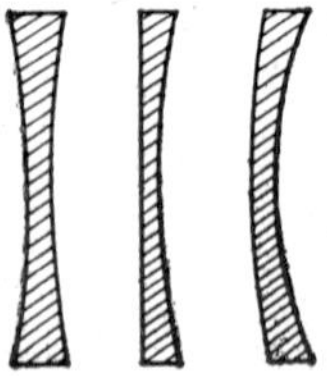

FIG. 16.07.—
CONCAVE LENSES.

(a) A ray which passes through the centre of the lens is undeviated,

(b) All rays parallel to the principal axis emerge from the lens as though they come from a point P′ on the principal axis (see figure 16.08).

The point P′ is called the principal focus of the lens. Since the rays from an infinitely distant point meet the lens as a set of parallel rays, the principal focus is the position of the image of an infinitely distant object. The distance CP′ is called the focal length of the lens.

The formation of images by a concave lens may be illustrated by means of light streaks diverging from a point, such as A (figure 16.09). In every case the rays leaving the lens do so

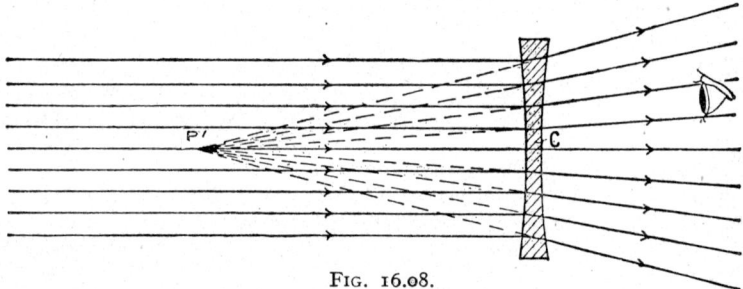

FIG. 16.08.

as though they were diverging from a second point B which is nearer to the lens than A, so the image is always nearer to the lens than its object, and is always virtual, since the rays only appear to pass through it. The ray from the object to the centre of the lens is undeviated by the lens, so the image lies

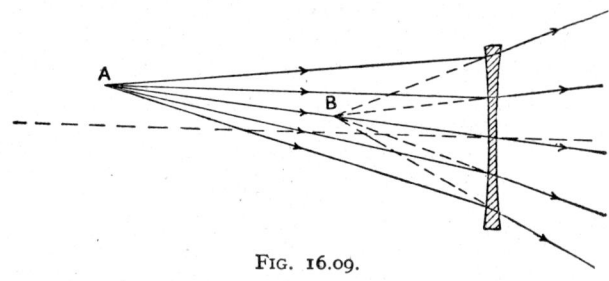

FIG. 16.09.

at some point on this ray. It is therefore on the same side of the principal axis as its object. Hence, *the image formed by a concave lens is an erect one.*

The formula, $\dfrac{1}{v} + \dfrac{1}{u} = F$, which was found for convex lenses, is also true for concave lenses, but the power F is negative in this case. The power and the focal length f are related by the formula, $F = \dfrac{1}{f}$, so the focal length is also negative. As in the case of the convex lens the magnification produced by a concave lens is given by the formula, $m = \dfrac{v}{u}$.

The following example illustrates the application of these formulæ to the case of a concave lens.

An object 1 cm. high is placed on the principal axis of a concave lens of power 5 dioptres. If the distance between the object and its image is 18 cm., find the positions of the object and image, and the magnification produced by the lens.

Since the lens is concave, its power is negative; *i.e.* $F = -5\cdot00\mathrm{D}$. The distance between the object and image is $(v + u)$, so $(v + u) = 0\cdot18$ metre. Hence, $v = 0\cdot18 - u$

$$\frac{1}{v} + \frac{1}{u} = F$$

$$\therefore \frac{1}{0\cdot18 - u} + \frac{1}{u} = -5\cdot00.$$

This gives a quadratic equation, the solutions of which are $u = +0\cdot30$, and $u = -0\cdot12$. We are only concerned with values for which u is positive, because negative values would mean that the rays did not actually come from the object.

$$\therefore u = +0\cdot30 \text{ metre, or } +30 \text{ cm.}$$
$$\therefore v = -12 \text{ cm.}$$

Hence, the object and its image are 30 cm. and 12 cm. distant from the lens, and are both on the same side of it. The magnification m is given by the formula

$$m = +\frac{v}{u}$$

$$\therefore m = +\frac{(-12)}{(+30)} = -0\cdot4.$$

Hence, the image is $0\cdot4$ times as long as its object, and is thus 4 mm. long. The negative sign indicates that the image is erect.

Figure 16.10 shows how the image is formed. AB is the object, DE its image, and the rays from the top of the object have been drawn. The ray BC is undeviated in passing through the lens, and the ray BL, parallel to the principal axis, is deviated so that after emerging from the lens it appears to come from the principal focus P'. Both of these rays emerge, therefore, as though they came from E, the top of the image. The other

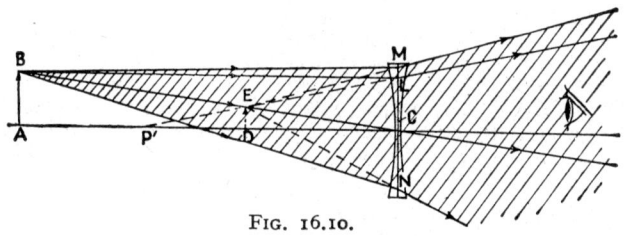

FIG. 16.10.

Horizontal scale : 1 unit represents 2 units.
Vertical scale : 2 units represent 1 unit.

rays BM and BN must also appear to come from E, so their paths after leaving the lens are as shown. The eye must be placed in the cone of rays emerging from the lens, and it must be at least 25 cm. from the image. A suitable position is that shown.

EXAMPLES 16

1. Explain with the aid of suitable diagrams the meaning of the terms *real image*, and *virtual image*.

2. A convex lens of power 5D forms an erect image twice the size of its object. Calculate the positions of the object and image, and draw a diagram to scale showing how the image is formed.

3. Describe an experiment to show how a convex lens forms a virtual image.

4. The virtual image formed by a convex lens is 10 cm. farther from the lens than its object. If the object is 20 cm. from the lens, find its focal length.

5. A convex lens forms a virtual image which is 10 cm. farther away from the lens than its object, and the magnification produced is 2. Find the power of the lens.

6. The real image formed by a positive lens is 20 cm. from the lens when the object is also 20 cm. from the lens. At what distance from the lens must the object be placed so that a virtual image is formed, twice the size of the object ?

7. A convex lens of power 4D is used to form (*a*) a real image ; (*b*) a virtual image. If the magnification is 4 in both cases, at what distances must the object be placed from the lens ? Draw a diagram to scale showing how the image is formed in case (*b*).

8. Describe an experiment to show how a concave lens forms an image of an object. Explain why the image formed must be (a) virtual, (b) erect.

9. Prove that for a concave lens the magnification m is given by the formula, $m = \dfrac{v}{u}$.

10. The image formed by a concave lens is 10 cm. and the object 20 cm. from the lens. Find the power and focal length of the lens, and draw a diagram to scale, showing how the image is formed.

11. An object is placed 30 cm. from a concave lens and the lens forms an image whose length is half that of the object. What is the power of the lens ? Show by means of a diagram drawn to scale how the image is formed.

School Certificate Questions

12. Draw diagrams to show the formation of images by a convex lens, when the object is placed at different distances from the lens. An object 1 cm. in height is placed at a distance of 10 metres from a screen. A lens is used to form on the screen an image of height 19 cm. What kind of lens must be used, where must it be placed, and what must be its focal length ?   (O.C)

13. An object is placed 10 cm. from (a) a converging lens of 20 cm. focal length, (b) a diverging lens of 20 cm. focal length. Calculate the position of the image in each case, and draw diagrams to show how the image is formed.   (O.C)

14. What is meant by the focal length of a lens ? Calculate at what distance from a converging lens of focal length 20 cm. an object must be placed in order that the image may be (a) real and three times the size of the object, (b) virtual and three times the size of the object. Draw diagrams to illustrate the two cases.   (O.C)

15. Describe the conditions under which you can obtain (a) a *real image*, and (b) a *virtual image* of an object by means of a convex lens. Define the terms in italics.   (B)

16. A convex lens of 10 cm. focal length is used to form an image of an object. Plot a curve showing the relation between the magnification and the distance of the image from the lens as the object is taken to different distances from the lens.   (L)

17. A convex lens of focal length 20 cm. is placed in the path of
(1) A parallel beam of light ;
(2) A divergent beam of light, diverging from a point 30 cm. from the lens ;
(3) A convergent beam of light, converging to a point 30 cm. beyond the lens.
Explain and construct scale diagrams for each case showing the effect of the lens on the beam.   (L)

CHAPTER 17

REFRACTION

17.01. The image formed by a lens is produced by the bending—or to use the scientific term, by the *refraction*—of the rays falling on the lens. The light is not refracted *in* the lens, however, but as it passes from the air to the glass, and again as it passes back from the glass to the air. Refraction occurs when light passes from one medium to another.

Two very old experiments illustrate some of the effects of refraction. If a coin is placed in an empty cup and the head is moved so that the coin is just hidden behind the rim, the coin becomes visible again when the cup is filled with water. Rays of light from each point on the coin are refracted as they pass from the water to air, and reach the eye, as shown in figure 17.01, as though they came from a point above the coin. Accordingly the eye sees an image of the coin in the cup.

Fig. 17.01.

The other experiment is the very simple one of placing a straight stick in water. The stick no longer appears straight (figure 17.02) because an image is formed by the refraction of the rays passing from the water to the air.

17.02. The refraction of light may be studied by means of the optical disc (figure 17.03). A narrow beam of light is allowed to pass along the face of the disc as shown, and at the centre of the disc the beam falls upon the plane face of a semicircular block of glass. As it enters the block the ray is refracted, but in whatever position the disc may be, the ray emerging from the glass meets the curved surface of the block normally, and passes straight through this surface. Hence, the directions of both the incident and the refracted ray may be measured by means of the scale marked on the edge of the disc.

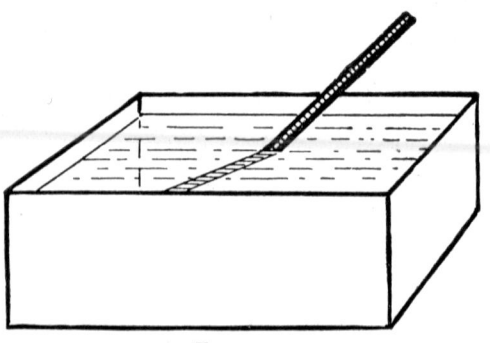

The angle between the refracted ray and the normal to the surface at the point where refraction occurs is called the *angle of refraction*. In the figure the angle of refraction is 41°.

There are two laws of refraction corresponding to the two laws of reflection.

(*a*) **The refracted ray, the incident ray, and the normal to the surface at the point of incidence, all lie in the same plane.** This is shown by the fact that, if the incident ray just grazes the face of the optical disc, the refracted ray does the same, and the plane of the disc also contains the normal to the refracting surface.

Although the second law is a simple one, it is not easily guessed, so we shall state it, and then see how it is verified by experiment.

(*b*) **The sine of the angle of incidence divided by the sine of the angle of refraction**

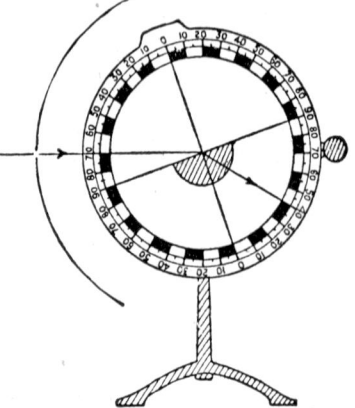

FIG. 17.03.—OPTICAL DISC.

is a constant for the two media at whose common boundary refraction occurs. In other words, using the glass block (say) to refract rays entering it from air at various angles of incidence, the same number is obtained in each case by dividing the

sine of the angle of incidence by the sine of the corresponding angle of refraction. In mathematics the phrase "the sine
of the angle" is abbreviated to "*sin*," so if i denotes the angle
of incidence, and r denotes the angle of refraction corresponding to this angle of incidence, the second law of refraction
states that, however i may alter,

$$\frac{\sin i}{\sin r} = \mu$$

where μ is a constant. This constant is called the **refractive
index,** or the **index of refraction** of the second medium with
respect to the first.

It is important to realize that the refractive index depends
upon *both* media, and not upon one only. Thus the index of
refraction for a ray passing from air to glass is different from
that for a ray passing from water to glass, from air to water,
or from glass to air. If there is any possibility of ambiguity
as to the surface at which refraction occurs, the refractive index
may be written $_{air}\mu_{glass}$, or in some similar form. $_{air}\mu_{glass}$ means,
for example, the refractive index for a ray passing from air to
glass.

Often, however, statements regarding refractive indices are
made in such a form as "the refractive index of water is 1·33."
This must be understood to mean that $_{vacuum}\mu_{water}$ is equal to
1·33. This may not appear to be a very useful fact, since we
seldom cause rays of light to pass from a vacuum into water.
If, however, $_{vacuum}\mu_{water} = 1·33$, it is also true that $_{air}\mu_{water} = 1·33$,
for it is found that the refractive index for a ray passing from
air into a given substance is nearly the same as the refractive index
for a ray passing from a vacuum into the same substance.

17.03. The second law of refraction may be verified by measuring angles of incidence and their corresponding angles of refraction by means of an optical disc. The sines of the angles can
then be found from books of tables. It may also be verified
using light streaks. In this case we can avoid the use of pro-
tractors and tables by the following easier and more accurate
method.

Let AO (figure 17.04) be the path of a ray which meets a
glass block at O, and is refracted along the line OB, and let
CD be the surface of the glass block. With centre O a large
circle is drawn cutting the lines AO and OB at E and G respec-

tively. KL is the normal to the surface at O, and EH and GJ

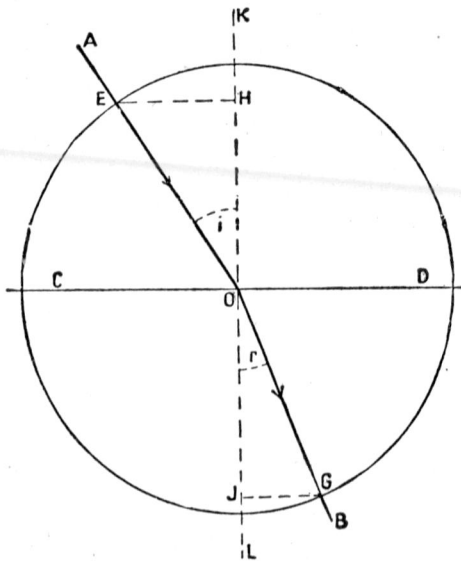

FIG. 17.04.

are the perpendiculars from E and G to this normal. The angle of incidence i is $\underline{\angle EOH}$, and the angle of refraction r is $\underline{\angle GOJ}$.

$$\mu = \frac{\sin i}{\sin r} = \frac{\sin \underline{\angle EOH}}{\sin \underline{\angle GOJ}}$$

$$\therefore \mu = \frac{EH}{EO} \Big/ \frac{GJ}{GO}.$$

But $EO = GO$

$$\therefore \mu = \frac{EH}{EO} \Big/ \frac{GJ}{EO} = \frac{EH}{GJ}.$$

Hence, by measuring EH and GJ, μ may be calculated, and by doing this for various angles of incidence, μ may be shown to be constant.

Substance	μ	Substance	μ
Ice	1·31	Rock salt	1·54
Water	1·33	Glass—varies for differ-	1·48 to
Alcohol	1·37	ent specimens	1·96
Fused quartz . . .	1·46	Ruby	1·76
Glycerol	1·47	Diamond	2·60

17.04. Any ray of light passing through a parallel-sided block of glass emerges from the block in a direction parallel to that of the incident ray. This fact is easily shown using light streaks. The emerging ray CD (figure 17.05) is parallel to the incident ray AB. The ray is not deviated by the block of glass. It is *displaced*, however —that is, it is moved sideways. The displacement of the ray shown in the figure is the distance BE.

At the middle of a lens the two faces of the lens are approximately parallel. Hence, a ray passing through the centre of a lens is not deviated, although it is displaced a short distance. All the lenses with which we shall deal are thin, however, and the displacement is in such cases negligible.

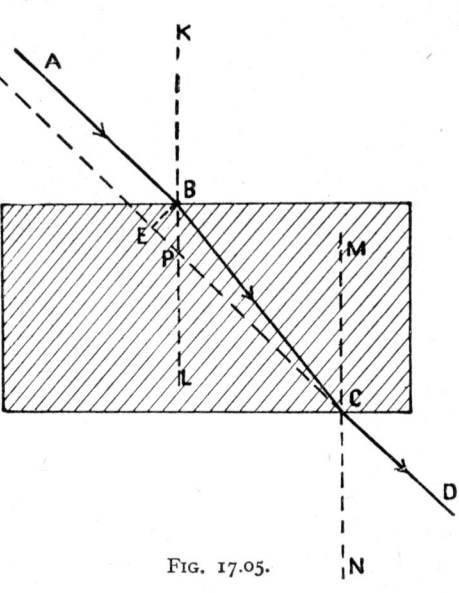

Fig. 17.05.

To return to figure 17.05; KL and MN are the normals to the faces of the glass block at the points where the ray enters and leaves the block.

$$_\text{air}\mu_\text{glass} = \frac{\sin \lfloor \text{ABK}}{\sin \lfloor \text{LBC}}.$$

But KL and MN are parallel, and AB and ED are parallel,

$$\therefore \underline{|ABK} = \underline{|EPB} = \underline{|NCD},$$

and

$$\underline{|LBC} = \underline{|BCM}$$

$$\therefore \text{air} \mu \text{glass} = \frac{\sin \underline{|NCD}}{\sin \underline{|BCM}}$$

$$\therefore \text{air} \mu \text{glass} = \frac{1}{\dfrac{\sin \underline{|BCM}}{\sin \underline{|NCD}}}.$$

$\underline{|BCM}$ is, however, the angle of incidence for the ray leaving the block, and $\underline{|NCD}$ is its angle of refraction, so

$$\text{glass} \mu \text{air} = \frac{\sin \underline{|BCM}}{\sin \underline{|NCD}}$$

$$\therefore \text{air} \mu \text{glass} = \frac{1}{\text{glass} \mu \text{air}}.$$

Similarly, for a ray passing through any o t h e r transparent substance,

$$\text{air} \mu \text{substance} = \frac{1}{\text{substance} \mu \text{air}}.$$

Hence, **the refractive index for a ray passing from one medium to a second is the reciprocal of the refractive index for a ray passing from the second medium to the first.**

17.05. Figure 17.06 shows the paths of rays meeting the surface of a medium of refractive index 1·5 at various angles of incidence. The ray AB is in each case

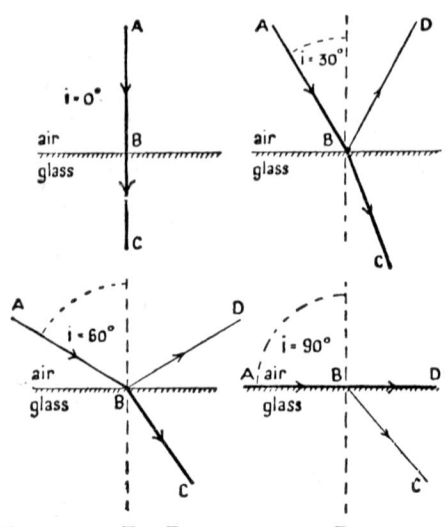

Fig. 17.06.—The Refraction and Reflection of Rays passing through Air and meeting a Glass Surface at Various Angles of Incidence.

the incident ray, and BC is the refracted ray. Some light is always reflected in such cases, and BD shows the paths of the light which is reflected. Unless the angle of incidence is large, the amount of light reflected is small. It should be noticed that the refracted ray makes a smaller angle with the normal than does the incident ray, and that, whatever the angle of incidence, *some* refraction always occurs.

17.06. Let us now consider the case of rays emerging from a substance of refractive index 1·5 into air. This is the case, for example, when rays emerge from a glass block. If $_{air}\mu_{glass} = 1\cdot50$, or $\frac{3}{2}$, $_{glass}\mu_{air}$ is the reciprocal of this, or $\frac{2}{3}$, so $\frac{\sin i}{\sin r} = \frac{2}{3}$. We shall consider three cases.

Case (1). *A ray meets the glass surface normally.*

$i = 0°$, and looking up $\sin 0°$ in the tables, we find that $\sin 0° = 0$

$$\therefore \frac{0}{\sin r} = \frac{2}{3}$$

$\therefore \sin r = 0$, so r must also be $0°$.

In other words, the ray which meets the surface at right angles passes straight through without deviation.

Case (2). *The ray meets the surface at an angle of incidence* 30°.

$$\frac{\sin i}{\sin r} = \frac{2}{3}, \text{ and } \sin 30° = \frac{1}{2}$$

$$\therefore \frac{\frac{1}{2}}{\sin r} = \frac{2}{3}$$

$$\therefore \sin r = \frac{3}{4}.$$

Looking up r in the tables, we find it to be 48° 36′. We may therefore draw a diagram with the aid of a protractor, making the angle of incidence 30° and the angle of refraction 48° 36′. Another and more accurate method of drawing the diagram to illustrate the path of the ray is that shown in figure 17.07.

AB represents the surface of the glass, and DC is the ray meeting the surface at C, at an angle of incidence of 30°. It is required to construct the path of the refracted ray.

$$\frac{\sin i}{\sin r} = \frac{2}{3}.$$

CR, 2 units of length, is marked off along AB, and CS is

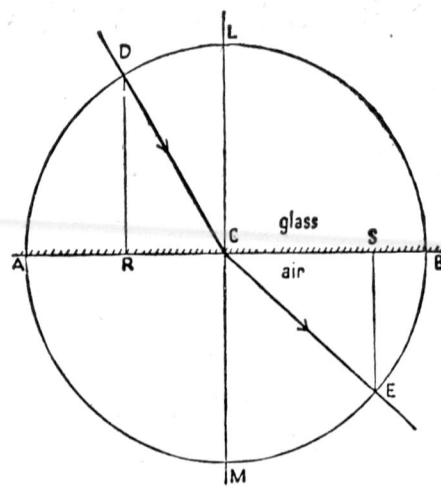

FIG. 17.07.

marked off equal to 3 units of length. The perpendicular RD is drawn at R meeting the incident ray at D, and with centre C and radius CD a circle is drawn. The perpendicular SE is drawn at S, cutting the circle at E. Then CE is the path of the refracted ray. Let LM be the perpendicular to the glass surface at C.

Since DR, LM, and SE are parallel,

$$\lfloor RDC = \lfloor DCL, \text{ and } \lfloor SEC = \lfloor MCE$$

$$\therefore \frac{\sin \lfloor DCL}{\sin \lfloor MCE} = \frac{\sin \lfloor RDC}{\sin \lfloor SEC}.$$

But

$$\sin \lfloor RDC = \frac{RC}{CD}, \text{ and } \sin \lfloor SEC = \frac{CS}{CE}$$

$$\therefore \frac{\sin \lfloor DCL}{\sin \lfloor MCE} = \frac{RC}{CD} \Big/ \frac{CS}{CE} = \frac{RC}{CD} \times \frac{CE}{CS} = \frac{2}{3},$$

since CD = CE, and RC = ⅔CS.

$\lfloor DCL$ is, however, the angle of incidence i, so $\dfrac{\sin i}{\sin \lfloor MCE} = \dfrac{2}{3}$, and, since $\dfrac{\sin i}{\sin r} = \dfrac{2}{3}$, $\lfloor MCE$ is the required angle of refraction.

Case (3).   *The ray meets the surface at an angle of incidence* 60°.

$$\frac{\sin i}{\sin r} = \frac{2}{3}$$

$$\therefore \quad \frac{\sin 60°}{\sin r} = \frac{2}{3}$$

$$\therefore \quad \sin r = \tfrac{3}{2} \times \sin 60° = \tfrac{3}{2} \times 0\cdot8660 = 1\cdot2990.$$

If you look in the tables for the angle whose sine is 1·2990, you will discover that there is no such angle. What does this mean ? A graphical construction similar to that used in the previous case does not help us to discover the angle, because, on drawing the figure, it will be found that the point S lies out-side the circle, so the per-pendicular from S does not meet the circle at any point. Apparently the only way of discovering the path of the refracted ray is to find it experimentally.

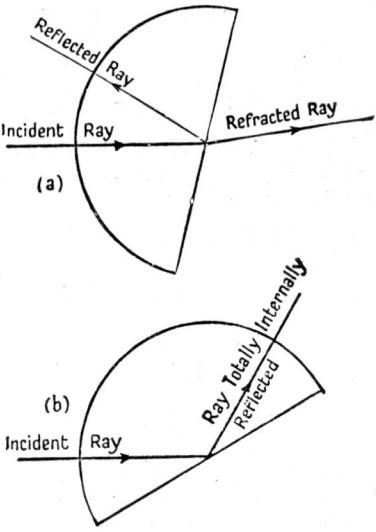

We allow a light streak to pass across the face of the optical disc, and turn the disc so that the rays enter the curved surface of the glass. The rays meet this surface normally, and no refraction occurs as they enter the glass, but the rays are refracted as they leave the plane face of the block. If the angle of incidence at this face is small, most of the light passes through the surface into the refracted beam. A little light is re-flected at the inner surface of the glass, however (figure 17.08(*a*)).

Fig. 17.08.—Partial Internal Re-flection and Total Internal Reflection.

As the angle of incidence is increased, the intensity of the reflected light increases, while that of the refracted light decreases. At the same time, the refracted beam approaches the surface of the glass block more and more nearly, until it lies along this surface. When the angle of incidence is still further increased, the refracted ray disappears altogether, and *all* the light is internally reflected (figure 17.08(*b*)). The beam is then said to be *totally internally reflected*. Our calculation was, after all, quite correct in not predicting an angle of refraction, for there is no refracted ray !

Figure 17.09 shows the refraction of rays incident upon the inner surface of a glass block, the thicknesses of the lines AB, BC, and BD indicating approximately the relative amounts of light in the incident, refracted, and reflected rays. The fraction of the incident light which is refracted decreases gradually as the angle of incidence increases, until the refracted ray lies along the surface. For greater angles of incidence *no* refraction occurs.

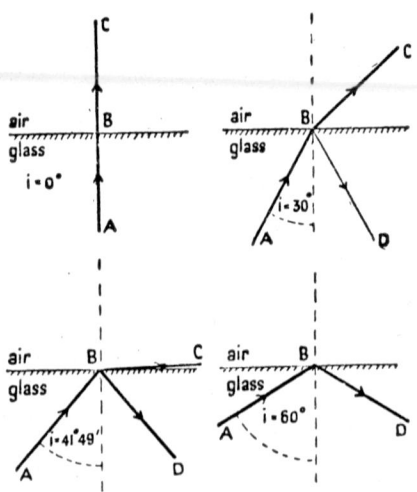

FIG. 17.09.—THE REFLECTION AND REFRACTION OF RAYS PASSING THROUGH GLASS AND INCIDENT AT THE GLASS-AIR SURFACE AT VARIOUS ANGLES.

The smallest angle of incidence at which total internal reflection occurs is called the **critical angle** for the two media. When total internal reflection is just about to take place, the refracted ray lies along the surface of the two media, so the angle of refraction is 90°. Let $_s\mu_a$ be the refractive index for a ray, passing from a given substance into air.

$$_s\mu_a = \frac{\sin i}{\sin r},$$ and when total reflection is about to occur $r = 90°$ and $\sin r = 1$. Hence, in this case,

$$_s\mu_a = \sin i.$$

This angle of incidence, however, is called the critical angle for the two media. Let us call it i_c. Then,

$$\sin i_c = {}_s\mu_a$$

$$\therefore \sin i_c = \frac{1}{{}_a\mu_s}.$$

In words, **the sine of the critical angle is equal to the reciprocal of the refractive index.** For glass $\mu = 1.5$, so the critical angle is given by the formula,

$$\sin i_c = \frac{1}{1.5}$$
$$\therefore i_c = 41° 49'.$$

17.07. If a ray travelling in glass meets the surface at an angle of incidence greater than $41° 49'$, total internal reflection occurs. This fact is applied when a glass prism is used as a plane mirror. A ray of light falling on a prism as shown in figure 17.10 is totally internally reflected twice, and returns in the direction from which it came, and such prisms are used as plane mirrors in field-glasses. Good prisms are expensive, but there is no silvering to be replaced at intervals as there is with an ordinary mirror.

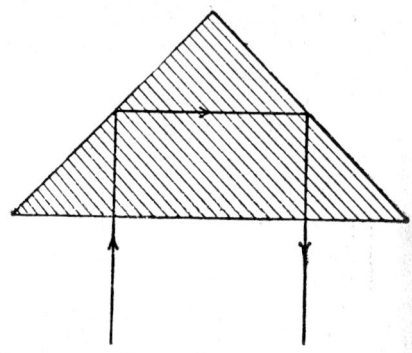

FIG. 17.10.—TOTAL INTERNAL REFLECTION IN A PRISM.

The critical angle for rays passing from water to air is $48° 35'$. If an iron ball is covered with soot and placed in water, the black ball shines like polished silver. The soot, being oily, prevents the water from wetting the ball, which is therefore surrounded by a thin film of air. The rays of light which fall on the ball at angles greater than the critical angle are totally internally reflected at the water-air surface instead of crossing the film and being absorbed by the soot. Hence, the ball appears shiny instead of black.

We have all heard of a " bird's-eye view." Have you ever

considered what a " fish-eye view " would be like ?   Figure 17.11
shows some of the rays which enter the eye of a fish at the

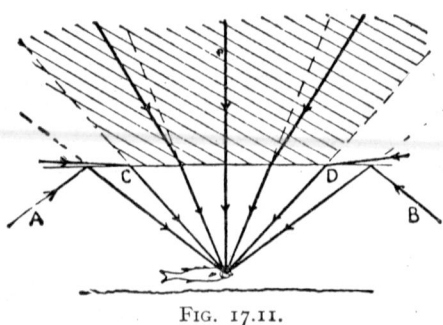

bottom of a pond,
and the dotted lines
show the directions
from which the rays
appear to come.
The rays from objects
above the surface of
the water all appear
to come from points
in the cone shaded.
Rays such as A and
B are totally intern-
ally reflected, so
around the central

FIG. 17.11.

cone which appears to contain the objects above the water, the
fish sees objects which are really at the bottom of the pond.

17.08. We must now
consider the appear-
ance of objects below
the surface of water,
when viewed from the
air above.   Here are
two facts for you to
observe next time you
are at the swimming
baths.   (1) The water
directly below you as
you stand at the side
of the bath appears
shallower than it really
is ; (2) the water at
the far side looks even
s h a l l o w e r, so the
bottom of the bath
appears to curve up-
wards towards the far
side.   You will under-

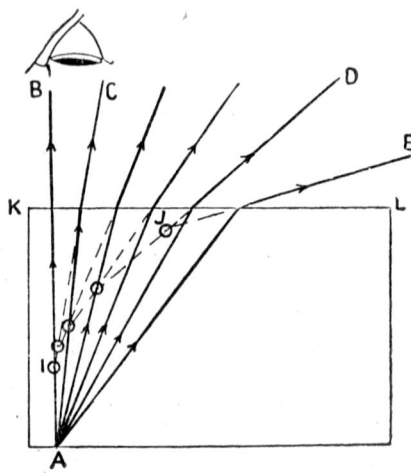

FIG. 17.12.

stand why this is so if you study figure 17.12, which is obtained
by shining a set of light streaks into a block of glass at the

point **A**. The light streaks enable the paths of rays proceeding from A to be seen.

The dotted lines show the paths along which the rays appear to have come when the eye is placed in the positions B,C . . . D,E. Thus the rays AB and AC, after leaving the block, appear to an eye, placed in the position shown, to have come from I, which is therefore the image of the point A. Hence, the block of glass appears to be shallower than it really is. In the same way, the rays AD and AE appear to come from J, so an eye placed to receive these rays will see an image of A at J, and when viewed from t h i s direction the block appears very shallow. Intermediate rays between AC and AD give images at the various points shown with a dot and circle, and as the eye moves from B to E the image of A moves along the curve on which these points lie, and the far side of the block appears to approach nearer and nearer to the surface KL. The curve on which the various images lie is called a *caustic curve*.

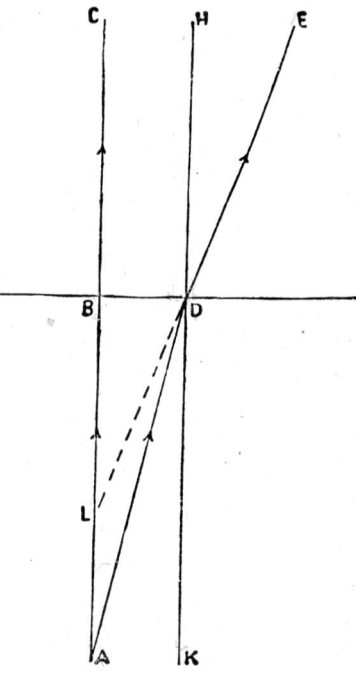

Fig. 17.13.

17.09. It is not difficult to c a l c u l a t e what the apparent depth of a pool will be when the bottom is viewed by means of rays which emerge almost at right angles to the surface.

Let A (figure 17.13) be a point at the bottom of some water whose surface is at BD. Let ABC be the ray which passes through the surface at right angles to it, and let ADE be the path of a ray very near the ray ABC. In order to obtain a clear diagram AD has been drawn making a considerable angle

with AB, but in practice this angle is a degree or less. HK is
the normal to the surface at D, and LD is the path the ray DE
appears to have traversed.

$$_{\text{water}}\mu_{\text{air}} = \frac{\sin i}{\sin r} = \frac{\sin \lfloor\text{ADK}}{\sin \lfloor\text{HDE}}.$$

Hence, since $_{\text{air}}\mu_{\text{water}}$ is the reciprocal of $_{\text{water}}\mu_{\text{air}}$

$$_{\text{air}}\mu_{\text{water}} = \frac{\sin \lfloor\text{HDE}}{\sin \lfloor\text{ADK}}.$$

CA and HK are parallel lines, so

$$\lfloor\text{HDE} = \lfloor\text{BLD, and} \lfloor\text{ADK} = \lfloor\text{BAD}$$

$$\therefore \;_{\text{air}}\mu_{\text{water}} = \frac{\sin \lfloor\text{BLD}}{\sin \lfloor\text{BAD}} = \frac{\text{BD}}{\text{LD}}\Big/\frac{\text{BD}}{\text{AD}} = \frac{\text{AD}}{\text{LD}}.$$

AD, however, is the real depth of the water, and LD is its
apparent depth.

$$\therefore \;_{\text{air}}\mu_{\text{water}} = \frac{\text{the real depth}}{\text{the apparent depth}}.$$

The index of refraction of water is 1·33, or $\frac{4}{3}$. Hence, water
which is actually 4 ft. deep will appear, when viewed from
directly above, to be 3 ft. deep.

17.10. The refractive index of the glass in a glass block may
be calculated from the above formula if the real thickness and
the apparent thickness of the block are measured. One method
of measuring the apparent thickness is illustrated in figure 17.14.

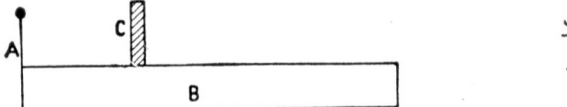

FIG. 17.14.—MEASUREMENT OF THE APPARENT DEPTH OF A GLASS BLOCK.

A pin A is placed against the middle of the narrow end of a
rectangular glass block, and a scale C is placed across the block.
With the eye in the position shown, the pin can be seen through
the block, and its image is below some division of the scale.
The scale is moved backwards or forwards until there is no
parallax between the image of the pin and a mark on the scale,
and since the image and the scale are then the same distance
from the eye, the apparent depth is equal to the distance from
the scale to the side of the block nearest the eye.

The apparent thickness can be measured more accurately

using a microscope mounted so that the microscope tube can be moved along its own axis, and provided with a scale and vernier for measuring the movement. A little lycopodium powder is sprinkled on a sheet of paper, and the tube of the microscope is moved until the grains are in focus. A thick block of glass is placed on top of the powder, and the microscope is moved until the grains are again in focus. Finally, some lycopodium is sprinkled on top of the glass, and this is brought into focus by a further movement of the tube of the microscope. The three positions of the microscope are read by means of the scale and vernier. The real thickness of the block is the difference between the first and third readings, and the difference between the second and third gives the apparent thickness.

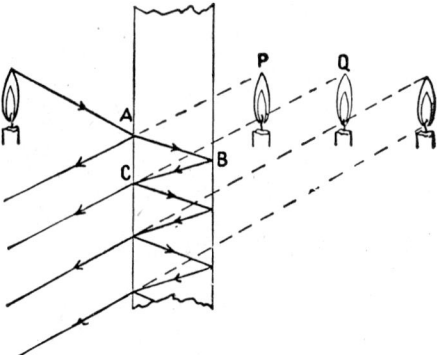

FIG. 17.15.—THE IMAGES FORMED IN A THICK MIRROR.

17.11. When light is reflected at a thick mirror a number of images may be seen behind the mirror. Their formation is illustrated in figure 17.15. The light from the object, striking the glass at A, is partly reflected and partly refracted. The reflected light produces a virtual image at P. The refracted beam, after reflection at the silvered surface at B, is partly refracted at C, and partly internally reflected. The beam which escapes at C produces an image at Q. Further reflections and refractions of parts of the beam produce other images in a similar way.

17.12. Objects which do not themselves emit light are rendered visible only when light is reflected or refracted from them to the eye. If a colourless transparent object is placed in a liquid of refractive index equal to that of the solid object, neither reflection nor refraction occurs at the boundary of the object, so the light passing through the liquid is quite unaffected by its presence, and the solid is completely invisible.

An interesting optical illusion may be prepared, using this fact, by balancing a steel ball on a glass tube standing in a bottle of glycerol. The glycerol and glass have nearly the same refractive index, so the glass tube is invisible and the steel ball appears to be floating in the liquid. Another illusion of the same kind is illustrated in figure 17.16. Water is run into a kettle through a bent glass tube as shown, and the water escaping from the kettle obscures the tube. If the kettle is suspended in mid-air, therefore, it appears that a continuous stream of water escapes from the kettle without any entering.

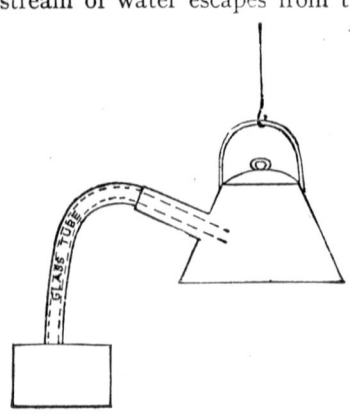

FIG. 17.16.—THE MAGIC KETTLE.

When ordinary transparent glass is powdered it appears white and opaque, because it now consists of innumerable tiny grains. Light falling on it is reflected at the surfaces of the grains, and causes the powder to appear white. If some water is poured over the powder, however, little reflection occurs at the surfaces of the glass, and the glass appears transparent again.

The frosting of the inside of electric lamp bulbs causes a similar effect. The inside surface is artificially roughened so that the light from the filament shall be refracted in all directions. Thus light enters the eye from all parts of the bulb instead of merely from the direction of the filament, and glare is reduced. It is interesting to note that the inside, and not the outside, of the glass is frosted. If the outside were roughened, much of the light would meet the glass surfaces at angles greater than the critical angle, and the light would be reflected back into the bulb. Roughening the inside surface, however, causes a loss of only 3% of the light.

Coloured glass owes its colour to the fact that light passes through it before entering the eye, and if such glass is powdered the rays of light are reflected at the glass surfaces before they have penetrated far, and the powder appears white. The colour may be restored, however, by moistening the powder, for less reflection then takes place, and the light travels farther through the glass before being reflected to the eye. By moistening or oiling paper, reflection at its rough surface is reduced, and the paper then allows more light to pass through it.

17.13. When light passes from a vacuum to air, or from air at one temperature and pressure to air at another temperature and pressure, the light is refracted, although the deviation is only small. Hence light entering the earth's atmosphere from the sun follows a path whose direction changes continually as the rays reach lower and lower levels. The refraction has been exaggerated in figure 17.17, but it is large enough to render measurements of the exact position of the sun and stars worthless, if the measurements are made while the stars are near the horizon. Astronomers apply a correction to their measurements of the positions of stars to allow for the refraction, but since the value of the correction depends upon the temperature and pressure in each layer of the atmosphere through which the rays pass, it cannot be calculated exactly. If the stars observed

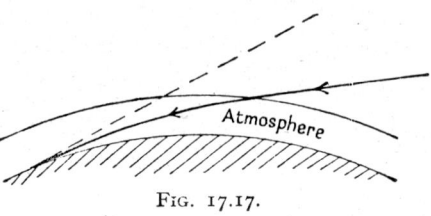

Fig. 17.17.

are high above the horizon, however, the rays from them enter the various layers of air at small angles of incidence, the deviation of the rays is small, and the correction is sufficiently accurate.

Since refraction in the earth's atmosphere causes rays to reach an observer as though coming from a point higher above the horizon than the actual position of the object, the sun appears to be just above the skyline when it is really just below it, and the day is longer than it would be if no atmosphere were present. Moreover, the daylight fades gradually, instead of disappearing instantaneously, as it would do in the absence of an atmosphere, for even after the sun has passed so far below the horizon that its rays are no longer refracted to an observer, some of the refracted light reaches clouds and dust particles overhead, and is reflected downwards.

The amount of refraction is greatest when the rays are travelling nearly tangentially to the surface of the earth, so the rays from the lower parts of the sun and moon are refracted more than rays from the upper parts. Hence, the sun and moon, when near the horizon, appear elliptical instead of circular.

The twinkling of stars is also caused by atmospheric refraction. Convection currents in the atmosphere continually alter the temperatures of the air through which rays from a star reach an observer, so the paths of such rays alter from instant to instant, and the rays travelling in a given direction are concentrated first at one point, then at another. Hence, the amount of light reaching the eyes of the observer changes continually.

17.14. The alterations of the temperature and pressure of the parts of the atmosphere through which rays pass to the eyes are the cause of the quivering and shimmering of objects seen near the surface of a tarred road on a hot day.

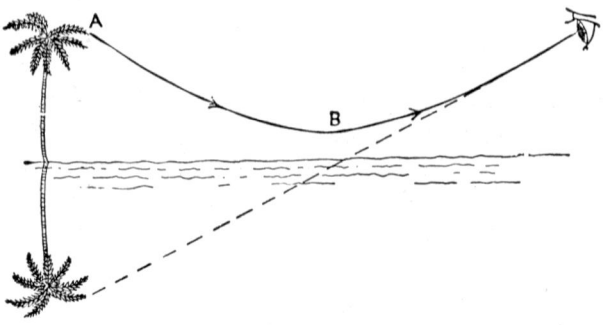

Fig. 17.18.—A Mirage.

If the surface of the earth is strongly heated by the sun's rays, layers of air near the ground may become warmer than the air above, and in such cases a *mirage* may be produced. The rays from a distant object are refracted as they pass from colder layers of air to warmer ones, and their path is a curve, such as AB (figure 17.18). The rays finally reach a still warmer layer at the level B at an angle of incidence greater than the critical angle, and are totally reflected. After further refraction they reach the eye as though coming from a point below the level of the ground, and form an inverted image of the object. Since rays of light from the sky are refracted and reflected in a similar way the image lies on a blue background, and is often mistaken for the image formed in an expanse of water.

EXAMPLES 17

1. Define *angle of refraction*. State and explain the two laws of refraction. What is meant by the statement that the refractive index of water is 1·33 ?

2. Show that the refractive index for a ray passing from air to a substance is the reciprocal of that for a ray passing from the substance to air.

3. With the aid of suitable diagrams describe what happens when a number of rays of light meet the surface of a pool of water at various angles of incidence. What are the chief differences between this case and that in which light travelling through the pond meets the air-water surface from below ?

4. Prove that, for light passing into air from a substance of refractive index μ, the critical angle is given by the formula,

$$\sin i_c = \frac{1}{\mu}.$$

5. Rays of light travelling in air meet the surface of a pond at angles of incidence of 30° and 60° respectively. Calculate the angles of refraction in the two cases, and verify your results by means of diagrams drawn to scale. [μ for water = $\frac{4}{3}$.]

6. Rays of light travelling upwards through a pond meet the surface at angles of incidence of 30° and 60° respectively. By means of diagrams drawn to scale find the subsequent paths of the light [μ for water = $\frac{4}{3}$].

7. A ray of light meets one of the shorter sides of a right-angled isosceles prism at an angle of incidence of 0°. Trace the subsequent path of the ray, and explain what the prism does to the incident light. [μ is 1·5 for the glass of which the prism is made.]

8. A parallel beam of light, travelling in a direction parallel to the longer side of a right-angled isosceles prism meets one of the shorter sides. The prism is made of glass of refractive index 1·5. Trace the paths through the prism of (*a*) a ray which is incident at the mid-point of the side, (*b*) a ray incident farther from the right angle of the prism. Using your results, explain what effect the prism has on the beam.

9. A fish is in a hemispherical glass bowl full of water, the bowl being supported so that it rests on the rounded surface. Assuming the fish to be just below the surface of the water, and at the centre of the water surface, explain, with the aid of a suitable diagram, the appearance of its surroundings as seen by the fish.

10. Explain with the aid of a suitable diagram, why (*a*) the water in a swimming bath looks shallower than it really is, (*b*) the bottom of the bath appears to slope upwards towards the far side.

11. Prove that when a block of glass of refractive index 1·5 is viewed along a line perpendicular to its nearer surface the apparent thickness of the block is two-thirds of its real thickness.

12. Explain why glass lamp bulbs are frosted, why they appear white, and why the inside and not the outside is frosted. What change in the appearance of the glass would occur if the bulb were filled with water?

13. The moon possesses no atmosphere. What influence would this fact have upon the appearance of your surroundings if you were able to spend a lunar day and night at its surface?

14. Observatories are often situated at the top of mountains far from towns. Give reasons why such sites are preferable to others near towns at sea level.

School Certificate Questions

15. Define, with reference to a diagram, the meaning of *refractive index*. A ray of light is incident at 45° on the upper surface of a rectangular block of glass. The glass is 2 in. thick and it is silvered on its under side. Draw a figure, full size, showing the complete path of the ray through the glass. [Refractive index of glass = 1·5.] (L)

16. Explain why an isosceles right-angled glass prism can be employed to reverse the path of a ray of light. Show by a diagram the formation of an image by such a prism and compare it with the image formed by a plane mirror. What are the advantages of the use of a prism over a plane mirror? (L)

17. What do you understand by the statement that the refractive index for an air-water interface is $\frac{4}{3}$? How would you confirm this statement by experiment? A ray of light is incident in water, at an angle of 30° to the normal, at a water-air interface. Find *graphically* the inclination of the emergent ray to the normal. Explain, with illustrative diagrams, what happens if the angle of incidence of the ray in the water gradually increases. (O)

18. A narrow parallel beam of white light is incident at 45° upon a rectangular block of red glass 5 cm. thick. Some of the light is reflected at the first surface. Call this "beam A." The remainder passes into the glass at an angle of refraction 30°, and falls upon the second surface of the block, where some of it passes out into the air ("beam B"), and the remainder is reflected back to the first surface and passes out into the air; call this "beam C." (a) Give a ray-diagram showing accurately the paths of the various beams. (b) Remembering that red glass is being used, discuss the differences in colour between beams A, B, and C. (O)

19. State the laws of reflection and the laws of refraction of light at a plane surface, and explain what you mean by *total reflection*. A ray of light is travelling in a liquid of refractive index 1·4 at an angle of incidence 44° to the surface. Will total reflection take place? Give reasons. (B)

20. A ray of light falls on the upper surface of a parallel-sided block of glass. Illustrate the laws of reflection and refraction by tracing out in detail the subsequent path of the ray of light as the angle of incidence is varied. If a cube of glass is placed on a page of a book, why is it not possible to read the print through the sides of the cube ? (B)

21. Show with the aid of an accurate diagram how a ray of light incident obliquely on a slab of glass of uniform thickness, emerges parallel to its original direction. An object is placed 2 in. behind such a slab 2 in. thick. Draw two rays, from a point on the object, incident on the slab at angles of 30° and 45 (with the normal) respectively. Trace the paths of these rays through the slab, and indicate the position of the image determined by them on emerging. Show also the position of the image obtained by simple reflection of these rays at the first surface. Take the refractive index of glass as 1·5 in each case. (J)

22. Explain clearly what is meant by the statement that *the refractive index of water is $\frac{4}{3}$*. A boy looking at a dark object on the bottom of a swimming bath with vertical sides, where the water is 8 ft. deep sees, in the same direction, the image of a small roof window formed by reflection at the water surface. The point where his line of vision cuts the surface is 14 ft. from the far edge of the water and the window is 20 ft. vertically above that edge. Find graphically (on a scale of 1 in. to 4 ft.) how far the object is from the far side of the bath. (J)

23. State the *laws of refraction of light*. Describe how you would measure, by an " apparent depth " method, the refractive index of water contained in a beaker. Prove the formula which you employ. (J)

24. Explain why, when looking vertically down into a vessel containing a transparent liquid, the bottom of the vessel is apparently raised. A pin A is fixed on the inside of the flat base of a glass vessel and a liquid is poured into the vessel to a depth of 20·0 cm. A second pin B is fixed parallel to A but 25·0 cm. above the surface of the liquid. A plane mirror is then adjusted between B and the surface of the liquid until, on looking vertically down, the image of B in the mirror appears to coincide with A for all positions of the eye. The distance between the pin B and the mirror is then found to be 19·3 cm. Calculate from these data the refractive index of the liquid. (L)

25. Explain with the aid of a diagram why a pool of water appears shallower than it is. A transparent cube of 15 cm. edge contains a small air bubble. Its apparent depth when viewed through one face of the cube is 6 cm. and when viewed through the opposite face it is 4 cm. What is the actual distance of the bubble from the first face, and what is the refractive index of the substance of the cube ? (C)

CHAPTER 18

SPHERICAL MIRRORS

18.01. A spherical mirror is a portion of a sphere which has been silvered on its outer or inner surface, to cause it to reflect light. If the inside of the silvered surface is used to reflect light it is a concave mirror, and if the outside of the silvered surface is used it is convex. The centre of the sphere of which the mirror forms a part is called the *centre of curvature* of the mirror (C, figure 18.01). The middle point of the mirror surface is called the *pole* (P in the diagrams), and a line through the centre of curvature and the pole is called the *principal axis* of the mirror.

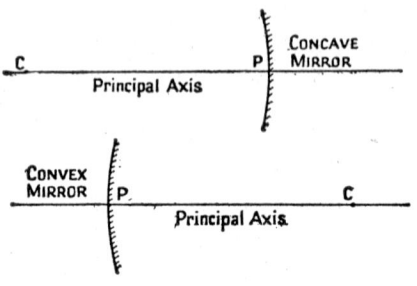

FIG. 18.01.—SPHERICAL MIRRORS.

18.02. Spherical mirrors form images just as lenses and plane mirrors do. When a concave mirror is held at arm's length an image of the face is seen. This image is inverted, but if the mirror is brought nearer, the image becomes blurred and disappears, and then reappears as an upright image.

How is the image formed? Using light streaks diverging from a point A (figure 18.02), we allow the light to fall on a concave cylindrical mirror as shown in the diagram. After reflection at the mirror the streaks converge to a second point B, and, to an eye placed at the position shown, the rays appear to start from B, so B is the image of A. Since the rays actually pass through the image, the latter is real. The concave mirror forms a real image by causing rays from each point on the object to converge to a second point which is the image of the first, and the complete image is the aggregate of all the image points formed in this way.

In the above experiment, only a narrow cone of rays diverges from the point A, and only a small part of the mirror surface is used. By using a wider cone of rays more of the mirror surface is used, but it is then found that the reflected rays no longer pass through a single point, so in this case no sharp image will be formed. **To obtain a sharp image with a spherical mirror only a small fraction of the sphere, of which it forms a part, must be used.**

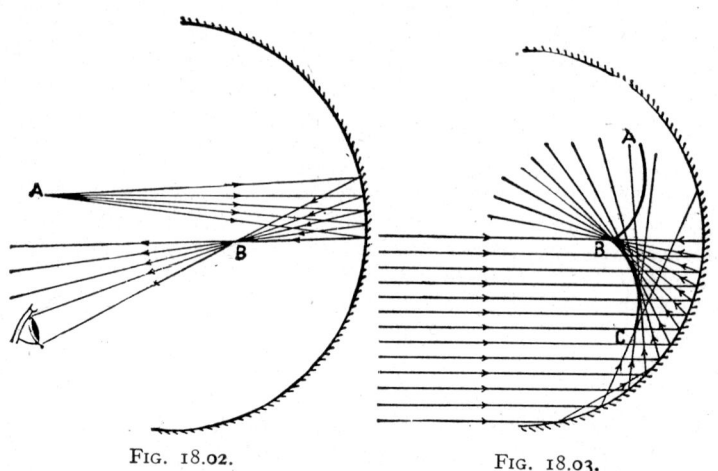

FIG. 18.02.   FIG. 18.03.

18.03. As shown by the light streaks in figure 18.03, a set of rays travelling parallel to the principal axis intersect, after reflection from the mirror, along a curve ABC, those rays drawn in the diagram intersecting along the portion BC. The reflected rays are tangents to this curve, and it appears bright because at each point on it several light streaks overlap. The curve ABC is called the *caustic curve* of the mirror. Since parallel rays, such as those from an object at infinity, are reflected to meet at various points along the caustic curve, and not at a single point, the concave mirror shown does not form an image of an object at infinity. If, however, the rays far from the principal axis are cut off by a screen, so that only a small portion of the mirror is used, the other rays do meet at a single point, and this point is found to lie on the principal axis, midway between the pole and the centre of curvature. This point is called the *principal focus* of the mirror.

The position of the principal focus may be deduced from the laws of reflection as follows :

Let AB (figure 18.04) be any ray parallel to, and near, the principal axis CP of the mirror, and let BD be the path of the

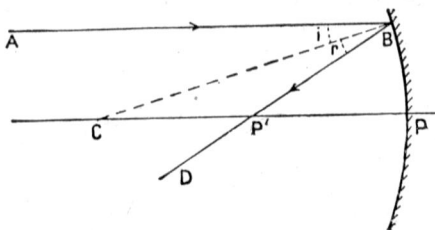

FIG. 18.04.

reflected ray. Since the incident ray AB and the normal BC lie in the plane of the diagram, the reflected ray BD does so as well. The principal axis CP also lies in this plane because C does so and CP is parallel to AB. Hence, BD cuts the axis at some point. Let P′ be this point.

Since C is the centre of curvature of the mirror, CB is a radius, and is therefore normal to the mirror at B. Hence, $\angle$ABC is the angle of incidence of the ray AB, and $\angle$CBP′ is the angle of reflection.

$$\therefore \; \angle \text{ABC} = \angle \text{CBP}.$$

But $$\angle \text{ABC} = \angle \text{BCP}' \; \text{(alternate angles)}$$

$$\therefore \; \angle \text{CBP}' = \angle \text{BCP}'.$$

Hence, the triangle CP′B is isosceles, and CP′ = P′B. If AB is close to the principal axis, B will be close to P, and in that case P′B is nearly equal to P′P.

$$\therefore \; \text{CP}' = \text{P}'\text{P}.$$

In other words, *any* ray such as AB, after reflection, passes through the point P′ on the principal axis, midway between the pole and centre of curvature ; *i.e.* passes through the principal focus of the mirror.

The distance of the principal focus from the pole of the mirror is called the *focal length* of the mirror. If f denotes the focal length and r the radius of curvature,

$$f = \frac{r}{2}.$$

Notice that the focal length and the radius of curvature are both measured along the paths of actual rays. We may agree to call the numerical values of both positive.

18.04. As noted above, lines from the centre of curvature of a mirror meet it normally. Hence, rays which travel from the centre of curvature of a concave mirror are reflected back along their own paths by the mirror, and are caused to converge again at the centre of curvature, and form an image there. **The image of an object at the centre of curvature is itself at the centre of curvature.** This fact is used in determining the radius of curvature of a concave mirror.

A light pin is set up on the axis of a concave mirror, and moved backwards or forwards until its image coincides with the tip of the pin, as shown in figure 18.05. The tip of the pin is

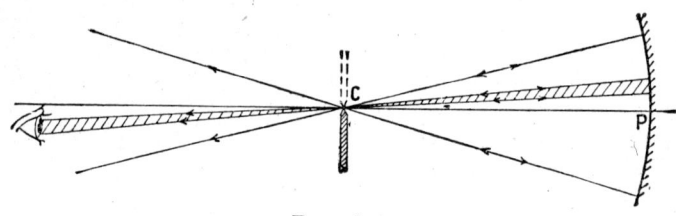

FIG. 18.05.

then at the centre of curvature, and the radius of curvature is the distance CP.

18.05. The Mirror Formula.—As in the case of the lens, there is a simple formula connecting the distances of the object and its image from a spherical mirror. We shall call u and v the distances of the object and image from the pole of the mirror, and shall use the same convention of signs as was used for a lens to determine whether the numerical values of u and v are positive or negative.

Let CP (figure 18.06) be the principal axis of the concave mirror, whose centre of curvature is at C and pole at P, and let A be the position of a small object on the principal axis. Let AB be any ray from A to the mirror. The normal to the mirror at B is the radius CB, so the ray AB is reflected at B in such a way that the angle of incidence $\lfloor ABC$ is equal to the angle of reflection $\underline{\lfloor CBD}$. Since AB and BC lie in the plane

I

of the diagram, the reflected ray also lies in this plane, **and** therefore cuts the principal axis at some point. Let this point be D.

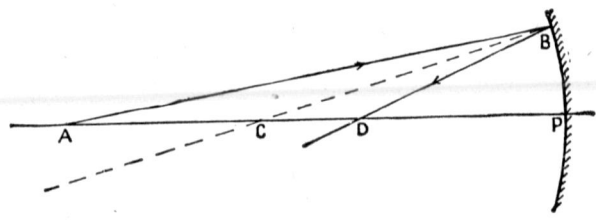

F$_{IG}$. 18.06.

In the triangle ABD the line BC bisects the angle ABD.

$$\therefore \frac{AC}{CD} = \frac{AB}{DB}.$$

Only a small fraction of the sphere through B and P is to be used as a mirror, and in this case B lies close to P, so AB is nearly equal to AP, and DB is nearly equal to DP. Hence,

$$\frac{AC}{CD} = \frac{AP}{DP}$$

$$\therefore \frac{AC}{AP} = \frac{CD}{DP}. \qquad \cdot \quad \cdot \quad \cdot \quad \cdot \quad \cdot \quad (1)$$

This equation states where the point D is situated relative **to** A, C, and P, and is the same wherever the point B is taken, so *all* the rays from A pass through the *same* point D. Hence, D is the position of the image of A.

The distance of the object is measured along the paths **of** actual rays, and is therefore positive.

$$\therefore \ AP = + u.$$

Similarly,

$$DP = + v$$
$$AC = (AP - PC) = + u - r$$
$$CD = (CP - DP) = + r - v.$$

Substituting these values in equation (1), we have,

$$\frac{u - r}{u} = \frac{r - v}{v}$$
$$\therefore + u.v - v.r = + u.r - u.v$$
$$\therefore u.r + v.r = 2u.v.$$

Dividing throughout by $u.v.r$,

$$\frac{1}{v} + \frac{1}{u} = \frac{2}{r}$$

18.06. The radius of curvature of a mirror is constant, so $\frac{2}{r}$ is also constant. Hence, the mirror equation may also be written :

$$\frac{1}{v} + \frac{1}{u} = F$$

where F is a constant, and is equal to $\frac{2}{r}$. This constant F is called the power of the mirror, and if r is measured in metres, the power calculated from the equation $F = \frac{2}{r}$ is said to be in dioptres.

The radius of curvature r of a concave mirror is equal to twice its focal length f.

$$\therefore \frac{2}{r} = \frac{1}{f}.$$

Hence, the mirror formula may also be written,

$$\frac{1}{v} + \frac{1}{u} = \frac{1}{f}.$$

18.07. The mirror formula may be tested in the laboratory using two light pins, one of which is used to mark the position of the image of the other. While performing the experiment, you cannot fail to notice that when the image of the first pin is vertically above the second pin, the image of the second pin is also vertically above the first pin. Hence, if $v = + 30$ cm. (say) when $u = + 15$ cm., it will also be true for this mirror that $v = + 15$ cm. when $u = + 30$ cm. This fact enables two sets of values of u and v to be obtained from each setting of the light pins—a useful fact when the values obtained are to be used for plotting graphs.

The graphs obtained with a concave mirror are similar to the corresponding graphs for a convex lens. Figure 18.07 shows, for example, the graph obtained by plotting the distances of the image against the corresponding distances of its object. If the object is at the centre of curvature of the mirror the image is also at that point, so u and v are equal, and each is equal to the radius of curvature. On the curve the point for which

$u = v$ is that where the line AB, the bisector of the angle between the axes, cuts the curve, so the mirror whose graph is

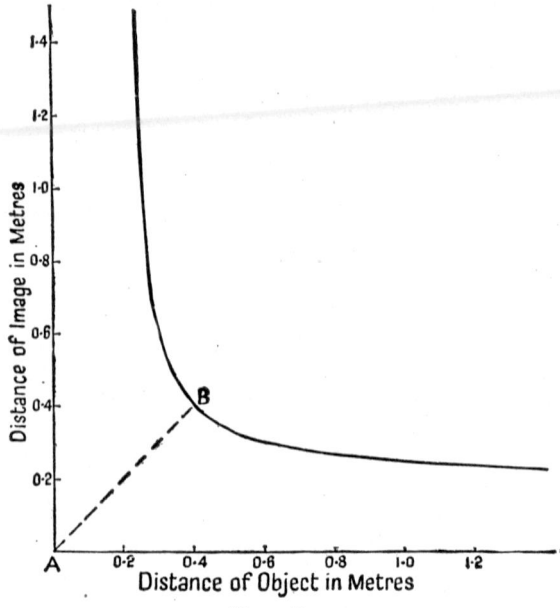

Fig. 18.07.

shown has a radius of curvature 0·40 metre; *i.e.* $r = + 0·40$ metre. Hence, $F = \dfrac{2}{0·40} = + 5·0\text{D}$, and $f = + 0·20$ metre.

18.08. As in the case of a lens, the **magnification** produced by a mirror is defined to be $\dfrac{\text{the length of the image}}{\text{the length of the object}}$, and in this case also, the magnification may be calculated from the values of v and u.

AB (figure 18.08) is the object, and DE is its image formed by the concave mirror, whose principal axis is AP and pole P. Since all the rays from B pass through E after reflection, PE is the path of the ray BP after it meets the mirror. The line AP passes through the centre of curvature, and therefore meets the mirror normally. Hence, $\lfloor$DPE is the angle of reflection corresponding to the angle of incidence $\lfloor$BPA.

$$\therefore \lfloor DPE = \lfloor BPA.$$

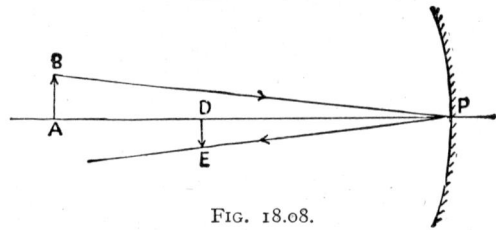

FIG. 18.08.

The angles BAP and EDP are equal, since each is a right angle, so the triangles BAP and EDP are similar.

$$\therefore \frac{DE}{AB} = \frac{DP}{AP}.$$

The magnification m is defined by the equation,

$$m = \frac{\text{the length of the image}}{\text{the length of the object}}$$

$$\therefore m = \frac{DE}{AB} = \frac{DP}{AP}.$$

$$DP = + v \; ; \; AP = + u$$

$$\therefore m = \frac{v}{u}.$$

As in the case of lenses the image is inverted if the numerical value of the magnification is positive; it is erect if the value is negative.

18.09. The following problem indicates the use of the mirror formula, and shows the graphical construction for obtaining the position of the image.

An object 1 cm. high is placed 30 cm. from the pole of a mirror of power + 5·00D. Find the size and position of the image.

$$F = + 5 \cdot 00D$$

$$u = + 30 \text{ cm.} = + 0 \cdot 30 \text{ metre}$$

$$\frac{1}{v} + \frac{1}{u} = F$$

$$\therefore \frac{1}{v} + \frac{1}{0 \cdot 30} = 5 \cdot 00.$$

Whence $v = + 0 \cdot 60$ metre, $= + 60$ cm.

The image is formed 60 cm. in front of the mirror, since the positive sign shows that the rays pass through it. Its magnification m is given by the formula

$$m = \frac{v}{u}$$

$$\therefore\ m = \left(\frac{60}{30}\right) = +2.$$

Hence, the image is inverted and twice the size of its object. It is therefore 2 cm. high.

AB (figure 18.09) is the object, DE its image. The ray BM travels along the radius through B, meets the mirror normally, and is reflected back along its own path. The ray BL is parallel

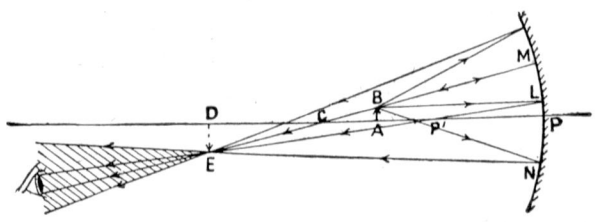

FIG. 18.09.

Horizontal scale : 1 unit represents 5 units.
Vertical scale : 1 unit represents 2 units.

to the principal axis CP, and is reflected from the mirror to pass through the principal focus P'. These rays meet at E, which is therefore the image of the point B. The path of any other ray such as BN may now be drawn, since, after reflection, the ray must pass through E. To see the image, the eye must be placed in the path of the rays coming from the image, and at least 25 cm. from it.

18.10. Consider now the following problem : *An object 1 cm. high is placed 10 cm. from the pole of a mirror of power + 5·00D. Find the position of the image.*

$$F = +5\cdot00D$$
$$u = +10\ \text{cm.} = +0\cdot10\ \text{metre.}$$
$$\frac{1}{v} + \frac{1}{u} = F$$
$$\therefore\ \frac{1}{v} + \frac{1}{0\cdot10} = 5\cdot00.$$

Whence $v = -0\cdot20$ metre, or -20 cm.

The negative sign shows that in this case the light does not pass through the image, which must therefore be formed behind the mirror. The magnification

$$m = \frac{v}{u} = \left(\frac{-\ 0{\cdot}20}{+\ 0{\cdot}10}\right) \text{ or } -\ 2.$$

Hence, the image is twice as long as the object, and is erect.

The graphical solution (figure 18.10) shows how the image is formed. The ray from B along the radius returns along its own path, and the ray parallel to the principal axis meets the mirror at M and is reflected through the principal focus P'. Both of

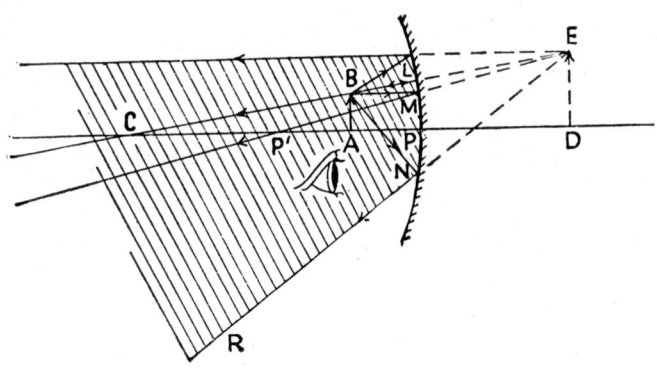

FIG. 18.10.

Horizontal scale: 1 unit represents 5 units.
Vertical scale: 1 unit represents 1 unit.

these reflected rays LC and MP' come from the direction of the point E, and since other reflected rays do the same, E is the image of B. The ray BN, for example, after reflection travels along NR, the continuation of the line EN. As before, the eye is placed to receive some of the reflected rays, and at least 25 cm. from the image.

18.11. The following table gives some details of the image formed by a concave mirror. The letters in the table refer to figure 18.11, where C is the centre of curvature, P' the principal focus, and P the pole of the mirror. The image formed is very small when at P', but its length increases and becomes equal to that of the object by the time it reaches C. Its length continues to increase until it reaches $+ \infty$, when it is very large. The virtual image is very large when it is far from the mirror,

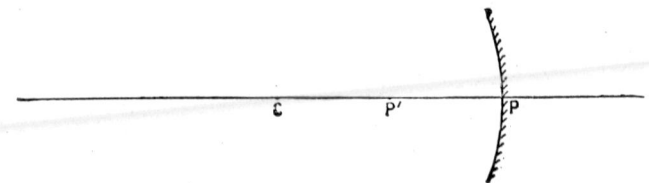

FIG. 18.11.

but decreases in size as it approaches it, and finally object and image become equal in length when both are at P.

As the Object moves from	The Image moves from	Character of the Image		
$+\infty$ to C	P′ to C	inverted	real	diminished
C to P′	C to $+\infty$	inverted	real	enlarged
P′ to P	$-\infty$ to P	erect	virtual	enlarged

It is worth noting that the image formed by a mirror is real, if the object and its image both lie on the *same* side of the mirror. The image formed by a lens, on the other hand, is real if the object and its image lie on *opposite* sides of the lens.

Convex Mirrors

18.12. When rays of light, coming from a point, are allowed to fall upon a convex mirror they are never reflected to one point by the latter, so a convex mirror does not form real images. The rays are, however, reflected in such a way that they *appear* to come from a second point, which is therefore the virtual image of the object point. The reflection of light streaks at a convex mirror is illustrated in figure 18.12.

Rays which travel parallel to the principal axis of the mirror appear after reflection to diverge from a point on the principal axis of the mirror. This point is called the principal focus, and lies midway between the pole and centre of curvature. Rays travelling along the continuation of a radius meet the mirror normally, and are reflected back along their own paths.

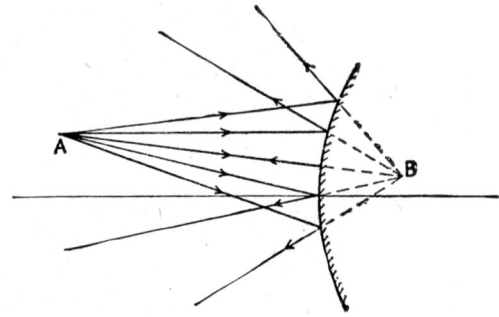

FIG. 18.12.

18.13. The mirror formula is true for convex as well as concave mirrors, and $\frac{1}{v} + \frac{1}{u}$ is equal to a constant which is written as F. F is called the power of the mirror, and if v and u are measured in metres, the formula $\frac{1}{v} + \frac{1}{u} = F$ gives the numerical value of the power in dioptres.

As in the case of the concave mirror, the power F of a convex mirror and its radius of curvature r are connected by the equation $F = \frac{2}{r}$. Moreover, since the focal length f is half the radius of curvature,

$$\frac{1}{f} = \frac{2}{r} = F.$$

Hence, for a convex mirror also,

$$\frac{1}{v} + \frac{1}{u} = \frac{2}{r}, \text{ and}$$

$$\frac{1}{v} + \frac{1}{u} = \frac{1}{f}.$$

The radius of curvature and the focal length of a convex mirror are both measured in the space behind the mirror, to which no rays can pass from the object, and both are negative.

The magnification m is given by the formula

$$m = \frac{v}{u}.$$

Its numerical value is always negative and the image is always erect.

18.14. EXAMPLE ON THE CONVEX MIRROR.—*A convex mirror of power* $- 5\cdot00D$ *is* 20 *cm. distant from an object* 2 *cm. high. Find the position, size, and nature of the image produced.*

$$F = - 5\cdot00D$$
$$u = + 20 \text{ cm.} = + 0\cdot20 \text{ metre}$$

$$\frac{1}{v} + \frac{1}{u} = F$$

$$\therefore \frac{1}{v} + \frac{1}{0\cdot20} = - 5\cdot00.$$

Whence $v = - 0\cdot10$ metre $= - 10$ cm.

$$m = \frac{v}{u} = \frac{- 0\cdot10}{+ 0\cdot20} = - \tfrac{1}{2}.$$

Hence, the image is virtual, erect, half the size of the object, and 10 cm. behind the mirror.

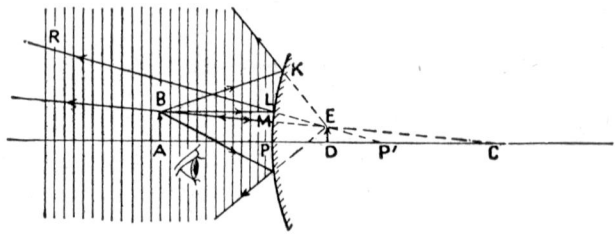

FIG. 18.13.

Horizontal scale: 1 unit represents 5 units.
Vertical scale: 2 units represent 1 unit.

AB (figure 18.13) is the object, AC the principal axis, C the centre of curvature, and P' is the principal focus. The ray BM, travelling along the continuation of the radius CM, meets the mirror normally and is reflected back along its own path. The ray BL travels parallel to the principal axis, and is reflected along LR as though coming from P', the principal focus. These rays MB and LR, when produced backwards, meet at E. They therefore appear to come from E, so E is the image of B. The other rays such as BK appear, after reflection at the mirror, to come from E, so their paths are as shown in the diagram. By measurement from the diagram the size and position of the image may be shown to agree with the values given by the calculation.

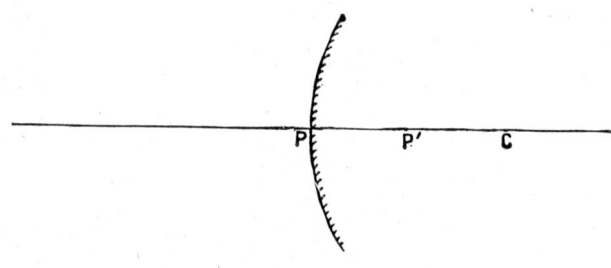

FIG. 18.14.

18.15. The table for the position and nature of the image formed by a convex mirror is a very simple one. The size of the image is very small when it is at P′ but becomes equal to that of the object when both arrive at P.

As the Object moves from	The Image moves from	Character of the Image		
+∞ to P	P′ to P	erect	virtual	diminished

18.16. The driving mirrors of motor-cars are usually convex. The image formed by such a mirror is erect, and the fact that it is diminished and near the mirror means that much of the road behind the driver is visible in a comparatively small mirror. If a plane driving mirror is used, it must be larger to give a similar field of view.

All the objects in the cone shaded in figure 18.15 (a) will be visible to an eye placed at the point E. The extreme rays of the cone may be found by joining I, the image of E, to the edges of the convex mirror, and producing these lines backwards. Light *from* the eye, E, is reflected from the mirror as though it came from I, so AC and BD are the paths of the rays EA and EB after reflection. Actually, the rays with which we are concerned are those travelling to the eye, and not those travelling from it. The rays DB and CA, however, follow the same paths as the rays EBD and EAC, but in the reverse direction. Figure 18.15 (*b*) shows the cone of rays reflected from a plane

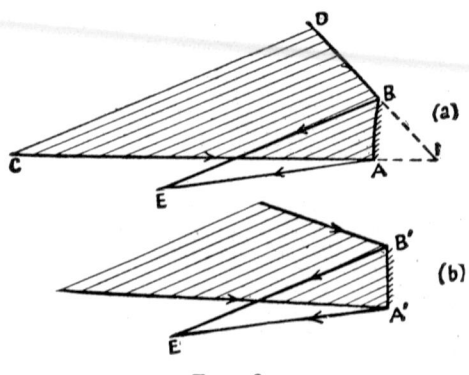

Fig. 18.15.

mirror of the same size to the eye at E′, and this cone of rays is narrower than that for the convex mirror. In other words, the field of view is narrower with a plane mirror. On the other hand, the plane mirror has the advantage that objects seen by means of it appear their correct sizes and distances. How is figure 18.15 (*b*) drawn?

When a magnified image is required, a concave mirror may be used. Shaving mirrors are of this type. To obtain an erect image, the object—in this case, the face—must be placed nearer the mirror than its principal focus, and to allow sufficient space for using the razor a concave mirror of long focal length is required.

If an object is placed at the principal focus of a concave mirror its image is formed at infinity, so the rays leaving the mirror form a parallel beam.

In the searchlight and in motor headlamps this fact is used in order to obtain a parallel beam of light. A large portion of a spherical mirror must not be used, however, if a sharp image is to be obtained at its principal focus by means of a parallel beam of light. In the same way, a spherical mirror produces a parallel beam of light, only if the rays from a point source at its principal focus gives light which is reflected near the pole of the mirror, and rays which are reflected far from the pole do *not* travel parallel to the principal axis. On the other hand, the reflector of a searchlight or motor headlamp must use the maximum possible fraction of the light from the source, and only if a large fraction of the mirror is used can much of the light be reflected.

The difficulty is overcome by using a parabolic mirror instead of a spherical one. A section through such a mirror is shown in figure 18.16, with a dotted semicircle for comparison. Notice that, although the semicircle and the parabola coincide at points near the axis, they do not do so at other points. Light from the principal focus of a parabolic mirror is reflected as an accurately parallel beam from all parts of the mirror. Such mirrors are, however, more difficult and expensive to make than are spherical ones, and are chiefly used where, as in the present case, a spherical mirror will not serve the purpose.

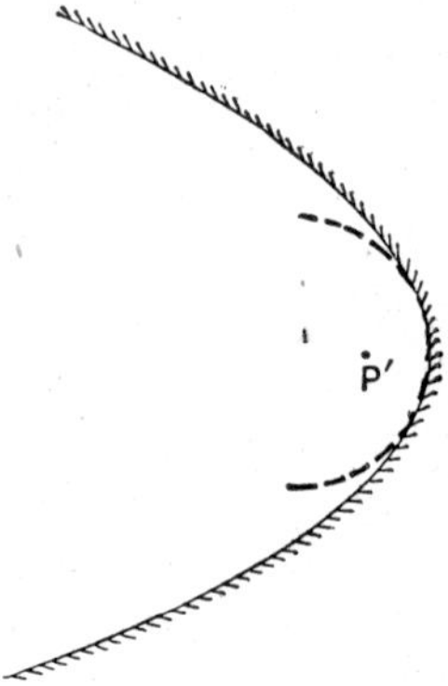

FIG. 18.16.—PARABOLIC MIRROR.

18.17. Concave mirrors are sometimes used in the laboratory in order to measure the refractive index of liquids. Figure 18.17 shows a spherical mirror containing a few drops of liquid. The centre of curvature of the mirror is at C, but when the mirror contains liquid the centre of curvature appears to be at some other point C'. The apparent centre of curvature is located by means of a light pin, and the apparent radius of curvature and the real radius of curvature are measured. Let μ be the refractive index of the liquid. μ is given by the equation

$$\mu = \frac{\text{the real radius of curvature}}{\text{the apparent radius of curvature}}.$$

Let C'BA be the path of any ray from C' to the mirror at the point A, when liquid is in the mirror. This ray is refracted where it meets the liquid, and if LBM is the normal to the surface of the liquid at B,

$$\mu = \frac{\sin i}{\sin r} = \frac{\sin \lfloor C'BL}{\sin \lfloor ABM}.$$

Since C' is the apparent centre of curvature, the ray C'BA returns to C' by reflection along its own path. It therefore

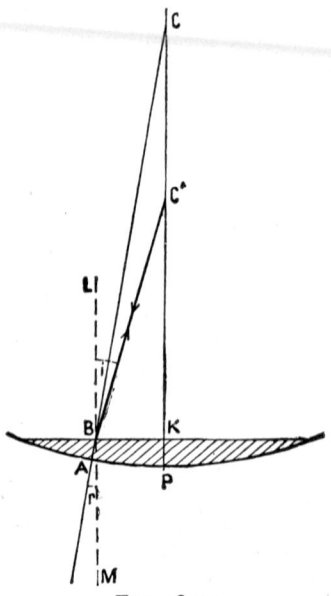

FIG. 18.17.

meets the mirror normally. The normal to the mirror at A is, however, the radius AC, so BA is part of this line; that is CBA is a straight line.

CP is parallel to LM,

$$\therefore \ \lfloor ABM = \lfloor ACP, \ \text{and} \ \lfloor C'BL = \lfloor BC'P$$

$$\therefore \ \mu = \frac{\sin \lfloor BC'P}{\sin \lfloor ACP}$$

$$\therefore \ \mu = \frac{BK}{BC'} \Big/ \frac{BK}{BC} = \frac{BK}{BC'} \cdot \frac{BC}{BK} = \frac{BC}{BC'}.$$

When only a few drops of liquid are used, and only a small portion of the mirror, BC is nearly equal to PC, and BC' to PC'

$$\therefore \ \mu = \frac{PC}{PC'} = \frac{\text{the real radius of curvature}}{\text{the apparent radius of curvature}}.$$

When the apparent radius of curvature is to be measured, the mirror must be placed horizontally so that the liquid in it does not run out. To avoid the troublesome setting of a light pin at a distance above the mirror a small right-angled prism may be used. The mirror is first clamped vertically, and its radius of curvature is measured in the ordinary way. It is now supported horizontally, the prism is placed at its centre, and a light pin is adjusted until the tip of its image lies at the tip of the pin (figure 18.18). The distance between the pin and

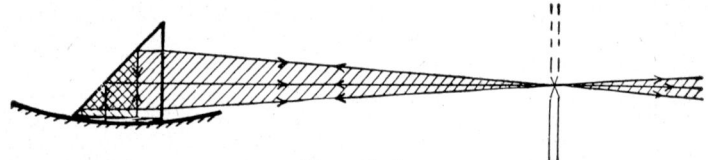

FIG. 18.18.

prism is measured. This distance is shorter than the radius of curvature, because part of the paths of rays travelling between the pin and mirror lies in the prism. By subtracting the distance between the pin and prism from the radius of curvature, we obtain the equivalent length of the ray paths in the prism. We may call this distance the " prism correction."

The prism is now removed, a few drops of liquid are placed in the mirror, and the prism is replaced. The light pin is moved until the tip of its image lies over the tip of the pin, and the distance between the pin and the prism is again measured. This distance is equal to the apparent radius of curvature with liquid in the mirror minus the prism correction, so the apparent radius of curvature is obtained by adding the prism correction to this third measurement.

EXAMPLES 18

1. Define *principal axis, pole, centre of curvature,* of a spherical mirror. Describe experiments to show how the image is formed by a concave mirror when the object is placed (*a*) farther from the

mirror than its principal focus, (b) nearer than the principal focus. Give diagrams to illustrate your answer.

2. Describe and explain with suitable diagrams what happens when (a) a broad beam of parallel rays, (b) a narrow beam of parallel rays, falls on a concave mirror.

3. Use the mirror formula $\frac{1}{v} + \frac{1}{u} = \frac{2}{r}$ to prove that a beam consisting of rays parallel to the principal axis of a concave mirror is brought to a focus at a point midway between the pole and the centre of curvature.

4. Deduce the mirror formula $\frac{1}{v} + \frac{1}{u} = \frac{2}{r}$, from the laws of reflection.

5. Draw a graph for a concave mirror of power 5D, plotting $\frac{1}{v}$ against $\frac{1}{u}$, and show how the power of the mirror could be deduced from such a graph.

6. Prove that, when a virtual image is formed by a concave mirror, the magnification m is given by the formula $m = \frac{v}{u}$.

7. The radius of curvature of a concave mirror is 20 cm. An object is placed 30 cm. from the mirror. Calculate the position of the image, and the magnification, and draw a diagram to illustrate your results.

8. A concave mirror of focal length 10 cm. forms an erect image 30 cm. from the mirror, and 5 cm. high. Find the position and size of the object, and show with a diagram drawn to scale how the image is formed.

9. The image formed by a concave mirror is virtual and magnified three times when the object is 8 cm. from the mirror. Where must the object be placed in order that the image should be real and magnified three times ?

10. An object 1 cm. high is placed 10 cm. from the pole of a convex mirror of radius of curvature 20 cm. Find the position and size of the image produced. Draw a diagram to scale to show how the image is formed.

11. A convex mirror of radius of curvature 1 ft. is used as a driving mirror and is 2 ft. distant from the eyes of the driver. A car 6 ft. high is 50 ft. distant from the mirror. Calculate the position and size of the image. Using this result draw a diagram showing the mirror, the image, and the eye of the driver, and find what width of mirror is required for the full height of the approaching car to be seen.

12. A plane mirror is substituted for the convex mirror in the previous problem. Draw a diagram (not to scale) showing the positions of the eye, the mirror, and the image of the approaching car, and by means of the properties of similar triangles find what width of mirror is required in this case. Compare this result with that of the previous problem, and draw any deductions you can from the results.

13. With the same scale for x and y, plot a graph for the equation $y = \dfrac{x^2}{4}$, using values of x between $+6$ and -6. The curve gives a section through a paraboloidal mirror whose principal focus is at the point $(0, 1)$. Draw a tangent to the curve at the point where $x = 5$, and draw a line from the principal focus to this point. The latter represents the path of a ray from the principal focus to the mirror. Using the fact that the angle of incidence is equal to the angle of reflection, find the path of the reflected ray, and discuss your result. Explain why paraboloidal mirrors are used for searchlights and motor headlamps.

School Certificate Questions

14. Draw diagrams to show how a concave mirror may be used to form (a) a real, (b) a virtual, image twice the size of the object. Assuming that the diameter of the moon is 2000 miles, and its distance from the earth is 240,000 miles, find the diameter of the image of the moon produced by a concave mirror of radius 100 ft. (C)

15. Explain, with the aid of a diagram, how a real image differs from a virtual image. An image four times as high as the object is formed on a screen by a concave mirror. If the distance of the object from the mirror is 60 cm., what is the distance of the image from the mirror? Find also the focal length of the mirror. (C)

16. Show with the aid of carefully drawn scale diagrams the formation of the image of an object placed 20 cm. from (a) a plane mirror, (b) a concave mirror of radius of curvature 25 cm., (c) a convex lens of focal length 25 cm. Give reasons for your construction in each case. (B)

17. (a) Explain the difference between a real and a virtual image. (b) Describe how the centre of curvature of a concave mirror may be found experimentally. State clearly the experimental operation and setting. Draw a ray diagram showing the paths of the various rays, and explain how you arrive at the conclusion that your method gives you the desired result. (c) A concave mirror of radius of curvature 10 cm. is to be used to form an upright image which is to be twice the length of the object. Find where the object must be placed and where the image will be formed. Give a scale ray diagram showing how the image is formed. (O)

18. State the laws of reflection of light and show by means of diagrams how these laws account for the formation of images by plane and spherical mirrors. An object placed 10 in. from a spherical mirror produces a virtual image 15 in. from the mirror. Find the radius of curvature of the mirror *either* by construction *or* calculation. State whether the mirror is convex or concave. (J)

19. A small object 2 in. in height is placed on the axis of a concave mirror 3 in. from its surface. If the mirror is of 4 in. focal length and an eye is situated 20 in. from the mirror near the axis, show by a diagram (quarter size) the pencils of light by which two points of the image are seen by the eye. (L)

20. Distinguish between a real and a virtual image. At what distance from an object should a concave mirror of 6 in. radius of curvature be placed to give an image magnified threefold when the image is (a) real, (b) virtual? Illustrate your answer by diagrams drawn to scale. (L)

21. Explain, with the help of sketches, why a convex mirror is to be preferred to a plane mirror of equal aperture for use as a driving mirror on a motor-car. Some drivers, however, use large plane mirrors in preference to small convex ones. Why? (J)

22. Define the *focal length* of a mirror or lens. Why are driving mirrors convex? A man 6 ft. high stands 16 ft. from the driving mirror of a car. If the radius of curvature of the mirror is 1 ft., how far from the mirror is the man's image and how high is it? Show on a diagram how the image is formed. (O.C)

23. Explain, with a diagram, how a concave mirror can produce both real and virtual images, and deduce the formula connecting the positions of the object and image with the focal length of the mirror. State any sign conventions you use. Find the distance from the face at which a concave shaving mirror must be held to give an image magnified twofold, if the radius of curvature of the mirror is 4 ft. (O.C)

24. Define "radius of curvature" and "focal length" of a concave mirror. Prove that the radius of curvature is twice the focal length. A concave mirror of focal length 12 in. forms an upright image three times the size of the object. Determine the position of the object. (O.C)

CHAPTER 19

THE PHOTOGRAPHIC CAMERA ; THE EYE ; THE OPTICAL LANTERN ; THE SEXTANT

19.01. The Photographic Camera.—Photographic plates and films and photographic papers are coated with a film of gelatine containing minute grains of silver bromide. This substance undergoes a chemical change when it is exposed to light, some of the silver bromide becoming converted into metallic silver. If a real image is formed on such a film or plate the chemical change is greatest at those points on the image which are most brightly illuminated, and these points correspond to bright portions of the object. The film or plate is then " developed." This process consists in placing it in a solution which reduces to metallic silver the rest of the silver bromide in those grains which have been affected by light, but has less action on the silver bromide in other grains. In this way the film is darkened at those points where the light produced chemical change. After removal from the developer, the film or plate is " fixed " by placing it in another solution (e.g. sodium thiosulphate solution) which dissolves the unchanged silver bromide, and thus prevents any further chemical changes when the film is again exposed to light. The picture thus formed is similar to the original image, except that the bright points on the image are dark on the film, and vice versa. Such a picture is called a " negative."

To obtain a print from the negative, the latter is placed on a piece of photographic paper and exposed to light. More light passes through those parts of the negative which are clear than through the darker portions, so the photographic paper undergoes chemical changes whose intensity is greatest at points where the negative is clear ; that is, at points which correspond to dark portions of the object photographed. Hence, when the paper is developed and fixed, it carries a picture of the object, and this picture is darkest where the object was darkest and lightest where the object was brightly illuminated. It therefore corresponds in appearance to the object, and is called a " positive " or " print."

The function of the camera is to produce a suitably illuminated, real, inverted image on the photographic plate or film. The simplest form of camera—the box type—consists of a light-tight box blackened on the inside to prevent the reflection of light from the sides to the film. The latter is held at one end of the box, and at the other end is an opening, behind which are a convex lens and a shutter. When the shutter is open light passes to the lens from objects outside, and the lens forms a real, inverted image on the film.

Let us suppose that the lens of such a box camera is of power 10D. The image of an infinitely distant object is formed at the principal focus of the lens, so a sharp image will be formed on the film if the film is in the focal plane of the lens ; *i.e.* the film must be 10·0 cm. behind the lens. The images of nearer objects will now be formed behind the film, and the " image " of such objects on the film will not be sharp, but slightly blurred. If the image formed by the lens is nearly on the film, however (within 0·1 cm. of it, say), the " image " on the film will be sufficiently sharp to give a satisfactory picture. Let us calculate how near the camera objects may be placed.

If the image is to be not more than 0·1 cm. behind the film, *v* must not be greater than 10·1 cm. Hence,

$$F = + 10\cdot00D$$
$$v = + 10\cdot1 \text{ cm.} = + 0\cdot101 \text{ metre.}$$

$$\frac{1}{v} + \frac{1}{u} = F$$

$$\therefore \frac{1}{0\cdot101} + \frac{1}{u} = 10\cdot00.$$

Whence $u = + 10\cdot10$ metres.

The object may be any distance greater than 10 metres from the lens, but if it is nearer than this, the image formed by the lens will be too much out of focus to give anything but a blurred picture. In practice the lens of a box camera is placed at such a distance from the film that objects at a certain distance—10 metres, say—are in focus. Distant objects are then slightly out of focus, but the camera may be used for taking photographs of such objects, and for objects a little less than 10 metres distant as well.

To obtain a sharp image of objects nearer the camera than
10 metres or so we may (*a*) use a more powerful lens, or (*b*)
move the lens and film farther apart. The first method is used
in certain types of box camera, but in more expensive cameras
the second method is used. In this case the lens and film-
holder are joined by flexible bellows (figure 19.01), and the lens
is moved to the correct distance before use. The correct position of the lens for an object at any given distance is calculated
by the camera manufacturer by means of the lens formula, and
a scale is engraved on the instrument showing where the lens
is to be placed. When the lens is correctly placed to photograph objects at any
given distance, objects at
other distances are out
of focus.

The amount of light
which reaches the film
must be carefully regu-
lated, and this may be
done by regulating the
time during which the
shutter of the camera is
open, or by introducing a
stop behind the lens.
The stop consists of a
piece of metal in which
a hole is cut, and by
using stops with holes of

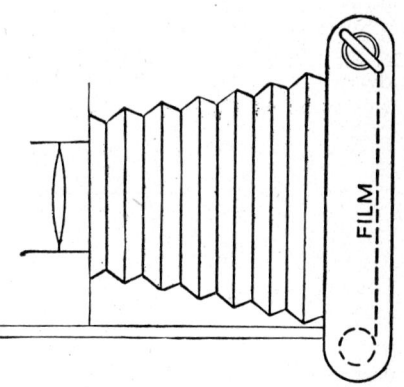

FIG. 19.01.—CAMERA.

various sizes, suitable amounts of light are allowed to reach
the film, whether the photograph is taken on a bright sunny
day or on a dull one.

19.02. The Pin-hole Camera.—A very simple camera, in which
no lens is used, can be made with a light-tight box. The film
or plate is placed at one end of the box, and a small pin-hole
at the other end allows light to enter. This light forms on the
film a real, inverted image of the objects in front of the pin-
hole. If the film and back of the box are removed and replaced
by a ground-glass screen, the image formed on the screen may
be seen from outside the box, when the camera is turned towards
a bright object, such as a lamp.

AB (figure 19.02) represents an object in front of the pin-hole E.

The rays which pass from A into the camera form a cone whose apex is at A, and these rays meet the back of the camera near the point C, where they produce a circular patch of light, slightly larger than the circular pin-hole through which they pass. If the pin-hole is very small, however, the cone of rays entering it from A is narrow, and in this case all these rays meet the back at points near C. Hence, all the light which passes from C to the eye comes in the first place from A ; in other words, C is the image of A. Similarly, corresponding to every other point on the object there is an image point on the back of the box, and the image CD must be thought of as the aggregate of all these points.

Since the pin-hole cannot be made infinitely small, the patch of light formed at C is never accurately a point, and this patch always overlaps to some extent the patches of light formed by rays from other points on the object near A. Hence, the image

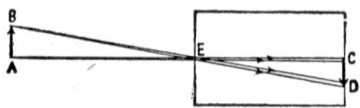

FIG. 19.02.—THE PIN-HOLE CAMERA.

formed by a pin-hole camera is never perfectly sharp. The smaller the pin-hole is, the sharper will be the image, for the patches of light decrease in size when the pin-hole decreases in size. A larger pin-hole gives a brighter, but less sharp, image.

In practice, the distance of the object from the pin-hole is much greater than that of the image. In this case, the width of the cone of rays from any point on the object is little greater at the image than at the pin-hole, and is nearly equal to its width at this point. This is true, whatever may be the distance between the photographic plate and the pin-hole, so although the image is never perfectly sharp, its sharpness alters little with changes in the distance between the pin-hole and photographic plate. Whether the plate is placed at C or at D [figure 19.03(a)], the rays passing from the object at A to the pin-hole at B affect the same area of the plate. Altering the distance of the plate makes little difference to the sharpness of the image, and the distance of the object also has little effect on its sharpness.

On the other hand, when a lens camera is focused to give a

sharp image of the object A at a photographic plate E [figure 19.03(b)], the image is sharp at this point only, and its sharpness decreases if the plate is moved in either direction to the position C or D. With the plate in either of these positions, the rays from A form a patch of light on the plate, and the size of this patch increases rapidly when the plate is moved to greater distances from E. The image thus becomes blurred. An object at one particular distance gives a sharp image on a plate at E, but if the plate is moved a short distance to bring an object at another distance into focus, the image of the first object becomes blurred. To sum up : *The images formed by a pinhole camera are equally sharp, whatever may be the distance of the objects ; the images formed by a lens camera are sharper than those given by the pin-hole camera if the object is correctly focused, but other objects at greater or smaller distances then form blurred images.*

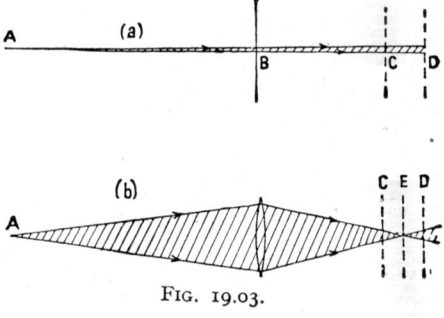

FIG. 19.03.

Let us call u the distance of the object AB from the pin-hole (figure 19.02), and v the distance of the image. The triangles EAB, ECD are similar.

$$\therefore \frac{CD}{AB} = \frac{EC}{EA} = \frac{+ v}{+ u}.$$

Hence, the magnification m produced by the pin-hole camera is given by the formula :

$$m = \frac{v}{u}.$$

The magnification is thus the same as would be produced by a lens camera, with a lens at E producing the image CD.

The image formed by a pin-hole camera is much fainter than that formed by a lens camera, because only a small fraction of the light from the object falls on the pin-hole, whereas a larger fraction falls on a lens. Hence, very long exposures are required to obtain photographs with a pin-hole camera, and if a street is photographed, the picture will show it as empty. During the time when they are present, vehicles reflect insufficient light to the film to affect it.

In summer, the gaps between the leaves of trees often act as pin-holes, and form numerous circular or elliptical images of the sun in the shade of the trees. The gaps are small compared with the distances of the sun and the ground from the leaves.

19.03. The Eye.—A horizontal section through the eye is shown in figure 19.04. On the outside is a tough, white, muscular coat S called the sclerotic.

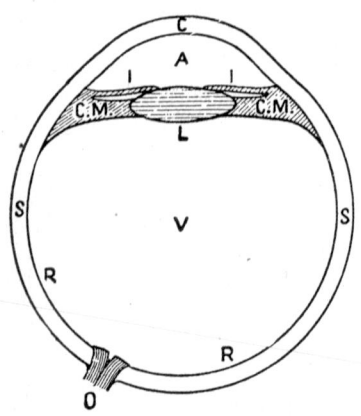

FIG. 19.04.—THE EYE.

A, aqueous humour; C, cornea; CM, ciliary muscle; I, iris; L, crystalline lens; O, optic nerve; R, retina; V, vitreous humour.

Part of this is visible as the white of the eye. At the front the muscular coat is transparent, and this part C, called the cornea, allows light to enter the eye. Behind the cornea is the iris I, which is the coloured portion. The iris serves as a stop to regulate the amount of light entering the eye. At its centre is a hole, the pupil, which appears black because light falling on it is not reflected, but passes through into the eye. In a dull light the iris draws back, enlarging the pupil, and allowing a bigger fraction of the light falling on the eye to enter it. In a strong light the pupil contracts.

The light which enters the eye falls upon the crystalline lens L, which forms a real, inverted image upon the retina R. The latter contains nerves which transmit messages to the brain by means of the optic nerve O, and enable the object whose image is formed on the retina to be " seen." Filling the space between the cornea and the lens is a transparent liquid A, called the aqueous humour, and the space between the lens and retina is filled with a jelly-like substance V called the vitreous humour. The aqueous humour and the vitreous humour press against the sclerotic and maintain the shape of the eye.

The lens of the eye corresponds to the lens of a camera, the iris to the stop, and the retina with its fine nerves to the sensitive film. Whereas the camera is usually focused by altering the relative positions of the lens and the film, the relative positions of the retina and the lens of the eye are fixed. How, then, are sharp images to be formed on the retina?

Instead of moving the lens relative to the retina, the eye produces sharp images by altering the power of the crystalline lens. It does so by means of the ciliary muscles CM which contract or relax to cause the crystalline lens to become thicker or thinner as required. When the eye views a near object, the crystalline lens is compressed, thickened, and rendered more powerful, and the image of the object is formed on the retina. When it looks at a distant object the ciliary muscles relax, the lens becomes thinner and less powerful, and the image is again formed on the retina.

There is a limit, however, to the amount by which the lens may be thickened. In a normal eye it may be made sufficiently powerful to form on the retina a sharp image of an object distant 25 cm. from the eye. If the object is nearer than at this least distance of distinct vision, the lens may be still further compressed to bring the image on to the retina again, but in doing so a severe strain is imposed on the eye muscles, and they can be kept in this state of strain for only a limited time. If the object is brought still nearer, no amount of strain renders the lens sufficiently powerful; the image is formed behind the retina, and the object appears blurred.

A normal-sighted person can thus see objects distinctly if they are at any distance from his eye between 25 cm. and infinity. This fact is sometimes expressed by saying that his *near point* is at 25 cm. and his *far point* is at infinity.

19.04. Two objects appear to the eye to be of equal lengths if they subtend equal angles at the eye. In figure 19.05 the

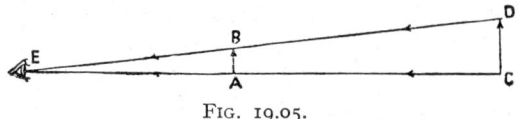

Fig. 19.05.

object AB subtends the angle BEA at the eye, and the object CD the angle DEC. Both of these objects appear, from the position of the eye, to be of the same size, because the object

AB just covers CD ; that is, it cuts off all the rays which travel from CD in the direction of E. The two objects subtend equal angles at the eye.

The triangles ABE, CDE are similar.

$$\therefore \frac{AB}{CD} = \frac{EA}{EC}.$$

Hence, *if two objects appear to be the same size, their lengths must be in the same ratio as their distances from the eye.*

19.05. Although a normal-sighted person can see objects at any distance from his eye between 25 cm. and infinity, many people are unable to do this, and the defects of their eyes have to be overcome by the use of spectacles. We have now to consider briefly some of the common defects of the eye.

Hypermetropia, or **Long Sight.**—Persons suffering from this defect of vision are not able to see farther than people with normal sight, for the latter are able to see clearly objects at infinity. The name " long sight " is given to this defect of the eye because persons suffering from it are able to see objects, *only* if their distances are sufficiently great. Objects nearer the eye than a certain point called the *near point* appear blurred and indistinct, although distant objects can be seen clearly. The defect arises from the fact that the lens of the eye is not sufficiently powerful, and the image of near objects is formed behind, instead of on, the retina.

A long-sighted person whose near point is at 100 cm. (say) is unable to read a book placed at 25 cm. from his eye, because the print appears blurred. He may, of course, place the book at 100 cm. from his eye and read it from this distance, because the print then appears sharp. There are two objections to his doing so, however. In the first place he will probably find it uncomfortable to hold the book at this distance, and will be tempted to bring it nearer and strain his eyes. In the second place the size of the print is chosen so that it can be easily read at a distance of 25 cm., and it will certainly appear too small for comfort when viewed from a distance of 100 cm.

Let us see whether we can find suitable lenses for the spectacles for this long-sighted man. If we provide him with lenses which form an image at 100 cm. of a book held at 25 cm., he will at least be able to see the image clearly, and, as we shall show, the print will also appear the correct size. Since he will wear his spectacles close to his eyes it will be sufficient if the lenses chosen are such that with the book at 25 cm. from the *lenses* the image is 100 cm. from them. Hence, when $u = + 25$ cm., v must be $- 100$ cm.

$$u = + 25 \text{ cm.} = + 0.25 \text{ metre}$$
$$v = - 100 \text{ cm.} = - 1.00 \text{ metre.}$$

$$\frac{1}{v} + \frac{1}{u} = F$$

$$\therefore \frac{1}{(- 1.00)} + \frac{1}{(+ 0.25)} = F.$$

Whence $F = + 3$D.

The lenses required are convex lenses of power 3 dioptres. Such lenses cause the rays from a point on the object to enter the eye as though they came from a point 100 cm. distant, and the crystalline lenses of the eye are sufficiently powerful to focus such rays on the retina.

The image is 100 cm. from the lens, and the object is 25 cm. distant, so the ratio of their distances is $\frac{4}{1}$. The magnification produced by the lens is:

$$m = \frac{v}{u} = \frac{- 100}{+ 25} = - \frac{4}{1}.$$

Hence, the image is four times as distant as the book, but it is also four times as large. In other words, the apparent size of the image is equal to the apparent size of its object when the latter is 25 cm. from the eye, so the print, as seen through the spectacles, will appear the same size as it does when a normal-sighted person holds the book 25 cm. from his eye.

19.06. Myopia, or Short Sight.—A person suffering from this defect of vision is able to see near objects clearly, but objects more distant than a certain point, called his *far point*, appear blurred and indistinct. The lens of the eye is, in this case, too powerful, and the image of distant objects is formed in front of the retina instead of on it.

Let us suppose that the far point for such a person is 50 cm. from his eye. What lenses does he require for his spectacles? He wishes to see distant objects clearly, so the lenses chosen must make objects at infinity appear to be 50 cm. from his eyes ; that is, the lenses must form the image of an infinitely distant object at a distance of 50 cm.

$$u = + \infty$$
$$v = - 50 \text{ cm., or } - 0\cdot50 \text{ metre.}$$

$$\frac{1}{v} + \frac{1}{u} = F$$

$$\therefore \frac{1}{- 0\cdot50} + \frac{1}{\infty} = F.$$

Whence $F = - 2D$.

Hence, the lenses required are concave lenses of power 2 dioptres. As before, it may be shown, by considering an object at a definite distance, that the object will appear its natural size when viewed through the spectacles, for although the image is closer than the object its size is also smaller.

19.07. Presbyopia.—As people grow older their eyes lose their power of *accommodation*, or ability to vary the focal length of the eye lens. They are then able to form on the retina a clear image of infinitely distant objects, but cannot see nearer objects clearly. They are, therefore, long-sighted, and require reading spectacles, of the kind prescribed for a long-sighted man, whose near point is at the same distance as their own. With such spectacles a man suffering from hypermetropia is able to see objects at a distance of one or two metres, by altering the power of his eye lenses. A man suffering from presbyopia, however, may be unable to vary the power of his eye lenses sufficiently to do this, and he therefore requires a second pair of spectacles to enable him to see objects at such distances.

19.08. Astigmatism.—When light from a point falls on a cylindrical lens, the light is not refracted to a single point, as is the case with a spherical lens, but converges to points on a straight line perpendicular to the principal axis of the lens. If, however, two cylindrical lenses are crossed, as shown in figure 19.06, with the direction of greatest curvature of one lens at right angles to that of the other, the combination acts as a spherical lens, and forms a point image of a point object.

Astigmatism is not caused by a defect of the eye lens, but of the cornea. In the case of persons suffering from astigmatism the cornea is not curved equally in all directions. Light entering the eye is refracted at the cornea as well as at the eye lens, and light entering such an eye reaches the lens as though it had passed through a cylindrical lens. The defect is overcome by placing in front of the eye a cylindrical spectacle lens, whose curvature is greatest in a direction at right angles to that in which the cornea is most curved.[1]

19.09. The Optical Lantern.— The lantern is used to form upon a screen brightly illuminated images of a slide, and the lens A (figure 19.07) is that which produces the image. This lens is called the objective. The slide and screen must, of course, be placed at the correct distances on either side of the objective, but this adjustment is not, in itself, sufficient to render the image visible. Of the light which falls on the lantern slide, only a small fraction is reflected

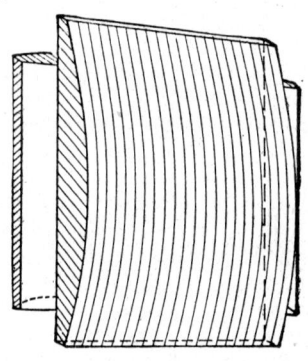

Fig. 19.06.

towards the objective and hence to the image, and only a small fraction of the light which does reach the screen is reflected to the eye. To render the image on the screen visible, an intense beam of light must pass from the slide to the screen.

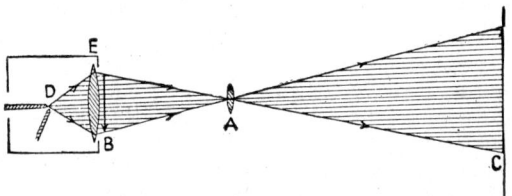

Fig. 19.07.—The Optical Lantern.

The beam of light is obtained by means of a powerful source of light D, and a condenser lens E. The function of this lens is to gather as much light as possible from that which is spreading out from the source, and to direct this light so that it passes first through the slide, and then through the objective to the screen. It must therefore be a convex lens, and it must be

[1] The earliest systematic treatise on the eye was written by Hunain ibn Ishaq in the ninth century. The Arabs made great advances in ophthalmology and optics.

large, and of short focal length. It must be large because it will then collect more light, and it must in any case be somewhat larger than the slide, because the whole of the slide must be illuminated by it. A small condenser would illuminate a part only of the slide. The condenser must direct the light which falls on it on to the objective, and for this purpose it is so placed that it forms an image of the source on the objective. Other things being equal, the shorter the focal length of the condenser, the nearer it must be placed to the source in order to form the image on the objective, and the greater will be the amount of light which it gathers.

To focus the lantern, the procedure is as follows : The source of light is placed in such a position that a sharp image of it is formed on the objective. A slide is placed upside down in the slide-holder, and the objective is moved until a sharp image of the slide is formed on the screen. This adjustment of the objective will probably have moved it away from the position of the image of the source, so the source is moved until its image again lies on the objective. The lantern is now ready for use.

Although the condenser is a large lens, it may be a cheap one, since it merely serves to concentrate light on the slide and objective, and need not form a clear image. The objective, on the other hand, must be a well-made lens, and is more expensive. It has to form a very much magnified image of the slide on the screen, and if the objective is not accurately made this image will be blurred and distorted. In practice, both the condenser and objective are double lenses. These double lenses act as the single lenses do in the theory explained above.

The optical arrangements of the cinema projecting lantern are similar to those of the lantern described. The pictures to be projected to the screen, however, are those on a film which passes in front of the condenser in the position occupied by the slide in the figure. About twenty pictures on the film pass in front of the condenser per second, and as each of these arrives in position, the film stops for an instant, and then passes on to the next picture. During the time when the film is moving a shutter cuts off the beam of light, but each time the film stops, the shutter is opened and the picture is projected to the screen. Hence, a series of images are formed at the screen, with an instant between each pair during which the film is not illuminated.

When the light passing from an object to the eye is suddenly shut off, the effect of the light upon the nerves of the retina does not cease instantaneously, but the object is still seen for a fraction of a second after light from it ceases to reach the eye. This phenomenon is called *the persistence of vision*. Owing to the persistence of vision the images projected to the cinema screen do not appear as distinct images separated by short intervals of time, but as a continuous picture which gradually alters.

19.10. ABC (figure 19.08) represents the path of a ray of light reflected from a plane mirror at B. BD is the normal to the mirror at B, so $\lfloor$ABD is the angle of incidence i, and the angle

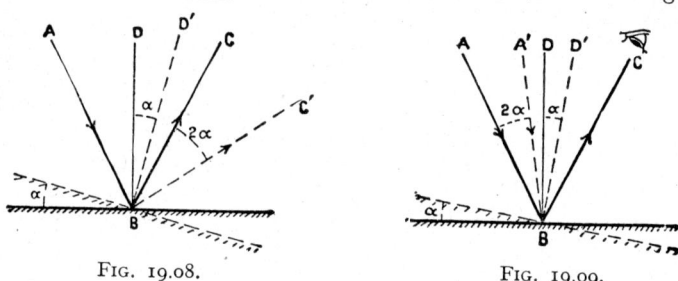

FIG. 19.08.   FIG. 19.09.

of reflection, $\lfloor$DBC, is equal to the angle of incidence. Hence, the angle ABC, which is the angle between the incident and the reflected ray, is equal to twice the angle of incidence ; *i.e.* $\lfloor$ABC = $2i$.

Let us suppose that the mirror is now turned about the point B through an angle α to the position shown by the dotted line. The normal to the mirror at B also turns through an angle α, and the angle of incidence increases by α and becomes $(i + \alpha)$. Hence, the angle between the incident and the reflected ray is now $2(i + \alpha)$; *i.e.* $\lfloor$ABC′ = $2(i + \alpha)$. The angle CBC′ is equal to the angle ABC′ minus the angle ABC.

$$\therefore \lfloor CBC' = 2(i + \alpha) - 2i = 2\alpha.$$

The angle CBC′ is the angle through which the reflected ray is turned when the mirror is turned through an angle α. Hence :
When an incident ray falls on a mirror from a given direction, and the mirror is turned through a given angle, the direction of the reflected ray is turned through an angle equal to twice that turned through by the mirror.

Similarly, it can be shown that if the eye receives rays reflected from a mirror in the direction BC (figure 19.09), then, on turning the mirror through an angle α, the direction of the incident ray (AB) changes by 2α (to the direction A′B).

19.11. The Sextant.—This instrument is used for measuring the angle between the directions of two distant objects. It may be used, for example, to measure the altitudes of the sun and stars, and is thus of use in determining the positions of ships at sea.

The arms A and B (figure 19.10) are rigidly fixed to the circular

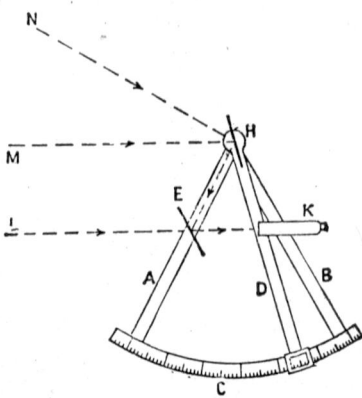

FIG. 19.10.—THE SEXTANT.

arc C, and the arm D is pivoted at the intersection of the arms A and B. A plane mirror H is attached to D, and another mirror E is attached to the arm A. The mirror E is silvered over half its surface only, so that the light which enters the telescope K is partly light reflected from the mirror, and partly light which comes from the direction of L.

When the arm D is turned so that the two mirrors are parallel, the ray MH from a distant object is reflected from both mirrors, and enters the telescope parallel to its original direction, and parallel also to the ray LE which passes from the object to the telescope through the unsilvered portion of E. Consequently, the distant object, and its image seen by reflection, appear to be in the same direction, and if the horizon is viewed from a ship the appearance will be that shown in figure 19.11. The two portions of the horizon, seen directly and by reflection, form one continuous line.

If the arm D is rotated until the image of a star in the direction N is formed in the direction of the horizon, the ray incident on the mirror H comes from a direction making an angle MHN with that of the rays incident from the horizon, and to reflect this ray along the path HEK the mirror H and the arm D must have been turned through an angle equal to half the angle MHN. Thus the altitude of the star is double the angle turned through by the arm D. The arm D carries a vernier which moves over

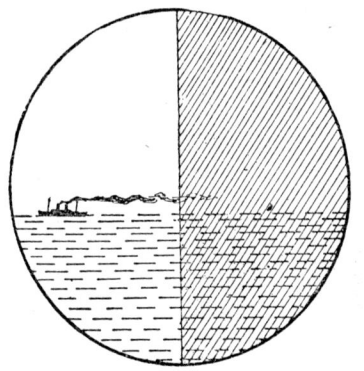

FIG. 19.11.—THE APPEARANCE OF THE HORIZON WHEN VIEWED THROUGH A SEXTANT HELD IN A VERTICAL PLANE.

a scale on C, and this scale is graduated to measure altitudes directly, each half-degree on the scale being marked as one degree.

EXAMPLES 19

Diagrams should be used to illustrate answers where possible.

1. Describe the action of the photographic camera. The lens of a camera is of power 12D. At what distances must the film be placed in order to photograph objects at distances of infinity, 10 metres, and 1 metre respectively? Explain why a single-lens box camera can be used for taking photographs of objects at any distance beyond 10 metres.

2. Explain what is meant by *short sight*, and how the defect of vision arises. The far point of a short-sighted man is at 30 cm. from his eyes. What lenses does he require in his spectacles to enable him to see distant objects?

3. How is the defect of vision called *long sight* caused? The near point of a long-sighted man is at 75 cm. from his eyes. What lenses does he require in his spectacles to enable him to read a book placed 25 cm. from his eyes?

4. The near point of a short-sighted man is at 15 cm. from his eyes. What lenses should be provided for his reading spectacles, if a book held 25 cm. distant is to appear to him as if at his near point?

K

5. What is *presbyopia*? A man suffering from presbyopia has his far point at 100 cm. and his near point at 50 cm. What lenses are required for his spectacles, (a) for reading, (b) for viewing distant objects?

6. Explain what is meant by *astigmatism*, and how this defect of vision arises. How is astigmatism overcome?

7. Give an account of the optical lantern. Explain what functions the objective and condenser lenses serve, and what kind of lenses are required.

8. Describe the sextant, and explain its action.

SCHOOL CERTIFICATE QUESTIONS

9. Explain with a diagram the optical system of a normal eye. The shortest distance of distinct vision for a certain person is 55 cm. What kind of spectacle lenses will he require and what must be their focal length in order that he may read in comfort a book at a distance of 25 cm.? (O.C)

10. Briefly describe " long sight " and " short sight " and explain how lenses are used to remedy these defects. Why do people who have had normal vision need glasses as they get older? (L)

11. Explain the action of the lens of the eye in vision and show how objects at different distances can be seen clearly. To what are short sight and long sight due, and how can they be overcome? (L)

12. Explain, with the aid of a diagram, the construction of a single-lens camera. Using a given camera it was found that in order to take a photograph of a distant object the photographic plate had to be at a distance of $7\frac{1}{2}$ in. from the lens. How far must the plate be from the lens when the object is only 10 ft. in front of the lens, and what will be the length of the image on the plate if the object is 3 ft. high? (J)

13. Describe a pin-hole camera, and explain how the definition of the image formed depends on the size of the pin-hole. The length of a pin-hole camera from front to back is 10 in. What will be the size of the image of an object 6 ft. high which is placed symmetrically with regard to the camera, and 30 ft. from it? (J)

14. Describe an experiment showing that light travels in straight lines. What is a pin-hole camera? Explain how images are formed in it, and show how their nature is changed by (a) altering the distance of the object, (b) increasing the size of the hole. (J)

15. Explain with the aid of a diagram the optical principle involved in the projecting lantern. Explain clearly the necessity of the condensing lens. A lantern has a focusing lens of focal length 11 in., and the distance of the slide from this lens is 12 in. Find how far the screen must be from the focusing lens. If the slide is a square of side 3 in., find the area of the image. (O)

CHAPTER 20

MICROSCOPES AND TELESCOPES

20.01. The simple microscope is merely a magnifying-glass or convex lens. When a small object is placed close to such a lens à virtual, erect, enlarged image is formed, and this may be viewed by means of an eye placed close to the lens (figure 20.01).

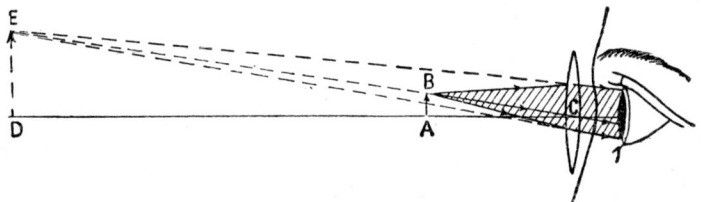

FIG. 20.01.—THE MAGNIFYING-GLASS OR SIMPLE MICROSCOPE.

The image DE is several times larger than its object AB. It is, however, several times as far away as the object. Will it appear larger ? The angles at the centre of the lens subtended by the object and image are equal. Since the eye is placed close to the lens, the angles subtended by the object and image at the eye are nearly equal also. In other words, the object appears nearly the same size as the image. If this is the case, of what use is the lens ?

The image can be seen clearly if it is at 25 cm. from the eye, and we may suppose that the image DE is 25 cm. distant. The object AB is then too close to the eye to be seen distinctly, and if the object were viewed without the aid of the lens, it would have to be moved back at least as far as the line DE, and it would then appear much smaller. Hence, *the lens enables the object to be placed nearer to the eye than would otherwise be possible.* When the lens is used an enlarged image at a distance of 25 cm. is viewed, instead of a small object at the same distance.

When using a simple microscope, the eye is placed close to

the lens, and since the image is to be formed at 25 cm. from the eye, it is nearly 25 cm. from the lens also. Whatever lens is chosen the image is to be at 25 cm. from the eye, so the lens which gives the image whose apparent size is greatest will be that lens which produces the greatest magnification when the image is 25 cm. from it. Let F be the power of a given lens in dioptres.

$$\frac{1}{v} + \frac{1}{u} = F.$$

Multiplying this equation throughout by v, we obtain:

$$1 + \frac{v}{u} = Fv$$

$$\therefore \quad \frac{v}{u} = Fv - 1.$$

$\frac{v}{u}$ is equal to the magnification m produced by the lens.

$$\therefore \quad m = Fv - 1.$$

When the lens is used as a simple microscope the image is to be at 25 cm. from the lens, so $v = -25$ cm., or $-\frac{1}{4}$ metre. Hence, in this case,

$$-m = \frac{F}{4} + 1.$$

The magnification produced by the lens when used as a simple microscope is one plus one-quarter of its power in dioptres. The magnification is greatest when F is as great as possible.

This fact may be verified using lenses in the laboratory. The lens whose magnification is to be measured is set up at the end of a desk, and a scale is placed 25 cm. from the lens. Another piece of scale is placed near the lens, and is moved until its image lies on the first scale, as shown by the no-parallax test. The adjustment is carried out by viewing the nearer piece of scale through the lens with one eye, and the distant scale round the edge of the lens with the other eye. When there is no parallax between the image and the distant scale, the required magnification is equal to the number of divisions of the scale corresponding to a division of the image.

20.02. There is a limit to the magnification which can be produced by a simple microscope because a powerful lens must be thick in comparison with its diameter, and very thick lenses do not produce sharp images. Much greater magnification can be obtained with a **compound microscope,** however. A simple type of compound microscope is shown in figure 20.02.

A powerful convex lens O, called the objective, is placed a little more than its focal length distant from the object AB, and the rays from AB form a real, inverted image CD. This image is much larger than the object, and is a little nearer the powerful convex lens E than the principal focus of the latter. The lens E is called the eyepiece. It serves as a simple microscope, and forms a virtual image FH of the image CD. It is this image which is viewed by the eye. The compound microscope thus magnifies in two steps, and if the magnifications produced are m_1 and m_2, the image CD is m_1 times the size of the object, and FH is m_2 times the size of CD ; it is therefore $(m_1 \times m_2)$ times the size of the object.

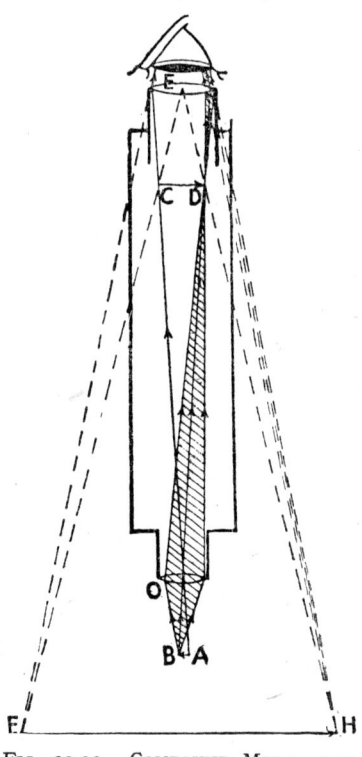

In drawing figure 20.02, the lines CE and DE, from C and D to the centre of the eyepiece, have been used. It is as well to remember, however, that there are no actual rays from C and D to the centre of the eyepiece, and that these lines are construction lines and nothing more. The paths of rays from the point B on the object to the eye are shown in the diagram.

FIG. 20.02.—COMPOUND MICROSCOPE.

The final image FH is formed at a distance of 25 cm. from the eye. Its position is *not* adjusted by moving the objective and eyepiece separately, but by moving the tube, which carries the

lenses, nearer to, or farther from, the object. As the tube is
moved towards the object, the image CD moves nearer to the
eyepiece, and this movement brings the final image FH closer
as well.

The eyepiece merely serves as a magnifying-glass, and to
obtain good magnification it must have a short focal length.
The objective must also be a powerful lens. The magnification
produced by this lens is equal to the ratio of the distances of
CD and AB from the objective. This ratio cannot be made
large by making the distance of CD large, because CD must lie
in the tube at a short distance from the eyepiece. The magnification produced by the objective can therefore be made large
only by making the distance between the object AB and the
objective small. The distance of the object must, however, be
greater than the focal length of the objective if the latter is to
produce a real image, so the magnification can only be large
if the focal length of the objective is small.

With compound microscopes, magnifications up to a thousand
diameters may be obtained, so that the area of the image may be a
million times that of the object. Since the light from the object
appears, after passing through the microscope, to come from
the image, the latter will appear very faint unless the object is
brightly illuminated. The object is therefore placed upon a
stand where it is illuminated by focusing light on it by means
of a concave mirror.

20.03. The Astronomical Telescope.—This is the simplest
type of telescope. For simplicity, only the rays from the top
of the object are shown in figure 20.03. These rays, coming
from the object at a great distance, meet the objective lens O
as a set of nearly parallel rays. If the object is large, however,
and the telescope is directed towards the middle of the object,
rays from the top of the object do not enter the telescope in the
direction of its principal axis, but are inclined to it at a small
angle. If the top of the object lies on the line CA, this angle
is the angle ACB. Such rays are brought to a focus at L, a
point near the focal plane of the objective. The real inverted
image KL, formed by rays from different points on the upper
half of the object, is viewed through the eyepiece E. This is a
short-focus convex lens used as a magnifying-glass, and forms a
virtual image MN of the image KL.

This image MN is *not* necessarily larger than the distant object.

Let us suppose that the objective O has a focal length of 1 metre, and that the telescope is used to view the moon, which is 4×10^8 metres distant. Considering the image KL we have, $u = + 4 \times 10^8$, $v = + 1$, so the magnification produced by the objective is $+ \dfrac{1}{4 \times 10^8}$; that is, this image is $\dfrac{1}{4 \times 10^8}$ times the size of the moon. The eyepiece forms an image which can

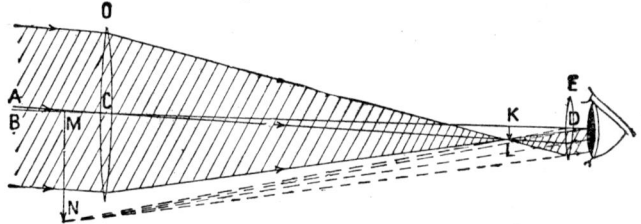

FIG. 20.03.—ASTRONOMICAL TELESCOPE.

be seen clearly if the image MN is 25 cm. or more from the eye. If it is 25 cm. distant the magnification produced by the eyepiece is,

$$- m = \frac{F}{4} + 1.$$

Assuming the eyepiece to have a power of 40D the magnification produced by it is $\left(\dfrac{40}{4} + 1 \right) = 11$ times. Hence, the image MN is $\left(\dfrac{1}{4 \times 10^8} \times 11 \right)$ times the size of the moon, or about one forty-millionth the size of the object. Nevertheless, even in this case the image formed by the telescope *appears* forty times as large as the moon does when viewed by the naked eye, because the image is so much closer.

It is possible to see the image MN clearly, provided this image is formed at any distance from the eye between 25 cm. and infinity, and the telescope is often used in such a way that the final image is formed at an infinite distance. This is the case when the eyepiece is drawn back until it is its focal length distant from the image KL, and the telescope is then said to be in *normal adjustment.* Hence, for a telescope in normal adjustment the distance CK is f_o, where f_o is the focal length of the objective, and the distance KL is f_e, the focal length of the eyepiece.

The power, or magnifying power, F, of the telescope is the ratio

$$\frac{\text{the angle subtended by the image at the eye}}{\text{the angle subtended by the object at the eye}},$$

the angles being measured when both the object and image are infinitely distant. Since the angles subtended at the eye by the image and the object are a measure of the apparent sizes of the image and object, the power of the telescope is a measure of the apparent magnification produced by it.

Referring again to figure 20.03 : The angle subtended by the final image MN at the eye is the angle MDN ; that subtended by the object is equal to the angle ACB.

$$\therefore F = \frac{|\text{MDN}}{|\text{ACB}}$$

But

$$|\text{MDN} = |\text{KDL, and } |\text{ACB} = |\text{KCL}$$

$$\therefore F = \frac{|\text{KDL}}{|\text{KCL}}.$$

Both of these angles are in practice small ; they are exaggerated in the figure in order to obtain a clear diagram. The ratio of two small angles is very nearly equal to the ratio of the tangents of the angles.

$$\therefore F = \frac{\tan |\text{KDL}}{\tan |\text{KCL}}$$

$$\therefore F = \frac{\text{LK}}{\text{KD}} \Big/ \frac{\text{LK}}{\text{CK}} = \frac{\text{CK}}{\text{KD}}.$$

But CK $= f_o$, and KD $= f_e$, when the telescope is in **normal** adjustment.

$$\therefore F = \frac{f_o}{f_e}.$$

In words, **the power of an astronomical telescope is equal to the ratio of the focal length of its objective to the focal length of its eyepiece.** To produce an image which appears large compared with its object, the objective lens should be of long focal length, and the eyepiece of short focal length. That is, the power of the eyepiece should be as large as possible, and the power of the objective should be small.

The eyepiece of a telescope need only be of small size. It should be large enough to cover the pupil of the eye, but need not be much larger than this, since any light which does not pass into the eye is lost. The objective, on the other hand, must be a large lens, because it has to gather sufficient light to form a bright image. The image appears many times as large as its object, and it will appear correspondingly faint unless the objective is large. The largest objective yet made is that of the Yerkes telescope. The diameter of this lens is 40 in., its weight is several cwt, and it has a focal length of 60 ft. The casting, grinding, and polishing of such enormous lenses, as well as their subsequent mounting and manipulation, present enormous difficulties, and recent large astronomical telescopes have been of the reflecting type (see section 20.08).

The action of the astronomical telescope may be illustrated by the following laboratory experiment. A long-focus convex lens is set up facing an open window, and a sheet of ground glass is placed behind it, and moved until a sharp image is formed on the glass. This real, inverted image is viewed through a powerful convex lens placed less than its focal length from the glass, and directly behind it. The glass merely serves to show that a real image is formed by the objective, so it may now be removed. The image formed by the eyepiece is then seen more clearly, since the glass stopped some of the rays travelling from the objective to the eyepiece.

20.04. The objective of a telescope forms an inverted image

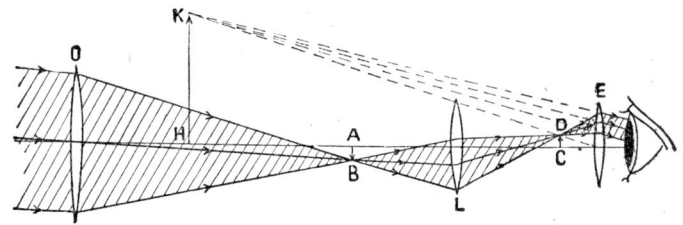

FIG. 20.04.—TERRESTRIAL TELESCOPE.

of the object, and since this image is not re-inverted by the eyepiece, the final image seen in an astronomical telescope is upside down. This is no disadvantage for the purposes of astronomy, but it would be troublesome if the telescope were used to view objects on the surface of the earth. Accordingly in the **terrestrial telescope** (figure 20.04) an extra lens is introduced to invert the image AB formed by the objective. The lens L is placed a distance equal to twice its focal length beyond AB, so the rays from AB emerge from L to form a real image CD. This image is at a distance from L equal to that of the image AB, and the lengths of these two images are equal. The extra lens L therefore produces no extra magnification, but merely inverts the image. The image CD is viewed in the ordinary way through the eyepiece, which forms the erect and virtual image KH.

20.05. The introduction of the extra lens in the terrestrial telescope increases its length considerably, and if it is to be carried about this is a serious disadvantage. Moreover, since some

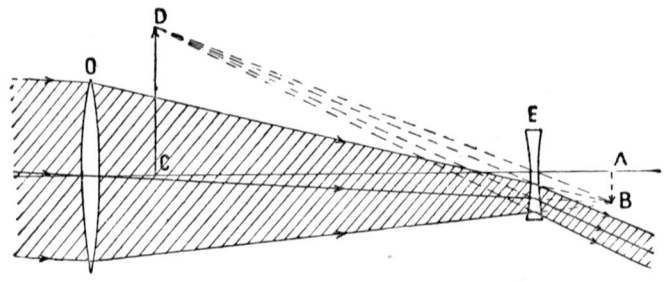

Fig. **20.05.**—Galilean Telescope.

light is reflected and lost at each glass surface, the extra lens renders the image fainter. In the type of telescope invented by Galileo these disadvantages are overcome by using a concave lens as eyepiece instead of a convex one.

Figure 20.05 illustrates the action of the **Galilean telescope.** The objective O causes the rays from the top of the object to converge towards the point B, and would form a real inverted image AB if the eyepiece E were not interposed. The eyepiece causes the rays which are converging towards B to diverge as though coming from the point D, so D is the virtual image of B, and CD is the virtual image of AB. The eyepiece must be placed at, or a little more than, its focal length distant from AB, and the eye is placed just behind the eyepiece.

Let us suppose that the eyepiece is placed a distance equal to its focal length from AB, and let its focal length be f. The image AB serves as object for the eyepiece, and its distance from the eyepiece is counted as negative since it is measured along lines which do not represent the paths of actual rays. f for a concave lens is negative, so in this case $u = f$.

$$\frac{1}{v} + \frac{1}{u} = \frac{1}{f}$$

$$\therefore \frac{1}{v} + \frac{1}{f} = \frac{1}{f}$$

$$\therefore \frac{1}{v} = 0, \text{ so } v = \pm \infty.$$

Hence, when the image AB is formed the focal length of the eyepiece beyond the eyepiece, the final image is formed at infinity, and the telescope is in normal adjustment.

The image AB is formed at a distance from the objective equal to the focal length of the objective, so the distance between the lenses is equal to the difference between their focal lengths. Hence, the Galilean telescope is much shorter than the terrestrial telescope. Opera glasses, and night glasses for use at sea, consist of two such telescopes placed side by side to enable both eyes to be used. In both of these cases it is essential that as little light as possible should be lost. The power obtainable with the Galilean telescope is smaller, however, than that which is possible with other forms. Moreover, the field of view is narrow. The rays leaving the eyepiece are deviated away from the principal axis of the telescope, so if the eye is placed on the axis to enable the part of the image at C to be seen, the rays which form the end of the image at D do not enter the pupil of the eye. Hence, only part of the image can be seen with the eye in the given position. Compare this with figure 20.03 where the rays from all parts of the image are deviated towards the axis, and thus into the pupil of the eye.

20.06. In field-glasses the astronomical form of telescope is used, but its length is decreased by using total reflection from glass prisms, so that the optical path of the rays in the instrument is longer than the actual length of the telescope. Two prisms are used in each tube of the field-glasses, and the prisms are placed in two planes at right angles, as shown in figure 20.06.

The image formed by the objective is inverted both laterally and vertically. Reflection at one of the prisms inverts the image laterally but not vertically, and reflection at the other prism inverts it vertically, but not laterally, so the final image formed is upright and the correct way round.

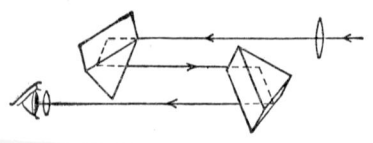

FIG. 20.06.—THE USE OF REFLECTING PRISMS IN FIELD-GLASSES.

20.07. The Periscope —The image formed by an astronomical telescope subtends a larger angle at the eye than does the object, and the rays from the top and bottom of the object are inclined to the axis of the instrument at a larger angle when they leave the telescope than when they enter it. If, however, the telescope is turned so that its eyepiece faces the object, the rays leaving the instrument are inclined at very small angles to the axis. This fact is used in the construction of periscopes.

The simplest form of periscope consists of two plane mirrors or reflecting prisms placed with their reflecting surfaces parallel as in figure 20.07 (a). Such an arrangement is of little practical use, however, for the objects which are visible through the periscope are only such as would be visible if the upper mirror were viewed from the position E'. The field of view is too small for practical purposes.

Figure 20.07 (b) shows the paths of the rays from a point on an object through a more useful form of periscope. The rays are reflected at the upper prism, and pass then through a short-focus lens to form a real image at P. The second lens, L, is a long-focus convex lens which is placed at a distance equal to its focal length beyond P, so that the rays from any point on the image P emerge from this lens as a parallel beam. The combination of the two lenses K and L acts as an astronomical telescope with its eyepiece K turned towards the object, so the rays leaving L emerge in directions inclined at small angles to the axis of the system. These rays can therefore pass down a long narrow tube without meeting the sides of the tube.

The rays reaching the bottom of the tube fall on the long-focus convex lens M as though coming from an object at infinity. Before they reach the point Q, where they would form an image, they are reflected by the lower prism to form the image R.

This image is viewed through the eyepiece N. The lenses M and N form an astronomical telescope with a prism between the objective and the eyepiece to deflect the rays, so the periscope consists essentially of two such telescopes with their objective lenses facing one another.

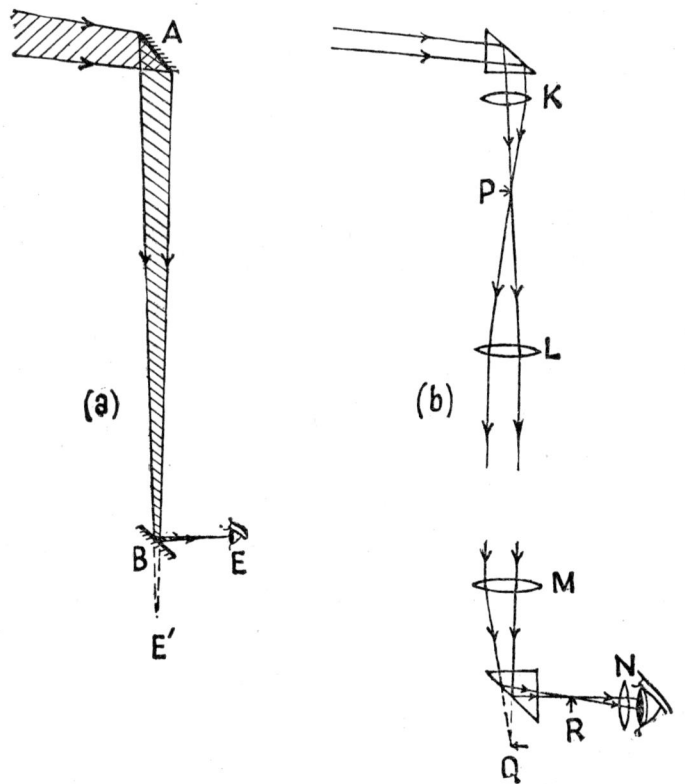

FIG. 20.07.—THE PERISCOPE.

20.08. Reflecting Telescopes.—Many difficulties are encountered in the manufacture of large lenses for astronomical telescopes. Apart from the difficulties of casting and supporting the huge blocks of glass required, the glass itself must be of the best quality and of extremely uniform composition. Moreover, as we shall see later, light of different colours is refracted by a lens by different amounts, and although this defect can be *reduced* by using a combination of two lenses of different kinds of glass to form the objective, light of different colours is brought to a focus at different points, and the image formed is never perfectly sharp in consequence. Finally, when the objective is very large an appreciable fraction of the light is absorbed in it, and when the reflection at the various glass surfaces is also taken into account, it is found that little more

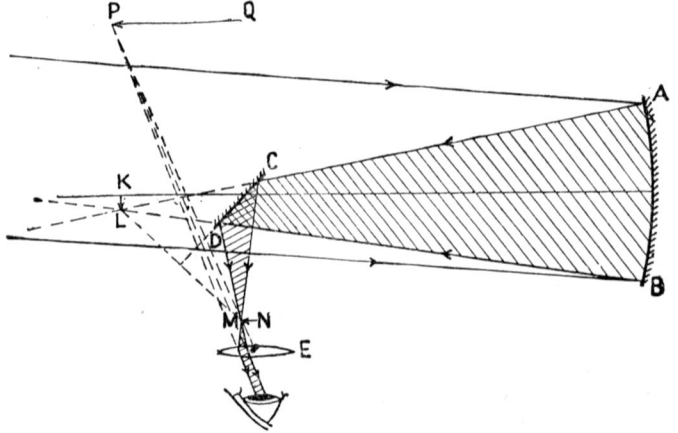

FIG. 20.08.—REFLECTING TELESCOPE USED IN THE NEWTONIAN FORM.

than half the light which falls on the objective passes through to form an image. Consequently, in the largest telescopes a concave mirror is used instead of a lens, in order to form the first real image, and the objective lens is dispensed with altogether.

Figure 20.08 shows one method of using such an instrument. Parallel rays of light from a point on a distant object are reflected by the concave mirror AB towards the point L in its focal plane. The concave mirror alone forms an image KL. To view this image directly, the eye would have to be placed to the left of KL in the diagram, and the head and body of the observer would then be in the path of the rays travelling from the object towards the mirror. To avoid this difficulty a plane mirror CD is placed as shown. In practice this mirror need not be large, and does not cut off much of the light travelling towards the concave mirror. The plane mirror forms an image of KL at MN, and this image is viewed by means of the eyepiece E, which forms a virtual image PQ of MN. In the figure, the paths of the rays from the top of the object are shown, and the shaded portion shows their paths after reflection at the mirror.

This method of using the telescope was first suggested by Newton, and when used in this way the telescope is said to be in the *Newtonian form*. The same concave mirror can, however, be used in other ways. Figure 20.09 shows the telescope

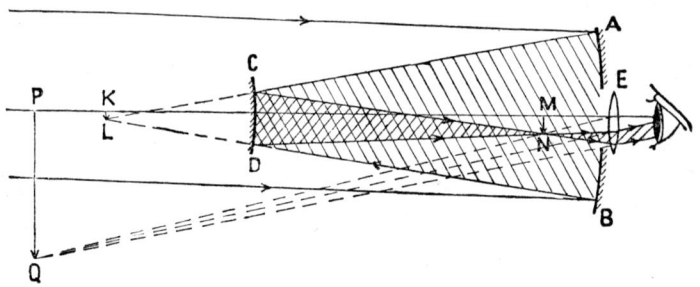

Fig. 20.09.—Reflecting Telescope used in the Cassegrainian Form.

used in the Cassegrainian form (so called after N. Cassegrain, a seventeenth-century physicist of Chartres). In this case the plane mirror is replaced by the convex mirror CD, and the latter forms an image MN, which is viewed through a hole in the large mirror by means of the eyepiece E. This lens forms the virtual image PQ. The concave and convex mirrors of a telescope used in the Cassegrainian form are equivalent as a combination to a single concave mirror of longer focal length than the actual mirror. The power of a reflecting telescope is equal to the ratio of the focal length of the mirror to that of its eyepiece; so by using the telescope in the Cassegrainian form its power is increased, and greater magnification is obtained. This is not always an advantage, because if the magnification is large the image will appear correspondingly faint. It is therefore an advantage to be able to use a given telescope in either of the two forms and this is done by making the small plane and convex mirrors interchange-able.

The largest reflector at present in use is that at Mount Wilson Observatory, California. The diameter of the concave mirror is 100 in. and has a focal length of 42 ft., but by using the tele-scope in the Cassegrainian form its effective focal length may be increased to 134 ft.

20.09. The manufacture of a large telescope mirror presents so many important applications of physics that it will not be out of place to consider it briefly here.

The glass for the disc from which the mirror is to be made must be uniform, and should have a small coefficient of expan-sion. The mirror is ground with an accuracy of one-millionth of an inch, and if any considerable expansion of part of the disc occurs, the correct shape of the mirror will not be maintained. The disc must also be perfectly rigid, and must therefore be thick. The largest mirror yet made has a diameter of 200 in., and if such a mirror were cast as a solid block its thickness would have to be 33 in. to ensure the necessary rigidity, and its weight would then be 40 tons. Such a mirror would be unnecessarily heavy, and the actual disc, weighing 18 tons, has been cast with a ribbed structure (see figures 7.02 and 7.03). The glass can then be made thinner without loss of rigidity, and since the thinner glass takes up the temperature of its surroundings more readily, the ribbed structure will also reduce to a minimum the strains caused when part of the disc expands more than other parts.

The glass is poured into its mould from huge ladles, and during this process it is impossible to avoid introducing air bubbles into the glass. These bubbles expand owing to the high tem-perature, and unless they are removed they leave " blow-holes." To remove the bubbles, the glass, after pouring, is reheated to a temperature of 1350° C., when it is sufficiently fluid to allow the bubbles to escape. It is now allowed to cool to 800° C., at which temperature it is sufficiently solid for removal to the annealing furnace. Here its temperature is kept constant at 500° C. for two months to remove strains set up during the cooling, and it is then cooled to room temperature at a rate of less than a degree per day. This slow cooling allows the disc to cool as a whole, and prevents the strains which would be set up if some parts cooled more rapidly than others.

The disc is now ready for grinding to its required shape. The mirror surface is ground by means of an iron tool (see figure 20.11), whose lower surface is convex and of the radius of curvature required for the mirror. Wet carborundum powder covers the mirror disc and performs the abrasion, smaller and smaller grains being used as the grinding approaches completion.

[*By courtesy of The Corning Glass Works.*

FIG. 20.10.—POURING THE GLASS FOR THE DISC OF THE 200-IN. MIRROR.

When the desired shape has been nearly attained, grinding is stopped and polishing commences. The polishing tool (see figure 20.13) carries numerous blocks of pitch to which the rouge used in polishing adheres. The grinding and polishing may be performed only slowly to allow the heat generated by friction to escape, and the preparation of the surface of the 200-in. reflector required three years.

The final process of polishing to shape is known as "figuring," and this is by far the most difficult of all. It consists first of preparing a surface which is accurately spherical, and then of

[By courtesy of Sir Howard Grubb, Parsons & Co.

FIG. 20.11.—GRINDING A 74-IN. MIRROR.

[By courtesy of Sir Howard Grubb, Parsons & Co.

FIG. 20.12.—GRINDING THE EDGE OF A 74-IN. MIRROR.

Note the central hole to permit the use of the telescope in the Cassegrainian form.

hollowing out the surface near the centre until the mirror is a paraboloid of revolution. During this stage frequent tests are required to see that polishing is bringing the surface nearer to the desired shape, the necessary adjustments of the polishing tool being made by cutting away pieces of pitch.

[*By courtesy of Sir Howard Grubb, Parsons & Co.*

FIG. 20.13.—THE HARTMANN DISC IN POSITION IN FRONT OF THE 74-IN. MIRROR.
The polishing tool is shown above.

The chief tests applied to the mirror are the Foucault knife-edge test, and the Hartmann test. If the mirror surface is spherical, the rays of light from a point A near its centre of curvature are caused by reflection to pass through a second point B as shown in figure 20.14. If, therefore, a knife edge C is slowly moved across the path of the rays at this point, the rays from all points on the mirror are cut off at the same instant, so the *whole* mirror darkens simultaneously. If no point can be found at which this occurs, the mirror is not truly spherical, and the positions of the shadows when the knife edge is moved into position indicate which parts of the mirror require further polishing. When the mirror is parabolized, different zones, from the centre outwards, must have increasing radii of curvature, and the test is applied to each zone separately by shielding the others with a wooden screen.

In the Hartmann test, the actual paths of rays reflected from the mirror are measured. To do this the mirror is covered with a screen containing holes (figure 20.13), and light is directed

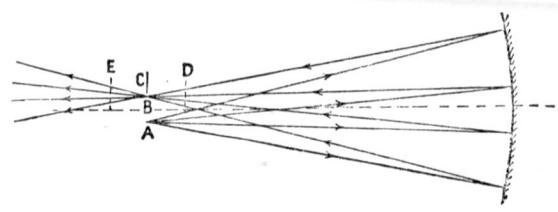

FIG. 20.14.

from a point source at A (figure 20.14), towards the mirror. Photographic plates are placed, first as shown by the dotted line D, and then at E. The rays returning from the various holes give patterns on these plates, and a comparison of the series of dots on the two plates enables the actual paths of the reflected rays to be calculated.

When the figuring is completed, the mirror is silvered on its concave surface, and it is then ready for use.

EXAMPLES 20

1. Describe with the aid of a diagram the use of a convex lens as a simple microscope. Calculate the magnification produced by a lens so used, the focal length of the lens being 5 cm.

2. Describe the construction of the astronomical telescope, and show by means of a diagram how the image is formed.

3. Prove that for an astronomical telescope in normal adjustment the power of the instrument is equal to the focal length of the objective divided by that of the eyepiece. Explain why an astronomical telescope is unsuitable for viewing objects on the earth. How would you modify the telescope for the latter purpose?

4. Show by means of a diagram how the Galilean telescope works. What are the advantages and disadvantages of this instrument, as compared with other types of telescope?

5. A small object is placed 5 cm. from the longer face of a right-angled isosceles prism, and parallel to this face. Find the positions of the images formed, neglecting any *refraction* at the glass-air surface, and use your result to explain the use of prisms in field-glasses.

6. A simple periscope consists of two parallel plane mirrors at the ends of a tube. Explain why such an instrument is of little practical use, and describe the construction and working of a more useful instrument.

7. With the aid of a suitable diagram describe the construction of the Newtonian type of reflecting telescope. What advantages does the reflecting telescope possess as compared with the refractor? Discuss the advantages and disadvantages of the Cassegrainian form of telescope.

8. You are provided with a concave spherical mirror of good quality. How would you test the accuracy with which its surface conforms to that of a true sphere?

School Certificate Questions

9. Explain the terms *principal axis, principal focus, focal length,* as applied to a convex lens, and describe how you would measure the focal length of such a lens. A convex lens is to be used as a simple magnifying glass by a person whose nearest distance of distinct vision is 12 in., and a magnification of 3 is to be produced. What must be the focal length of the lens? Illustrate your answer by a diagram to scale. (B)

10. An illuminated object of height 2 in. stands on the principal axis of a double-convex lens and at a distance of 14 in. from it; the lens has a focal length of 10 in. Obtain graphically the distance from the lens at which a screen must be placed to receive the image of the object, and determine the magnification produced. Explain by means of a sketch how such a lens, when held close to the eye, acts as a magnifying glass. (J)

11. Draw a diagram to show how a convex lens is used as a magnifying-glass. An object 1 cm. high is viewed through a convex lens of focal length 5 cm., and the image is found to be 6 cm. high and erect. Find the distances of the object and image from the lens. (O.C)

12. How would you arrange two lenses to make a simple form of compound microscope? Give a diagram showing how the images are formed. What is the purpose of a microscope, and how is this purpose achieved? (J)

13. A compound microscope is made of two thin convex lenses, each of focal length 1 in. The final image seen by the eye is formed 10 in. from the eyepiece. Find the distance of the object from the objective if the lenses are 8 in. apart. Sketch the path through the

instrument of a narrow pencil of light from a point on the object, and off the axis, to the eye. (C)

14. Explain, giving a sketch to show the path of rays from a distant object to the eye, the construction of a simple astronomical telescope. On what does the magnifying power of such a telescope depend ? (J)

15. How would you arrange two convex lenses of focal lengths 5 cm. and 15 cm. respectively so as to form a simple telescope ? Draw the course of a pencil of rays through the instrument, and show how to calculate its magnifying power when it is focused for infinity. (O.C)

16. Describe the Galilean telescope (converging object glass and diverging eyepiece) and illustrate your answer by means of a diagram. (O.C)

17. State the laws of reflection of light, and describe an experiment, which you have seen or done, to prove them. Draw and describe a simple form of periscope, and say how it works. (J)

CHAPTER 21

PHOTOMETRY

21.01. When light falls on the surface of any material and is absorbed, the temperature of the material rises. Light, like heat, is a form of energy, and the quantity of light absorbed at a surface might be found by measuring the heat produced by it.

The quantity of light which reaches each square centimetre of such a surface as that of a book illuminated by an electric lamp depends upon two factors—the angle at which the book

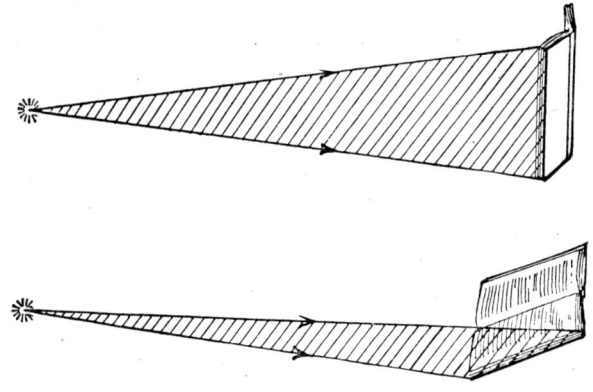

Fig. 21.01.

is held, and its distance from the lamp. As shown in figure 21.01 a greater quantity of light falls on the book when it is held at right angles to the rays, than when the rays meet the book at large angles of incidence.

How does the quantity of light reaching the book change when the distance of the source of light is increased? Let S (figure 21.02) represent a small source of light, from which rays emerge equally in all directions, and imagine two spheres with their centres at S, and having radii r_1 and r_2 respectively. If both spheres are perfectly transparent, all the light which passes through the inner sphere passes through the outer one also, so the quantities of light falling on the spheres per second are equal. Let Q be the number of units of energy emitted as light in each second by the source. The area of a sphere is $4\pi \times$ (radius)^2, so Q units of light energy fall upon $4\pi r_1^2$ units of area of the first sphere,

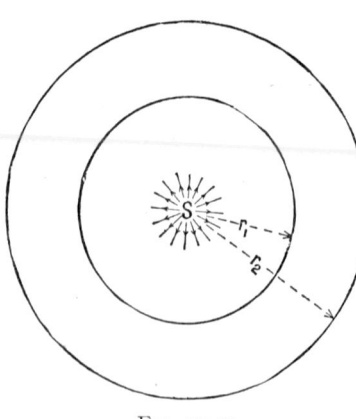

FIG. 21.02.

and $\dfrac{Q}{4\pi r_1^2}$ on each unit of its area. Similarly, the energy of the light falling on unit area of the other sphere per second is $\dfrac{Q}{4\pi r_2^2}$. Hence,

$$\frac{\text{the light energy falling on unit area of the first sphere}}{\text{the light energy falling on unit area of the other sphere}}$$

$$= \frac{Q}{4\pi r_1^2} \bigg/ \frac{Q}{4\pi r_2^2} = \frac{r_2^2}{r_1^2}.$$

In words : **The quantity of light energy falling on each unit of area varies inversely as the square of its distance from the source.**

21.02. The eye is unable, without the assistance of instruments, to estimate how much light energy falls upon various surfaces. If two pages of a book illuminated by a lamp are so held that one page receives more light than the other, the eye is quite unable to judge whether one page is receiving twice as much light as the other. It is able to estimate, however, whether the quantities of light received at two surfaces are *equal*, if the colours of the light are similar in the two cases. In this book we shall limit ourselves to the comparison of lights of the same type.

The intensity of illumination at a given surface is defined to be the quantity of light which falls on unit area of it per second, when the surface is perpendicular to the direction of the incident light. Since the quantity of light falling on unit area varies inversely as the square of the distance of the surface from a point source of light, the intensity of illumination at a distance of 2 ft. is one-quarter of that at 1 ft. ; is one-ninth at 3 ft., and so on. This is accurately true, only when the source of light is a point. We shall assume, however, that the sources of light used are so small compared with the distances of the surfaces where the intensities are measured that they may be regarded without serious error as point sources of light.

The illuminating power of a source of light is the intensity of illumination which it produces at unit distance from the source. The quantities of light emitted by various sources are compared by measuring the intensities of illumination which they produce.

Illuminating powers might be measured in ergs per sq. cm. per sec. per cm., or in some similar unit. Such measurements, however, are difficult to make, and in practice it is usual to measure illuminating powers in terms of the illuminating power of a standard lamp. It is necessary, therefore, to choose some standard source of light with which other sources may be compared. One such standard source is the Vernon-Harcourt lamp. This is a special type of lamp, so constructed that, under certain specified conditions, it always emits the same quantity of light. It emits about as much light as 10 candles, and is *defined* to have an illuminating power of 10 candle-power. Hence, one candle-power is the illuminating power of a source of light whose illuminating power is one-tenth of that of the Vernon-Harcourt lamp.

Intensities of illumination are measured in units called foot-candles. One foot-candle is the intensity of illumination produced by a source of one candle-power at a distance of one ft.

EXAMPLE : *A lamp produces an intensity of illumination of 10 ft.-candles at a distance of 3 ft. Find the illuminating power of the lamp, and calculate the intensity of illumination produced by it at 5 metres, expressing the result in metre-candles.*

The intensity of illumination varies inversely as the square of the distance, so at a distance of 1 ft. from the source it is 3^2 times as great as at 3 ft., and is therefore 90 ft.-candles.

$$\therefore \text{ illuminating power of the lamp} = 90 \text{ c.p.}$$

One metre-candle is defined as the intensity of illumination produced by a source of one candle-power at a distance of 1 metre. At 5 metres such a source would give an intensity of illumination of $\frac{1}{5^2}$ metre-candle. Hence, the 90 c.p. lamp gives an intensity of illumination at a distance **of** 5 metres, of $90 \times \dfrac{1}{5^2}$ = 3·6 metre-candles.

The candle-power of a few sources of light in common use are shown below :

Gas burner with mantle . . . 45 c.p.
Electric lamps for domestic use . 20 to 130 c.p.
Carbon arc . . . . . 1000 to 2000 c.p.

21.03. We have now to show how the candle-powers of various sources are compared.

The Rumford Shadow Photometer.—An upright rod A (figure 21.03) is placed in front of a white screen, and the two sources of light, whose illuminating powers are to be compared, are placed behind the rod. Each of these sources S_1 and S_2 casts a shadow (S_1' and S_2') on the screen, and these shadows are brought close together by placing the sources near the normal from

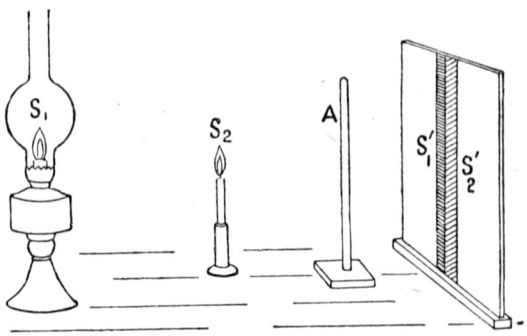

FIG. 21.03.—RUMFORD SHADOW PHOTOMETER.

the rod to the screen. Light from the source S_1 reaches the shadow S_2', and light from the source S_2 reaches the shadow S_1'. The source S_1 is now moved nearer to, or farther from, the screen, until both shadows are equally dark. The intensity of illumination is then the same in each shadow, and if the intensities of illumination produced at the two points by the light from the windows and the walls are equal, the intensities of illumination produced by the sources S_1 and S_2 at the screen must be equal. The distances S_1S_2' and S_2S_1' are measured. Let these distances be a ft. and b ft. respectively, and let J_1 and J_2 be the illuminating powers of the sources S_1 and S_2.

S_1 produces an intensity of illumination of J_1 ft.-candles at I ft. distance, and therefore an intensity of illumination of $\frac{J_1}{a^2}$ ft.-candles at the distance of a ft. Similarly, S_2 produces an intensity of illumination of $\frac{J_2}{b^2}$ at b ft. distance. These are equal, since the shadows are equally dark.

$$\therefore \frac{J_1}{a^2} = \frac{J_2}{b^2}$$

$$\therefore \frac{J_1}{J_2} = \frac{a^2}{b^2}.$$

21.04. Bunsen's Grease-spot Photometer.—When a grease spot is formed on a sheet of paper, light is more readily transmitted through the grease spot than through other portions of the paper. Hence, if the paper is viewed from the side opposite a source of light, the grease spot appears brighter than the rest of the paper, but if it is viewed from the same side as the source of light the grease spot appears dark. With two sources of light, one on each side of the sheet of paper, the grease spot tends to fade into its surroundings when the intensity of illumination is the same on both sides. This is the principle of Bunsen's grease-spot photometer.

The two sources S_1 and S_2 (figure 21.04) are set up on the normal to the paper AB, and the distance from the paper of one of them is varied until the intensity of illumination is the same on both sides. The distances a and b are then measured. If J_1 and

FIG. 21.04.—BUNSEN'S GREASE-SPOT PHOTOMETER.

J_2 are the illuminating powers of the sources, the intensity of illumination produced at the paper by the first is $\frac{J_1}{a^2}$ and that produced by the second is $\frac{J_2}{b^2}$.

$$\therefore \frac{J_1}{a^2} = \frac{J_2}{b^2}$$

$$\therefore \frac{J_1}{J_2} = \frac{a^2}{b^2}.$$

To obtain accurate results, the experiment must be performed
in a darkened room, the walls of which are blackened to prevent
reflection of light, so that light can reach the two sides of the
paper by direct paths from
the sources only, for if light
can reach the apparatus from
a window it is unlikely that
equal amounts of this light
will reach the two sides of the
paper.

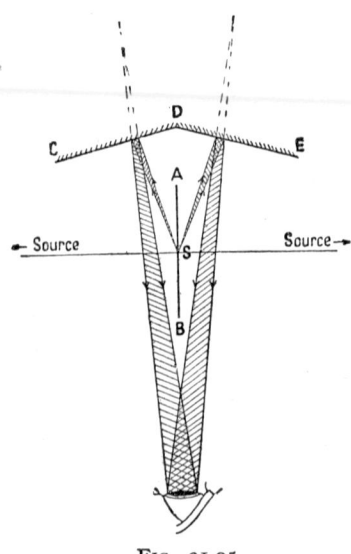

In practice it is not found
that the grease spot disappears
completely; the matt surface
of the paper can always be
distinguished from the smooth
greased portion. It is therefore necessary to view the two
sides of the paper at the same
time, and to adjust the distances of the sources until
both sides of the grease spot
present the same appearance.
This is done by means of two
plane mirrors placed behind
the paper, as shown in figure
21.05. AB is the paper, with
the grease spot at S. Two images of this are formed by the
mirrors CD and DE as shown.

Fig. 21.05.

21.05. The intensity of illumination of daylight in England
between sunrise and sunset varies between 10 and 5500 ft.-
candles according to the weather, the time of day, and the
season of the year.

The best intensity of illumination for reading and writing is
one of 3 to 6 ft.-candles. Both greater and smaller intensities
of illumination cause eye-strain; the smaller because the surface
of the paper is not bright enough for the print to be easily
distinguished, and the greater because the glare is trying to the
eyes. When a room is illuminated by means of a lamp hung
near the ceiling, light is reflected from the ceiling and walls, and
the intensity of illumination may be 50 per cent. greater than that
which would be provided by the direct rays of the lamp. The

lamp should be placed behind a translucent surface, or placed in such a position that it cannot be seen directly by the eye.

Shadows may be avoided by the method of indirect lighting. In this case the light is first thrown on to the ceiling and walls, and reaches the book or paper from various directions. Indirect lighting produces a pleasant, soft light, suitable for many purposes, but the absence of shadows is a disadvantage for such occupations as sewing, where the outlines of the thread must be seen.

Electric lamps often emit more light in one direction than in another. To obtain a more even distribution of light, and to reduce glare, electric lamp bulbs are usually " frosted." Owing to the structure of the human eye, eye strain is more easily caused by intense beams of light reflected upwards than by similar beams coming from overhead. In a room, therefore, the lamps should be placed above the level of the eyes.

21.06. *An electric lamp is required for reading at a distance of 5 ft. from the lamp. Assuming that the best intensity of illumination for this purpose is 4 ft.-candles, and that 20% of the light reaching the book does so by reflection at the ceiling and walls, what candle-power lamp should be used ?*

80% of the light reaches the book by direct rays from the lamp, so the direct rays should provide an intensity of illumination of $\frac{4 \times 80}{100}$ ft.-candles.

Let x be the candle-power of the lamp. The intensity of illumination at 5 ft. $= \frac{x}{5^2}$ ft.-candles,

$$\therefore \frac{x}{5^2} = \frac{4 \times 80}{100}$$

$$\therefore x = 80.$$

The lamp required is one of 80 c.p. A 60-watt lamp gives 80 to 90 c.p., and would serve the purpose.

EXAMPLES 21

School Certificate Questions

1. Explain the meaning of (a) illuminating power, (b) intensity of illumination, and state the unit in which each is measured. Describe the construction and explain the use of some form of photometer.

Two lamps, A and B, are balanced on a photometer when A is 60 cm. and B is 40 cm. from the photometer head. B is a 40 candle-power lamp; find the candle-power of A. A reflector is then placed close to B so that it throws more light on to the photometer head, and in order to obtain a balance A has to be placed at 50 cm. from the photometer head. Calculate the apparent increase of candle-power of B due to the reflector. (O)

2. State and deduce the relation connecting the intensity of illumination on a screen with the distance of the screen from a small source of light. A square frame ABCD has a small light source at A and a small plane mirror fixed at the centre of the side CD. Light from A strikes the mirror and is reflected to B. If the intensity of illumination at B due to direct light received from A is 10, calculate (a) the intensity of illumination at the mirror, (b) the intensity of illumination at B due to reflected light only, assuming that no light is lost by reflection. (O)

3. Explain the principle on which the use of a photometer depends, and describe any simple laboratory form of photometer. A 40 c.p. lamp and a 65 c.p. lamp are placed respectively on opposite sides of an opaque white screen, and at 50 cm. from it. Where must a 100 c.p. lamp be placed so as to make the intensity of illumination the same on both sides of the screen ? (B)

4. What do you understand by the terms *illuminating power*, and *intensity of illumination* ? Describe some simple form of photometer by means of which these quantities can be measured. Two lamps of 25 and 36 candle-power respectively are placed 110 cm. apart. At what position must a screen be placed between them to be illuminated equally on both sides ? (B)

5. Define units in which " illuminating power " and " illumination " may be measured. The powers of two sources of light are as 3 : 4. They are placed at 5 ft. and 6 ft. respectively from a screen. Compare the illuminations produced. What distances from the screen would give equal illuminations ? (L)

6. Explain what is meant by the description " 100 candle-power " as applied to a lamp. Describe in detail any one practical method of comparing the candle-powers of two lamps. Explain whether your measurements should be carried out in a darkened room, or whether this is not necessary. (J)

7. Explain how Rumford's shadow photometer can be used to compare the illuminating powers of two small electric lamps. Give the principle of the method. Two lamps of 24 and 6 candle-power respectively are placed 60 cm. apart, and a cardboard screen is placed perpendicular to the line joining the two lamps. Find the position (a) between the lamps, (b) beyond one lamp where the screen is equally illuminated by each. (J)

8. When the illuminating powers of two lamps A and B are to be compared, it is usual to place a third lamp C at a fixed distance from the photometer head, and using lamps A and B in turn, to move these until each produces an intensity of illumination equal to that given by C. Since A and B in the given positions produce equal intensities of illumination at the photometer their illuminating powers may be compared in the ordinary way. What advantages will be possessed by this " substitution " method, as compared with the method of measuring the intensity of illumination of A in terms of B by the direct method ?

CHAPTER 22

REFRACTION BY A PRISM—SPECTRA

22.01. A ray of light passing through a block of glass with parallel sides emerges from the block in a direction parallel to that of the incident ray. If, however, the sides of the block are not parallel the ray emerges in a different direction. Figure 22.01 shows the paths of a number of parallel rays through a glass prism. Each ray in passing through the prism has its

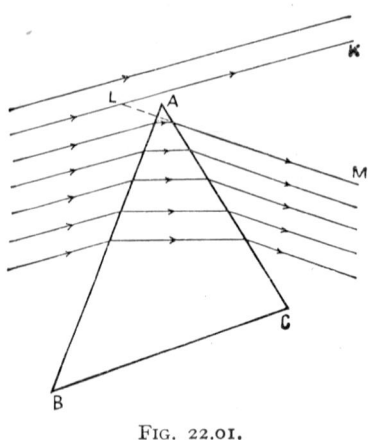

direction altered by an amount equal to the angle KLM, and this angle between the direction of the incident and emerging rays is called the *angle of deviation*. The angle BAC subtended by the paths of the rays in the prism is called the *angle of the prism*.

The deviation of the rays may be studied by means of the light streaks apparatus, and if it is arranged that some of the rays pass the apex of the prism, the angle of deviation can be seen as the prism is turned

FIG. 22.01.

to various positions. Keeping the apex of the prism fixed at A (figure 22.01), the prism is first turned until the angle of incidence is as great as possible. The prism is then slowly rotated. As the angle of incidence is decreased the angle of deviation decreases also. Presently, however, the angle of deviation ceases to decrease, and then becomes larger again. This is illustrated in the graph (figure 22.02), where the angles of deviation are plotted against the corresponding angles of incidence. It will be seen from the graph that, for the particular prism used in this experiment, the smallest

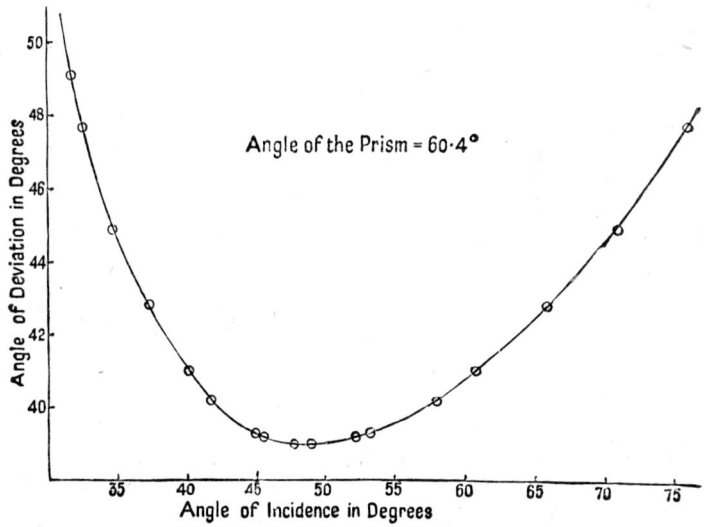

Fig. 22.02.

value of the angle of deviation is 39°. The least value of the angle of deviation is called the *angle of minimum deviation*.

22.02. A ray passes through a prism with minimum deviation when it passes through the prism symmetrically. Figure 22.03 shows such a ray PQRS passing through the prism BAC with minimum deviation. KL and ML are the normals to the glass surfaces where the ray enters and leaves the prism. The ray passes through in such a way that $\underline{|\text{KQP}} = \underline{|\text{MRS}}$, and $\underline{|\text{LQR}} = \underline{|\text{LRQ}}$; that is, the angle of incidence at the first surface is equal to the angle of refraction at the second, and

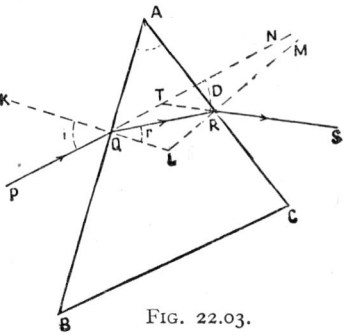

Fig. 22.03.

L

the angle of refraction at the first surface is equal to the angle of incidence at the second surface.

The angle of minimum deviation, $\lfloor D$, is the angle NTS, and the angle of the prism, $\lfloor A$, is the angle BAC.

The four angles of the quadrilateral AQLR together are equal to 360°, and since $\lfloor AQL$ and $\lfloor ARL$ are each a right angle,

$$\lfloor QLR + \lfloor A = 180°.$$

But, $\lfloor QLR + \lfloor LQR + \lfloor LRQ = 180°$ (three angles of a triangle)

$$\therefore \lfloor A = \lfloor LQR + \lfloor LRQ.$$

But, $\lfloor LQR = \lfloor LRQ$;

$$\therefore \lfloor A = 2\lfloor LQR \quad . \quad . \quad . \quad . \quad . \quad (1)$$

$\lfloor D$ is the exterior angle of the triangle TQR;

$$\therefore \lfloor D = \lfloor TQR + \lfloor TRQ$$
$$= (\lfloor TQL - \lfloor LQR) + (\lfloor TRL - \lfloor LRQ).$$

But $\lfloor TQL = \lfloor KQP$ (opposite angles); $\lfloor TRL = \lfloor MRS$, and is therefore equal to the angle KQP.

$$\therefore \lfloor D = (\lfloor KQP - \lfloor LQR) + (\lfloor KQP - \lfloor LQR)$$
$$\therefore \lfloor D = 2(\lfloor KQP - \lfloor LQR) \quad . \quad . \quad . \quad . \quad . \quad . \quad (2)$$

Adding equations (1) and (2), we obtain the equation:

$$\lfloor A + \lfloor D = 2\lfloor KQP$$

$$\therefore \lfloor KQP = \frac{\lfloor A + \lfloor D}{2} \quad . \quad . \quad . \quad . \quad . \quad . \quad . \quad (3)$$

Let μ be the refractive index of the glass of the prism.

$$\mu = \frac{\sin i}{\sin r}.$$

But $i = \lfloor KQP$, and $r = \lfloor LQR$. Substitution of the values for these angles given by equations (1) and (3), gives:

$$\mu = \frac{\sin\left(\dfrac{\lfloor D + \lfloor A}{2}\right)}{\sin \dfrac{\lfloor A}{2}}.$$

This formula enables the refractive index to be calculated from the values of the angle of the prism and the angle of minimum deviation. The angle of a prism and the angle of minimum

deviation can be measured by special methods with much greater
accuracy than can angles of incidence and refraction, so this
formula enables μ to be determined with great accuracy.

In the case of the prism used for obtaining the graph of
figure 22.02, $\underline{|A} = 60° \; 24'$, and from the graph $\underline{|D} = 39° \; 0'$.
Hence, for this glass,

$$\mu = \frac{\sin\left(\dfrac{39° \; 0' + 60° \; 24'}{2}\right)}{\sin\left(\dfrac{60° \; 24'}{2}\right)},$$

whence $\mu = 1\cdot52$.

22.03. There is another fact which you cannot fail to notice
when you measure the deviation produced by a prism. Although
the light streak produced by light entering the prism is white,
the streak which leaves the prism is not white, but coloured.

The production of these colours can be shown better by means
of the apparatus shown in plan in figure 22.04. Light from a

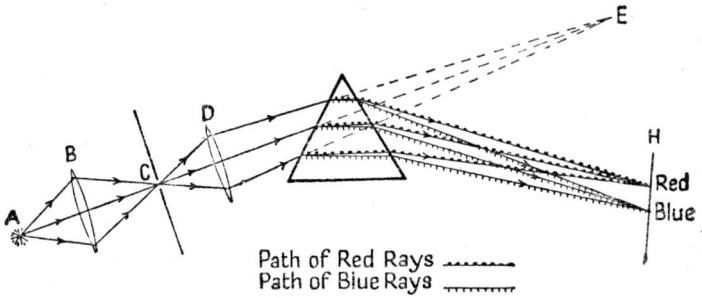

Path of Red Rays ....
Path of Blue Rays ....

Fig. 22.04.—Production of a Spectrum.

bright source A, such as a carbon arc, is concentrated by a
condenser lens B on a narrow slit C. The light from the slit
passes to the lens D and forms a real image of the slit at E.
When a prism is interposed between the lens and the point E,
the rays of light are deviated, and form a band of colour, red
at one end and blue at the other, on the white screen at H.
This band of colour is called a *spectrum*.

The spectrum is formed in this way because all the red rays
which leave the prism are brought to a focus at one strip on

the screen, all the blue rays to another strip, and so on. In other words, the spectrum consists of a large number of images of the slit C, each image having its own particular colour. That this is the case may be shown by replacing the ordinary straight slit [figure 22.05(a)] by a slit of a different shape, such as that shown in figure 22.05(b), when each band of colour is found to

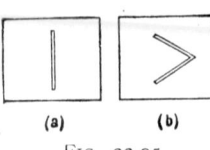

(a)   (b)

Fig. 22.05.

have the same shape as the slit. White light passing through a prism is thus not only deviated by the prism, but is converted into beams of light of various colours as well. This formation of coloured beams of light travelling in different directions is called *dispersion*.

Sir Isaac Newton, who first investigated the formation of the spectrum about the year 1666, distinguished seven different colours. Passing from the red end of the spectrum to the other these are : red, orange, yellow, green, blue, indigo, and violet. There are, however, a very large number of different shades of colour, and each colour shades off gradually into the next, so it is well to remember that, although it is usual to speak of these seven colours as the colours of the spectrum, there is no sharp dividing line between these colours, and the spectrum is divided only in imagination into the variously coloured bands.

22.04. We must now inquire how the colours of the spectrum are formed when white light passes through a prism. The simplest suggestion to test is that the light is somehow " stained " in passing through the glass. If this is the case we should expect that, if the light, after passing through one prism, is passed through a second, the " staining " will be carried a stage further, and that yet other colours will be produced. When the experiment is performed, however, it is found that the spectrum is spread out (figure 22.06), but the colours are the same as before. The second prism causes a greater deviation of the blue light than of the red, but does nothing more.

There is another possible method by which a spectrum might be formed by a prism. Suppose that the light which appears to our eyes as white, really consists of light of all the colours of the spectrum, but that our eyes are unable to distinguish this fact. As the previous experiment shows, blue light is deviated by a prism more than red light, so a prism might form a spectrum, not by " staining " the white light, but merely by separating out the various colours in the mixture. If this is actually what happens, it is obvious why the second prism produces no new colours. It cannot do so because there are no more colours for it to separate from the mixture. As a matter of fact the prism does " produce " colour by separating light of various colours from the beam of white light and not by staining the light. The next experiment shows this clearly.

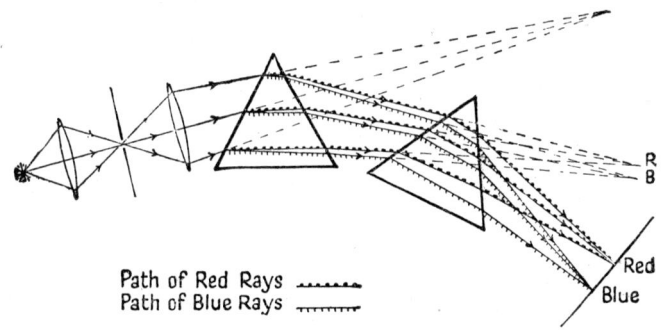

Path of Red Rays ....
Path of Blue Rays ....

R
B

Red
Blue

FIG. 22.06.

A spectrum is formed in the ordinary way on the screen at K (figure 22.07). The light leaving the prism has been split up into beams of different colours, each beam forming a coloured

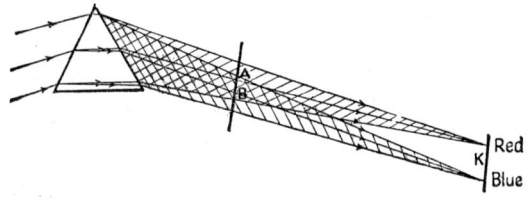

Red
Blue

FIG. 22.07.

image of the slit on the screen K. If, however, a white screen is placed at AB the beams of light of various colours overlap at the middle of the screen and this part of the screen does not appear coloured, but white. In other words, ordinary white light can be split up into all the colours of the spectrum, but white light is again obtained if beams of light of these colours are mixed. **Ordinary white light is a mixture of light of the spectrum colours.**

22.05. If, in a spectrum, light of only one colour is received at any given point on the screen the spectrum is said to be *pure*. If the images of the slit formed by a prism are not sharp, the image of one colour will overlap that of a neighbouring colour, and the spectrum will not be pure. It can be shown that a prism forms a sharp image of a slit, only if the rays which form the image pass through the prism with minimum deviation, and this is necessary when it is desired to form a pure spectrum as shown in figure 22.04.

Theoretically the slit used for forming a pure spectrum should have no width, for, however narrow it is made, the images formed will also have some width and will overlap those of neighbouring shades of colour. Reducing the width of the slit, on the other hand, reduces the amount of light which passes to the screen, and hence the brightness of the spectrum. In practice, therefore, when a pure spectrum is required a compromise has to be made, and the slit is made as narrow as possible, consistent with the spectrum being of the necessary brightness.

22.06. A prism of large angle used for producing a spectrum may be considered as equivalent to two prisms of smaller angle arranged as in figure 22.06. If the angle of the prism is large the spectrum formed is a wide one, and if it is desired to form a spectrum in which the red is widely separated from the green (say) a prism of large angle may be used. The angle of deviation is then large also, so this method of preparing a wide spectrum really consists in refracting the rays through a large angle.

Is it possible to produce a wide separation of the colours without increasing the deviation—by using prisms made of other materials, for example ? By using prisms of different kinds of glass, so shaped that they produce equal deviations, it may be shown that flint glass separates the colours of the spectrum into a wider band of colour than most other varieties of glass. This fact is expressed by saying that flint glass produces a large dispersion. For a given angle of deviation the separation of the colours produced by a prism containing carbon disulphide is even greater, and this substance is often used in the production of spectra.

22.07. We have seen that heat radiation is extremely similar to light ; it travels at the same speed as light, and is reflected in the same way. We may now show that it is also refracted in a similar way. For this purpose a spectrum is formed on a screen in the manner described, but since glass is nearly opaque to heat radiation, it is necessary to use quartz lenses and a quartz prism instead of glass ones.

A linear thermopile is placed so as to receive the light of some particular colour, say blue. The blue light falling on the thermopile produces a small deflection of the galvanometer. The thermopile is placed first in the middle, and then at the red end of the spectrum, and the increasing deflections of the galvanometer show that the light at the red end of the spectrum causes the greatest heating effect at the thermopile. This merely shows that the amount of energy emitted by a carbon arc as red light is greater than that emitted as blue light.

It may be expected that when the thermopile is placed beyond the red end of the spectrum the galvanometer deflection will decrease to zero. Instead of doing this, however, the deflection *increases*, and it is not until the thermopile is far beyond the red end of the spectrum that the deflection decreases to zero. Obviously the spectrum extends beyond the red end, although the eye is unable to detect the radiation. It is this *infra-red radiation* as it is called, which forms what we have hitherto called heat radiation, and this radiation bears the same relationship to red light that red light bears to blue. It is merely a radiation of the same type as light, but is refracted less than red light is. By means of experiments beyond the scope of this book, it has been shown that wireless waves are of a similar nature, and short wireless waves are nothing more nor less than radiation whose place in the spectrum lies just beyond the infra-red.

22.08. There is an invisible radiation beyond the red end of the spectrum. Is there an invisible type of radiation beyond the violet end also ? The thermopile will scarcely show the presence of such radiation, because the amount of energy emitted to this part of the spectrum by a carbon arc is small, but the presence of *ultra-violet radiation*, as it is called, may be shown using a photographic plate. A photographic plate is particularly sensitive to ultra-violet radiation, and if such a plate, or even a piece of gas-light printing paper, is exposed to the radiation of the spectrum it is darkened on developing, and is blackest at those points which were beyond the violet end of the spectrum.

The ultra-violet radiation from the sun has a beneficial effect upon health, although an excess causes sunburn and a great excess would be fatal. It is absorbed, however, by the ozone layer of the atmosphere, by clouds and by the smoke particles present in the air above large towns, and for this reason modern factories endeavour to remove the smoke particles from the fumes of their chimneys, thus enabling more of the beneficial ultra-violet rays to reach the earth. Ultra-violet rays are also absorbed by ordinary glass, so people working indoors lose much of the benefit of the sunshine passing through the glass windows. Of late years, however, special types of glass have been produced which are partly transparent to the ultra-violet light, and although these glasses are expensive, the extra cost is repaid by improvement of health where windows made of them are installed.

The ultra-violet rays are the most effective in photography, and the photographs taken on a cloudy day, when such rays from the sun are absorbed by the clouds, require longer exposures than those taken on a bright sunny day. The infra-red radiation, on the other hand, penetrates cloud and fog readily, *provided it is not radiation of the infra-red far removed from the visible spectrum*. Figure 22.08 shows two photographs, one taken by means of ordinary light, the other taken immediately afterwards by means of a photographic plate specially prepared to render it sensitive to infra-red rays. The latter are not scattered by the haze, and give a clear picture. If the infra-red radiation is of the type which lies far from the visible spectrum it is absorbed by clouds and mist just as ordinary light is. This is the type of infra-red radiation chiefly emitted by cold bodies such as the earth, and for this reason clouds prevent cooling of the earth by radiation at night.

Beyond the ultra-violet region of the spectrum lies still another —the region of the X-rays. Hence, the following types of radiation are all similar and are arranged in order : X-rays, ultra-violet radiation, light radiation, infra-red radiation, wireless waves.

22.09. The method of forming a spectrum described above is suitable when the spectrum is to be demonstrated to an audience. Another, and for many purposes a better method, is as follows. Rays from a brightly illuminated slit A (figure 22.09), fall on

[*By courtesy of Ilford Ltd. and J. Dixon Scott.*

Two photographs of the same subject; the upper taken with an ordinary photographic plate the latter by means of an infra-red sensitive plate.

FIG. 22.08.

a lens B which is placed its focal length from the slit, so that the rays emerge from the lens as a parallel beam. This beam passes through the prism C with minimum deviation, and rays of any given colour then form a parallel beam travelling in a direction different from that of the parallel beam of light of any other colour. These beams of light are focused by the lens D and form coloured images of the slit in the focal

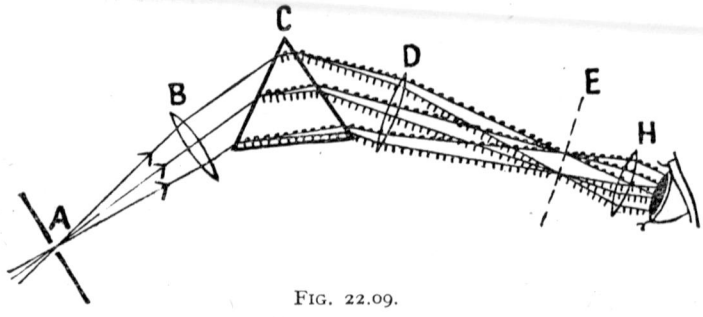

FIG. 22.09.

plane of the lens. The spectrum so produced may be caught on a screen placed at this point. More usually it is viewed by means of the eyepiece H, which forms a virtual, magnified image of the spectrum.

This is the principle of **the spectrometer**, one form of which **is** shown in figure 22.10. In this instrument the slit A and the

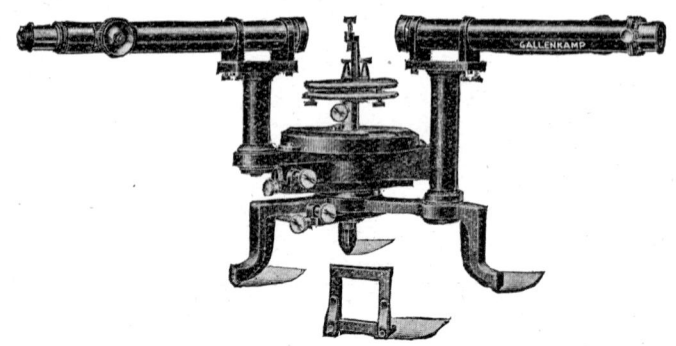

FIG. 22.10.—SPECTROMETER.

lens B of figure 22.09 are carried in a tube called the collimator, and the lenses D and H are carried in a second tube, the telescope. Between these is the prism table on which the prism is placed. The chief advantages of forming a spectrum in this way are that the apparatus is more compact, and that, since the spectrum is viewed directly by an eyepiece instead of by rays reflected from a screen, a much fainter spectrum may be used. This means that a narrower slit will allow sufficient light to pass, so a purer spectrum is obtainable. Moreover, the actual directions of the incident and refracted rays may be measured by turning the telescope and focusing it on any given part of the spectrum.

It is to be noted that a spectrum is formed only if a series of coloured images of a slit is formed. Hence the arrangement shown in figure 22.11 does *not* produce a spectrum on the screen AB, since the rays of any given colour in the beam diverging from the source S do not form an image. With such an arrangement, light of all the spectrum colours reaches the

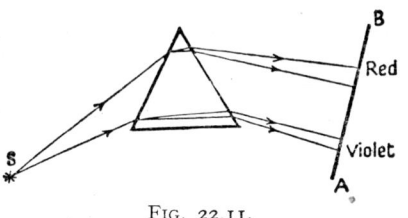

FIG. 22.11.

middle of the screen, so this portion of the screen appears white. This patch of light is surrounded by coloured edges. The edge nearer B is red because only red light reaches the screen here. Inside this narrow red edge is a band of colour formed where beams of light of various colours overlap. Similarly, at the edge of the patch of light near A another band of colour is formed with violet as the colour at the extreme edge.

22.10. The spectrum of the light from a carbon arc is a continuous band of colour ranging from a deep red to a deep violet. Such a spectrum is obtained whenever a solid body or a liquid is sufficiently hot to emit light, and is called a *continuous spectrum*.

The spectra obtained when light is emitted by hot gases, however, are of a completely different type. If, for example, a little common salt is evaporated in a Bunsen flame, the flame assumes a bright yellow colour, and on viewing the spectrum so produced by means of a spectrometer, it is found that the entire spectrum consists of nothing more than two bright yellow lines. Light of two neighbouring shades of yellow forms two bright images of the slit, but light of no other colour is emitted. The two yellow lines are typical of sodium, and are formed whenever a sodium salt emits a spectrum. Such a spectrum is called a *line spectrum* (figure 22.12).

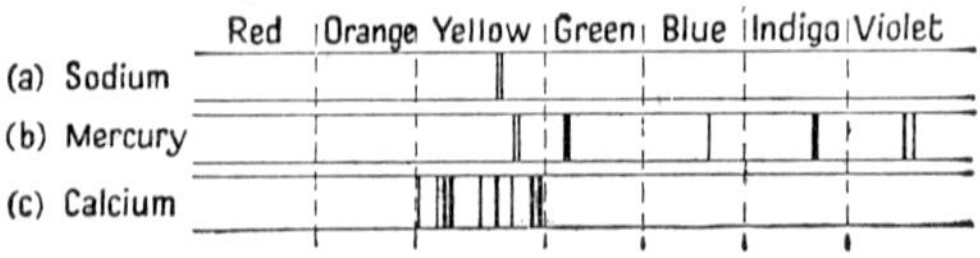

FIG. 22.12.—LINE SPECTRA.

Each substance in the gaseous state has its own particular line spectrum, the lines of which always occupy the same positions in the spectrum. Some of these, like the sodium spectrum, are simple ; some, like the iron spectrum, consist of many hundreds of lines. Since each substance possesses its own peculiar line spectrum, the presence of a certain set of lines in a spectrum indicates that this or that element is present in the material emitting the light. Extraordinarily small quantities of certain substances can be detected in this way.

22.11. When white light is allowed to pass through a liquid or a solution, and the transmitted light is examined with a spectrometer, the continuous spectrum of the white light is often found to be crossed by dark bands, showing that the solution has absorbed light of certain colours, and allowed light of other colours to pass through. Such a spectrum is called an *absorption spectrum*. The amount of light of any particular colour absorbed depends upon the substances, and the amounts of them in solution, so that if a slow chemical reaction occurs in the solution it is often possible to follow its progress by measuring the percentages of light absorbed at different times.

The absorption spectra of gases are of particular interest. The absorption by a gas is illustrated by the following experiment. The flame of a Bunsen burner (figure 22.13) plays upon an asbestos ring soaked in common salt, and the sodium vapour produced emits the characteristic yellow sodium light. The lens A concentrates light from the flame on the slit B of a spectrometer, by means of which the sodium spectrum is observed. A lamp C and a lens D are so placed that light from the lamp is focused on the flame, and the light which passes through the flame passes into the spectrometer. The lamp is placed in series with a resistance which enables its brightness to be altered at will.

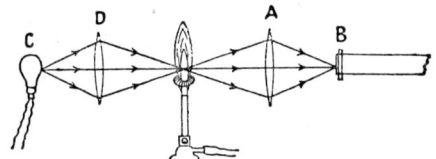

FIG. 22.13.—TO SHOW THE ABSORPTION SPECTRUM OF SODIUM.

The lamp is switched on, but kept faint. Then, while the spectrum is viewed, the brightness of the lamp is increased gradually. At first the sodium lines only are seen as bright yellow lines crossing a black background, but as the lamp becomes brighter its spectrum becomes visible and grows in intensity until the sodium lines become first dull in comparison with the rest of the spectrum, and then appear quite black.

The explanation is that the sodium vapour in the flame absorbs that light from the lamp which is of the same colours as the sodium itself emits. All the light of those colours is absorbed, but practically no other light, so the continuous spectrum of the lamp is crossed by the absorption lines of sodium. The sodium vapour in the flame continues to emit light, but the intensity of the light emitted by it is small compared with that of the light emitted by the lamp, so its own lines are *comparatively* dark. Other gases and vapours behave in a similar way, so absorption spectra may also be used to detect the presence of substances in the gaseous state.

22.12. The spectrum of the sun consists of a continuous spectrum crossed by a large number of dark lines. The continuous spectrum is produced by light from the intensely hot surface of the sun, and the lines are absorption lines caused by absorption of light of the continuous spectrum as it passes through the gaseous atmosphere of the sun. These absorption lines are called Fraunhofer lines, after their discoverer, Fraunhofer (1787–1826), and a knowledge of what lines are present is important, as showing what elements are present in the solar atmosphere. Many of the elements known on earth have thus been shown to exist in the sun and stars also, and one element, helium, was actually discovered in the sun twenty-six years before it was known on the earth !

When an eclipse of the sun occurs there is an instant—just as the surface of the sun disappears—when its atmosphere alone is visible. Since the solar atmosphere is extremely hot, it emits light, and when the surface of the sun is hidden this light is sufficiently bright to be examined with a spectrometer. As is to be expected, the spectrum then observed is a bright line emission spectrum in which the Fraunhofer lines appear in their natural colours against a dark background.

EXAMPLES 22

1. A ray of light passes with minimum deviation through a prism of angle 30°. The glass of the prism has a refractive index 1·5. Draw a diagram to scale showing the path of the ray, and measure the angle of deviation. Verify your result by calculating μ from the measured angle of minimum deviation and the angle of the prism.

2. What is meant by *dispersion* ? Describe with the aid of a diagram what experiments you would perform to show that a flint glass prism produces greater dispersion than one of crown glass.

3. How would you show the presence of (a) infra-red, (b) ultra-violet radiation beyond the ends of the visible spectrum ? Give a short account of these two types of radiation.

4. Describe and explain the use of a spectrometer. What advantages are there in forming a spectrum by means of this instrument rather than on a screen ?

School Certificate Questions

5. Describe an experiment to show that white light is of a composite nature. In what respects do lights of different colours differ in their physical properties ? (L)

6. A diverging beam of white light after passing through a glass prism is intercepted by a white screen. Describe and explain the colour effects exhibited. What means would you take to make these colours well defined ? (L)

7. How would you use a prism, lenses, and a slit to produce a pure spectrum of a source of light (*a*) on a screen, (*b*) for direct observation by eye ? (C)

8. How would you show that a ray of light is deviated by passage through a glass prism ? How must the prism be arranged so that the deviation is a minimum ? A narrow beam of white light is passed through a prism and then received on a white screen placed at right angles to the path of the emergent beam. What would you observe about the image on the screen, and why ? (J)

9. State briefly the evidence which leads us to believe that the processes by which light and radiant heat travel are very similar. Describe an experiment which you would perform to study the laws of reflection of radiant heat, and state the results you would expect. (J)

10. Describe, with a diagram, an arrangement for producing a pure spectrum. The spectrum of a sodium flame contains bright lines, and the spectrum of the sun dark lines. What are the causes of the difference ? (O.C)

11. Explain what you understand by a *pure* spectrum and describe how you would produce a pure spectrum on a screen using a light source, slit, a pair of convex lenses, and a prism. Draw a diagram of the arrangement of the apparatus. State, with reasons, whether the spectrum so produced is real or virtual. How could you test by experiment whether the spectrum produced was actually pure ? (O)

12. Describe the principal parts of a spectroscope and explain their action. What would be the nature of the spectra of the following sources of light : (*a*) an electric bulb, (*b*) the sun, (*c*) a neon lamp ? (O.C)

CHAPTER 23

COLOUR IN NATURE

23.01. Ordinary white light is a mixture of light of the various colours of the spectrum. The light of a particular colour produced in a spectrum is, however, not a combination of light of other colours, for it is not further split up by passing it through a second prism. We might conclude that white light is composite, whereas light of any other colour is simple. Such a conclusion would be incorrect, however, for there are certain colours—brown, for instance—which are not present in the spectrum, and such colours are produced by mixing light of the spectrum in the right proportions. Moreover, although such colours as yellow *may* be formed by yellow light only, a mixture of various other coloured lights in the right proportions also gives a yellow colour which is indistinguishable *by eye* from the yellow of the spectrum.

Figure 23.01 shows in plan an apparatus suitable for mixing light of various colours. Light from an arc-lamp is concentrated by a condenser lens on the slit A, whence it passes to the

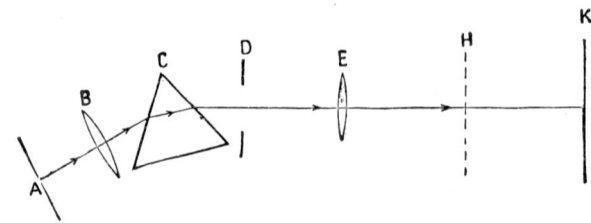

Fig. 23.01.

lens B, situated its focal length from the slit. The parallel rays of white light so produced pass through the prism C, where dispersion occurs. The light leaving the prism then consists of beams of various colours, light of each spectrum colour travelling in a direction different from that of light of every other colour.

These beams meet the lens E, and are brought to a focus to form a spectrum in its focal plane H. A screen D, with a round hole in it, is placed between the prism and the lens E, in such a position that only the central parts of the beam of light leaving the prism pass through the hole. This light contains all the constituent colours which make up white light. The screen K is placed at such a distance that the lens E forms on it a real image of the hole in D. This image is a white circle.

Although the rays forming an image on the screen combine there to produce a white image, the light is separated into its constitu-ent colours at H. Hence, by placing a tiny prism in the yellow part (say) of the spectrum at this point, the yellow rays may be deflected to a different part of the screen. The appear-ance of the screen is then that shown in figure 23.02. The upper portion appears yellow because yellow light, and only yellow light, reaches this portion of the screen. The blue of the lower portion is a composite colour

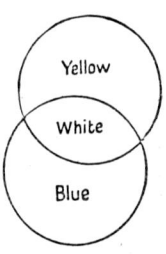

Fig. 23.02.

formed by the combination of all the spectrum colours except yellow. At the middle, both the yellow light and that which forms the blue light are mixed, so a mixture of what appears to the eye as blue light and yellow light gives white. Two such colours are said to be *complementary*. In a similar way, it may be shown that red and peacock blue are comple-mentary ; green and magenta are also complementary colours.

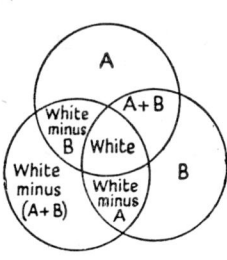

Fig. 23.03.

If two prisms are used to throw out the light of two different spectrum colours, the effect is similar to that shown in figure 23.03. Here the colours A and B have been thrown to the sides. The diagram indicates how the different colours are formed.

23.02. Light of various colours may also be mixed, using three lanterns, each of which directs a beam of light to the same portion of a screen. Various coloured filters are placed in front of the three lamps. Such filters allow light of only particular colours to pass through them, and red, green, and blue light, for example, may be mixed by using in front of the first lamp a filter which allows only red light to pass through, in front of the second a filter which transmits only green light, and in front of the third lamp a filter which transmits only blue light. The method of mixing light by means of the lanterns has the advantage that the intensity of the light of any given colour may be altered at will by changing the electrical resistance in series with the lamp in the lantern projecting this colour. It suffers from the disadvantage that the colours transmitted by the filters are never quite pure, so the colours formed are not so brilliant as those produced by the other method.

23.03. It is a peculiar fact that any colour whatever may be matched by mixing the light of three particular colours in the correct proportions. The three colours required are called the three *primary colours*. They are particular shades of red, green, and blue. These three colours, if mixed in other proportions, produce white light, and when they are projected together on to a white screen, the effect is indistinguishable *by eye* from that obtained by projecting ordinary white light on to the same screen. Keeping in mind the fact that white light is produced only if the three colours are mixed in the correct proportions, we may write the result in the form of an equation:

$$\text{Red} + \text{blue} + \text{green} = \text{white light} \quad . \quad . \quad . \quad (1)$$

Similarly, by mixing light of other colours it may be shown that:

$$\text{Red} + \text{blue} = \text{magenta} \quad . \quad . \quad . \quad . \quad . \quad (2)$$
$$\text{Blue} + \text{green} = \text{peacock blue} \quad . \quad . \quad . \quad (3)$$
$$\text{Red} + \text{green} = \text{yellow} \quad . \quad . \quad . \quad . \quad (4)$$

Suppose, now, that the green light is removed from a beam of white light falling upon a white screen. What colour will be observed on the screen? Our problem may be written:

$$\text{white light} - \text{green light} = \text{unknown colour.}$$

White light, however, is equivalent, as far as the eye is concerned, to a mixture of red, green, and blue light, and we may write (red + green + blue) light instead of white light in our problem. This then becomes:

$$(\text{red} + \text{green} + \text{blue}) - (\text{green}) = (\text{red} + \text{blue}).$$

The result is thus the same as is obtained by mixing red and blue light. According to equation (2) above, a mixture of red and blue light gives magenta. Hence, the result of removing the green light from ordinary white light will be to give a patch of a magenta colour on the screen. This result may be confirmed by experiment. Other problems of a similar kind may be solved in the same way.

23.04. Objects, which are not themselves luminous, appear coloured only if they reflect light to the eye. In a dark room, for example, no light from the objects passes to the eye, and everything appears black. Black is, therefore, not a colour like red, blue, etc., but results merely from the absence of reflected light.

Since coloured objects appear black in a dark room, and of various colours when sunlight falls on them, it is obvious that their colour is in some way due to their action upon the light which falls on them and is reflected to the eye. Mere *reflection*, however, *does not, in itself, produce colour*. Thus, if a beam of white light is reflected at the surface of a sheet of red glass and the reflected beam falls upon a white screen, it is found that the reflected light is not red, but white. If, on the other hand, the beam is allowed to pass *through* the glass, the light emerging is found to be red. Coloured objects appear coloured because the light falling on them *penetrates* them for a short distance before it is reflected.

It may, at first sight, appear surprising that light penetrates apparently opaque objects, even if for only a short distance. We are so accustomed to regarding objects such as pieces of metal as completely opaque, that it is difficult to imagine that light ever penetrates their surfaces. Nevertheless, it does do so, as may be shown if a sufficiently thin film of metal is available. Gold may be rolled into exceedingly thin sheets, and if a piece of gold leaf is held in a beam of white light, some of the light passes through it.

When white light falls on a body, and penetrates its surface, some of the light is absorbed as it passes through the material, and the reflected light appears coloured, because some colours are absorbed more strongly than others. The colour of the reflected light is not due to the addition of something to the incident light ; it is caused by the *subtraction* of particular colours from the white light. This may be shown by holding various objects in different parts of a spectrum. The light reaching the green part (say) of such a spectrum is green light only, and if light is subtracted when a beam is reflected from an object placed there, the object will appear either green or black —green if only part of the incident light is absorbed, and black if all of it is absorbed. If, however, reflection *adds* something to the light falling on an object, the objects held in the green parts of the spectrum will sometimes appear a colour other than green. In practice, it is found that this is never the case, so **the colours of objects are due to the fact that they absorb some colours from the incident light more readily than other colours.**

A white object held in a spectrum reflects all the spectrum colours. It also reflects all the colours when a beam of white light falls on it, and appears white for this reason. Most red objects reflect red light only, and hence appear red when viewed in white light. Similarly, green objects appear green because they reflect little except the green light falling on them. An object may, however, appear of a particular colour, not because *all* the other colours are absorbed, but because one or two colours are absorbed, and the remainder, which are reflected, produce in the eye the sensation of the given colour. Thus, most yellow objects reflect all the colours except those at the blue end of the spectrum, and the mixture of red, orange, yellow, and green light which is reflected to the eye is observed as yellow.

Hence, in order to determine what colour an object will appear to the eye, it is necessary to know three facts : (*a*) what colours are present in the light falling on the object ; (*b*) which of these colours are absorbed by the object ; and (*c*) what sensation of colour will be produced in the eye by the colours which are not absorbed.

We shall apply these facts to the following examples : (1) *A piece of red paper with yellow stripes on it is held in* (a) *the red part of a spectrum,* (b) *in the blue part. Describe its appearance in the two cases.*

(*a*) Only red light reaches the object. Hence, only red light or none can be reflected. The red part of the paper can reflect red light, and the yellow portions can reflect all colours except blue. Both parts will therefore reflect red light, and will appear red.

(*b*) Only blue light reaches the paper. Neither portion can reflect blue light, so no light is reflected. The whole paper, therefore, appears black.

(2) *A red handkerchief with white spots is held in beams of*

(a) *pure red light*, (b) *pure green light*, (c) *a mixture of red and green light. Describe its appearances in the three cases.*

(*a*) The red background and the white spots can both reflect red light, so the whole handkerchief will appear red if illuminated by red light only. If the colour of the handkerchief is of the same shade as the red light, the background and spots will reflect the light equally well, and the spots will not be distinguishable from their background.

(*b*) The white spots reflect green light and appear green. The background cannot reflect green light. It therefore reflects none of the incident light, and appears black.

(*c*) The white spots reflect both the red light and the green light. The mixture of red and green light reflected by them appears to the eye as yellow, so the spots appear yellow. The red background reflects red light, but not green, so it appears red.

23.05. When blue and yellow lights are mixed, white light is produced, for blue and yellow are complementary colours. Mixing blue and yellow **pigments** produces a pigment which is not white, but green.

Mixing light of different colours is equivalent to the addition of the colours. The colours produced by objects when white light falls on them are not formed by adding something to the white light, but by subtracting light of particular colours from it. A yellow pigment appears yellow because it absorbs blue light and reflects all the other colours. A blue pigment absorbs all the light except blue and green. Hence, the only colour not absorbed by one or other of the components of a mixture of blue and yellow pigments is green. Only green light is reflected from such a mixture, so the mixture appears green.

23.06. Transparent objects, like opaque objects, owe their colour to the absorption of particular colours from the white light falling on them. Thus, a piece of blue glass may appear blue because it allows blue light only to pass through it, and absorbs other colours. It may also appear blue because it transmits violet, indigo, blue, and green light in those proportions which produce in the eye the sensation of blue. If a piece of blue glass which transmits indigo, blue, and green light is laid on a piece of orange glass which transmits red, orange, yellow, and green light, the only colour which is transmitted by both is green, and this colour will be seen when a lamp is viewed through the combination. When, however, the same piece of blue glass is laid on a piece of red glass which transmits red light only, no colour is transmitted by both, and the combination appears black.

During the war, ships were camouflaged by painting broad bands of colour in various directions on their sides. This " dazzle painting," as it was called, rendered it difficult to judge the size of the ship and its course, and made submarine attack more difficult. At first many bright colours were used, but the enemy put this fact to advantage by fitting coloured screens in the periscopes of his submarines. Viewed through a dark-blue filter of this kind, a red band on the side of a ship does not appear different from a neighbouring black band, since the red does not reflect blue light, and only the latter colour is trans-mitted by the filter. Consequently a ship painted in red and black appears as a black silhouette in the periscope. Later, only the colours blue, white, and black were used for dazzle painting, and in this case little advantage is obtained by using a colour filter.

If coloured glass is finely powdered, the light falling on the mass of powdered material must pass through many glass-air surfaces in order to penetrate even a short distance through the material. As light passes from air to glass, or from glass to air, some light is reflected, so little of the incident light pene-trates far into the material. Since particular colours are absorbed only when light is being transmitted through the material, the white light falling on powdered glass undergoes little change before it is reflected to the eye, and powdered glass appears white. The original colour may be seen again, however, if water is poured on to the powder, for less reflection takes place at a glass-water surface than at one where air and glass are in contact, and the incident light thus penetrates farther before being reflected to the eye.

23.07. The spectrum of any solid body is a continuous one, and all such spectra contain the same spectrum colours. There is one respect, however, in which the spectra produced by dif-ferent hot bodies differ—the intensities of the various colours depend upon the particular hot body which is emitting the light, and upon its temperature. Generally speaking, the hotter the body, the more intense is the blue end of the spectrum as compared with the red end. The effective temperature of the sun is 6000° C., and its radiation contains a greater percentage

of blue light than that emitted by such sources of light as a
candle, an electric lamp, or even a carbon arc. Consequently,
objects which reflect chiefly blue light, and thus appear blue in
daylight, reflect practically no light at all when viewed by
artificial light from which the blue is absent. Dark-blue objects
tend to appear black by artificial light.

23.08. **The Rainbow.**—When a ray of light from the sun meets
a raindrop, as shown by the full line (figure 23.04) a small fraction

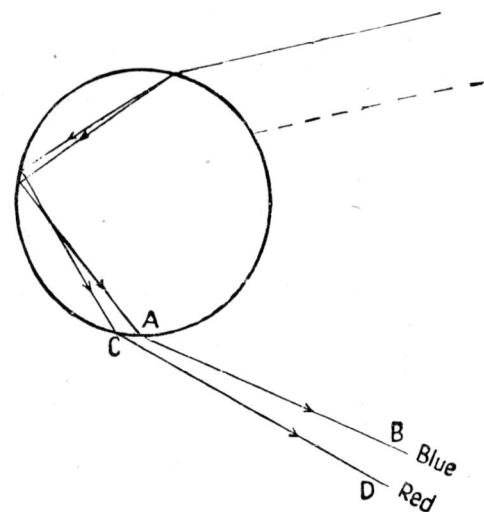

FIG. 23.04.—REFRACTION AND REFLECTION IN A RAINDROP.

of the incident light enters the drop and is refracted, is reflected
at the back of the drop, and is again refracted as it leaves it.
In consequence of the two refractions, the red light leaves the
drop in a direction different from that of the blue light. Those
rays which meet the drop at angles of incidence nearly equal
to that shown in the figure are reflected and refracted in such
a way that the light of any given colour leaving the drop forms
a number of nearly parallel rays, and the intensity of such beams
decreases little as the distance from the drop increases.

The refraction of rays which enter the drop at other angles
of incidence (*e.g.* as shown by the dotted line) also produces

dispersion, but in such cases the beam of light of any particular colour leaving the drop consists of rays which are not parallel. The intensity of such emergent beams diminishes rapidly, and at a short distance from the drop these beams are imperceptible. Hence, the blue light leaving the drop will only be perceived if the eye is placed somewhere on the line AB, and the red light will be seen from the direction CD. An eye placed at E (figure 23.05) therefore receives red light from the drop at A, and blue

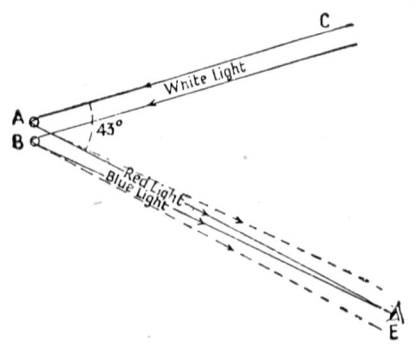

Fig. 23.05.—The Production of a Rainbow.

light from the drop at B, and sees a band of red above a band of blue, owing to the light from a number of drops near A and B. The intermediate colours of the rainbow are formed in a similar manner.

The red light leaving a raindrop in the manner described does so in a direction which makes an angle of 43° with that of the incident light. Let us take some distant object in the room where you are sitting to represent the position of the sun. The sun's rays approach the raindrops along the line CA (figure 23.05). Turn the book until the distant object representing the sun lies along this line. Now, keeping AC pointing to the object, turn the book about the point E. The point A describes a circle in a plane perpendicular to the line AC, and this circle shows the positions of the raindrops which are so placed that the red light is reflected to the eye at E. Since such drops lie on a circle, the colours seen are in the form of a bow.

EXAMPLES 23

1. Explain what is meant by *complementary colours*, and *primary colours*. How would you show the results of mixing lights of various colours ?

2. Explain with suitable diagrams the formation of a rainbow.

3. A piece of glass appears red when viewed in daylight. Explain why the glass appears coloured. What would be its appearance if viewed in the light of a sodium flame ?

4. An electric lamp is viewed through two pieces of glass laid on top of one another. What would you expect to observe if the colours of the glass are (*a*) red and blue respectively, (*b*) red and green respectively ? Give reasons.

5. A red book lies on a white sheet of paper, and is illuminated by sunlight. Describe and explain its appearance when viewed through (*a*) a red glass, (*b*) a blue glass. What differences would it make to the appearances in the two cases if the book and paper were illuminated by sodium light instead of by daylight ?

6. Explain why the result of mixing light of two different colours is unlike the result of mixing two pigments.

7. When two pieces of cloth are matched by means of artificial light, they often appear of different colours when viewed by daylight. Explain this fact.

SCHOOL CERTIFICATE QUESTIONS

8. Give an explanation of the cause of the colour of (1) a piece of red cloth, (2) a piece of red glass when viewed in daylight. Describe experiments you would make to justify your answer.   (L)

9. On what does the apparent colour of an object depend ? What would be the appearance of a green paper carrying black print, when viewed (*a*) in the light of a red lamp, (*b*) in the light of a sodium flame ? Give reasons for your answers.   (O.C)

10. Describe experiments with a prism to demonstrate the nature of white light. Explain how some objects when illuminated with white light appear to be coloured. A picture is composed entirely of red and green paints. Describe how its appearance changes if it is illuminated, first with red and then with yellow light.   (C)

11. Describe an experiment by which you could show that the different colours of which white light is composed have different refractive indices. For which colour is the refractive index greatest ? A beam of red light is allowed to fall successively on a (*a*) black, (*b*) white, (*c*) red, (*d*) blue surface. Describe and account for the various appearances presented.   (J)

SOUND

CHAPTER 24

WAVE MOTION—THE VELOCITY OF SOUND

24.01. No one who stands upon the seashore and watches the ceaseless ebb and flow of the surging water in the waves near the beach, and the quieter heaving and swell in the deeper water beyond, can fail to be impressed by the grandeur of the scene. The quieter progress of tiny ripples across a pond or stream, and their soft murmuring as they reach the shore, seem to bear little relation to the tumble and roar of the waves of the sea. It is appropriate, however, that some of the sweetest and some of the grandest sounds of nature should be produced by the waves at the shores of lakes and seas, for there is a close similarity between water waves and sound itself.

In the laboratory, wave motion may be studied by means of the apparatus called the ripple tank. This consists of a shallow tank, the bottom of which is of glass. Below the tank is placed a powerful source of light, and when waves are produced in the ripple tank, their progress may be followed by their shadows which are cast on the ceiling.

When the surface of the water is disturbed at any point, a wave is produced, which spreads out as an ever-growing circle until it reaches the edge of the tank. If the surface is disturbed at regular intervals, a series of waves—or as it is called, a *wave train*—is sent out, and at any given instant the shadows on the ceiling form a set of concentric circles. If the waves travel at a constant velocity, the distance between one wave crest and the next is the same for every pair of waves, and this distance is called the *wave length* of the wave train. In figure 24.01, which represents a section through such a wave train, the distance l is the wave length.

Let us suppose that n waves are produced per second, and that the waves advance with a velocity V. If the wave train travels forward as a whole, without any bunching together at a particular point, n waves pass any given point per second.

The first wave to pass the given point during any particular second will have advanced a distance V by the end of the second, and there will now be n waves occupying the space between

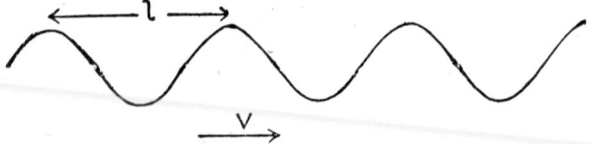

FIG. 24.01.—A WAVE TRAIN.

this wave and the given point. The space occupied by each wave is therefore $\dfrac{V}{n}$, and this is equal to the wave length l. That is,

$$l = \frac{V}{n}$$

$$\therefore \ V = n.l.$$

The number of waves produced per second is called the *frequency* of the wave train. Hence, **the velocity of a wave train is equal to the product of the frequency and the wave length.**

24.02. If you have watched an object floating in the sea at a distance from the shore, you may have been puzzled to observe that it was not carried rapidly towards the shore by the waves. We are apt to be misled by the fact that the water near the beach continually advances and recedes as wave after wave reaches the shore, for only the water in a wave which is break-

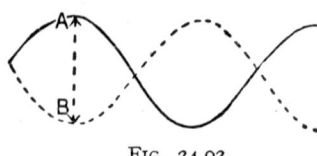

FIG. 24.02.

ing advances with the wave. Farther from the shore, where the waves do not break, only the *shape* of the wave moves forward, and the water itself merely rises and falls without approaching the shore. The motion of a particle of water in a wave is shown by the dotted line AB in figure 24.02. When the crest of a wave reaches the position shown, the particle is lifted to the point A; when a trough takes the place of the crest, the particle of water occupies the position B.

Figure 24.03 shows a machine designed to illustrate the motion of the particles in such a wave. When the handle is turned, the balls on the upper ends of the rods move up and down, reaching in succession their highest points, and although the balls themselves do not move horizontally, the wave advances in this direction. Since the motion of the particles in such cases is at right angles to the direction of motion of the wave, the wave is said to be **transverse.** Another example of a transverse wave is that formed when a long piece of rubber tubing, supported by one end from the ceiling, is made to transmit a wave by shaking the lower end.

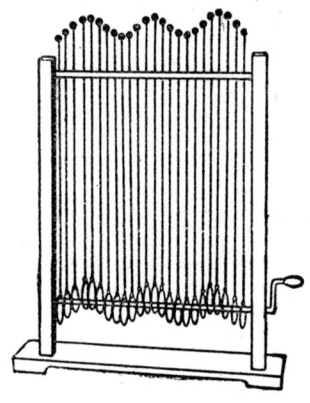

FIG. 24.03.—WAVE MACHINE.

It is possible, however, to form waves such that each particle in the wave executes a backward and forward motion in the same direction as that in which the wave travels. A large spring (figure 24.04) is supported horizontally from threads, two of which are attached to each coil of the spring. When one end of the spring is struck, the compression is communicated to neighbouring coils, and a compression wave passes through the spring from one end to the other. In the figure, the compression has reached the point A. As the wave passes, each particle in the spring moves first in the direction of the wave, and then in

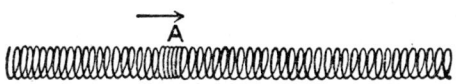

FIG. 24.04.

the reverse direction. In both cases its motion is along the line in whose direction the wave travels. Such a motion as this is said to constitute a **longitudinal** wave.

24.03. When a loud, deep note is played on a church organ it is often to be noticed that the objects in the building are vibrating. The organ vibrates so violently in sounding the note, that other objects are caused to vibrate too. **Whenever a body**

emits sound the body is in a state of vibration. The vibration of such objects as a sounding tuning-fork, or the wire of a piano, can be shown by holding a light pith ball on a thread, and allowing the ball to touch the sounding body. The ball receives a sharp blow from the latter.

When a metal plate is bowed at the edge with a violin bow, it emits sound. In this case, parts of the plate are caused to vibrate, while other parts remain stationary, and if a little sand is strewn on such a plate, the sand is thrown away from the vibrating parts, and heaped up along the lines where the plate is stationary. By means of a Chladni's plate, as the apparatus is called, beautiful patterns may be formed by bowing the plate at one point while other points are held stationary with the fingers.

A body in a state of rapid vibration sets up vibrations in the air around it. Each particle of air communicates its motion to neighbouring particles, and in this way particles at greater and greater distances from the source of sound are set in vibration. Some of these moving particles impinge on our ears, and cause us to "hear" the sound.

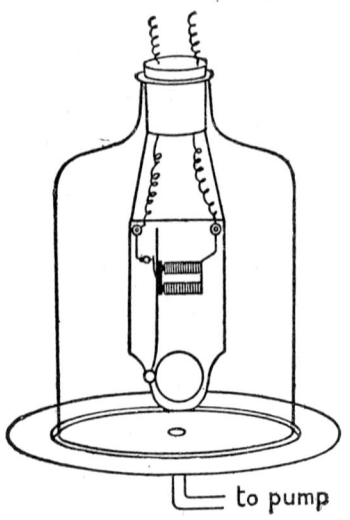

FIG. 24.05.—SOUND IS NOT TRANSMITTED THROUGH A VACUUM.

The following experiment shows that sound is transmitted to the ear by means of the air. An electric bell is suspended inside a bell-jar (figure 24.05) by means of strings. The bell-jar rests upon a ground-glass plate, and its rim is greased to render the joint airtight. A tube leading from the apparatus is connected to an air-pump, by means of which the air inside the bell-jar may be removed. Air is pumped out while the bell is ringing, and as pumping proceeds the sound of the bell becomes fainter and fainter, and finally almost disappears. When air is re-admitted to the bell-jar the sound is again loud.

It is quite clear from this experiment that it is the air which transmits sound, and that sounds are heard, not because something is shot out of the bell to reach our ears, but because the vibrations of the sounding bell are transmitted to our ears. The removal of the air from the bell-jar would not prevent particles travelling from the bell to our ears; it does prevent the vibra-

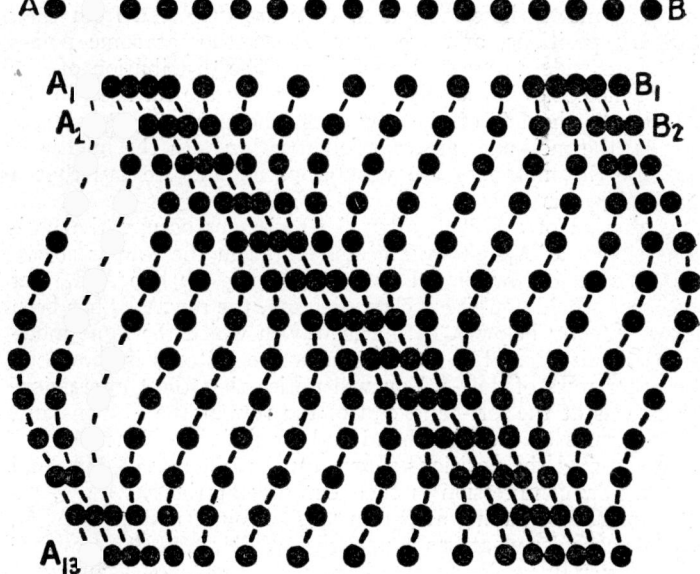

FIG. 24.06.—THE MOTION OF THE MOLECULES IN AIR THROUGH WHICH SOUND WAVES ARE PASSING.

tions of the bell from affecting our ears, because these vibrations are transmitted by waves in the air.

In this experiment the sound of the bell can always be heard, although it is only faint when the air is removed. This is because the vibrations of the bell set up vibrations in the supporting threads and wires, and these in turn cause the bell-jar and the surrounding air to vibrate. Sound vibrations can be transmitted by any material, whether it is gaseous, liquid, or solid, and if the bell in the above experiment stands on the glass plate under the bell-jar, or dips into a dish containing

M

mercury, the sound of the bell is readily transmitted by the glass and mercury to the air outside, and the bell sounds loudly even in a vacuum.

24.04. Figure 24.06 illustrates the movement of the molecules of a gas when sound waves pass through it. The row of dots AB represents a set of molecules in their positions before the sound waves reach them. When a wave, travelling from left to right, meets these molecules, they are displaced from their ordinary positions, and are crowded together at some points and more widely scattered at others. The distribution of the row of molecules is then like that shown by the set A_1B_1 in the figure. At the left of the row A_1B_1 there is a *compression*— that is, the molecules are crowded together. In the middle of the row the molecules are widely spaced and we say that a *rarefaction* exists here.

A fraction of a second after the molecules occupy the positions shown at A_1B_1 they are distributed in the row as shown at A_2B_2. This row should be drawn along the line A_1B_1, but since this would not give a clear diagram, the row A_2B_2 has been drawn directly below A_1B_1. The way in which the same molecules are distributed at further successive instants is shown by the other rows of dots. You will notice that the compression, which was at the left-hand end of the row at the first instant, passes across to the right-hand end by the time the molecules have assumed the positions shown by the last row of dots, and that a new compression is then entering at the left.

If, instead of paying attention to the row of molecules A_1B_1, we now consider what has happened to the first molecule, we see that it merely moves from left to right and back again, in a manner similar to that of the bob of a pendulum. The same is true of each of the other molecules, and the dotted lines in the diagram have been drawn to enable any particular molecule to be identified in its various positions. It is important to note that *the molecules do not travel forward with the waves*, but merely move backwards and forwards in the direction of the waves. Since the molecules vibrate in the same direction as that in which the sound travels, **sound consists of a longitudinal wave motion.** In this respect it resembles the waves in the spring shown in figure 24.04.

24.05. Sound travels through still air at a speed of 1100 ft. per second, so that in one second it travels about one-fifth of a mile. Each soldier in a column marching behind a band puts his foot to the ground at the instant when he hears the beat of the drum, but since the sound takes an appreciable time to reach the soldiers at the rear of a long column, the soldiers at the front and rear are seldom in step with one another. When large numbers of people take part in community singing, the sounds from those more distant reach any point some time after the same notes have been sung by those nearer, and since each person tends to wait for everyone else to " catch up," the tune usually becomes slower and slower. Similarly, a flash of lightning often precedes by some seconds the roll of thunder which is produced simultaneously with it. We have now to see how the speed of sound is measured.

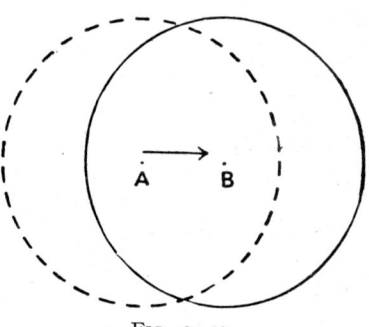

FIG. 24.07.

A stone thrown into water produces waves which spread out in circles, and if the stone falls into the water at the point A (figure 24.07), the wave produced forms a circle round A, such as that shown dotted in the figure. When the water is moving, the waves are carried forward with the stream, and if the stone falls at the point A, and by a certain instant the water originally at A has been carried forward to B, then at this instant the wave forms a circle round the point B.

Sound waves are carried forward in moving air in a similar manner. If the velocity of the wind is v, and that of sound is V, the sound waves travel relative to the ground with a velocity of $(V + v)$ in the direction of the wind, and with a velocity of $(V - v)$ in the opposite direction. The average of these two velocities is $\dfrac{(V + v) + (V - v)}{2}$, or V. Hence, the velocity of sound in still air is equal to the average of its velocities with and against the wind, and can be calculated if the latter are known.

The velocity of sound was first measured accurately by French physicists at the beginning of the eighteenth century. The

principle of the method used is as follows : Observers with
cannon are posted at two stations about 10 miles apart. A
cannon is fired at station A, and an observer at station B
measures the interval of time which elapses between the arrival
of the flash of the cannon and the report. Light travels almost
instantaneously between the two stations, so this interval is
equal to the time required for sound to travel from A to B,
and the velocity of the sound in this direction is calculated by
dividing the distance between the stations by the time interval.
Immediately the sound is heard at station B, a cannon is fired
there, and an observer at A notes the time interval between
the arrival of the flash and the report. This enables the velocity
of sound from B to A to be calculated, and the average of the
two velocities so found is the velocity of sound in still air.

In this way it was shown that :

  (a) **The velocity of sound does not depend upon the barometric
    pressure.** It is the same at high altitudes as near sea level.

  (b) The velocity increases when the temperature increases.
    **The velocity varies directly as the square root of the
    absolute temperature.**

  (c) The velocity of sound in dry, still air at 0° C. is 332 metres
    per second (1090 ft. per second).

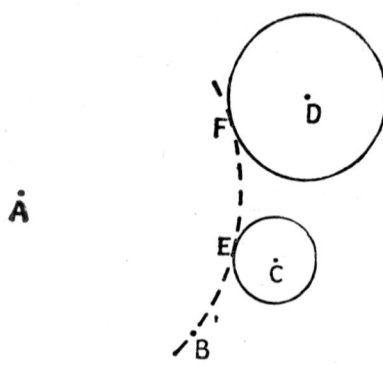

FIG. 24.08.—SOUND RANGING.

Since the tune played
by a distant band sounds
fainter, but otherwise
similar to that which is
heard nearer the band,
it is obvious that *high
notes and low notes all
travel at the same speed.*

24.06. During the war
of 1914–18 a knowledge
of the velocity of sound
was put to use in locating
enemy guns. Suppose
that the three observa-
tion stations B, C, D in
figure 24.08 are fitted

with apparatus which enables the times of arrival of the sound
of gunfire to be compared accurately, and suppose that station
C observes a report t_1 seconds after station B, and station D

observes the same report t_2 seconds after B. During t_1 seconds sound waves travel a distance $V.t_1$ where V is the velocity of sound. Hence, the sound waves were a distance Vt_1 from C when they were observed at B, and were therefore at this instant at some point on the circle of radius $V.t_1$ drawn round C. Similarly, they were at the same instant at some point on the circle of radius $V.t_2$ drawn round D.

The sound waves themselves form circles at any given instant round the gun which fired, so at the instant when the wave reached B its front must have been the circle BEF, which passes through B and touches the other two circles at E and F. Hence, the gun which fired was at A, the centre of this circle. In practice six observation posts were used to obtain greater accuracy, and enemy guns could be located in this way to within about 50 yards.

EXAMPLES 24

1. Distinguish between transverse and longitudinal wave motion, and give two examples of each.

2. The velocity of sound in still air at 0° C. and barometric pressure 76 cm. is 1090 ft. per second. Calculate its velocity in air at 60 cm. pressure and at 20° C.

3. How would you find the distance of a thunderstorm, the thunder and lightning of which can be heard and seen ?

4. When the end of an iron pipe a hundred yards long is tapped once with a hammer, a person at the far end hears two taps. Explain why this is so.

5. Give an account of sound ranging as applied to the location of enemy artillery.

School Certificate Questions

6. Sound waves are passing through a substance. Describe with the help of careful diagrams (a) the movement of a particle of the substance, (b) how this movement changes from particle to particle along the line of propagation. Describe briefly one method of measuring the velocity of sound in air. (C)

7. Explain what you understand by wave motion, using as an example the ripples formed when a stone is dropped into water. How do the sound waves from a tuning fork differ from these ? Define frequency, wave length, and wave velocity, stating the relation between them. (L)

8. Describe *one* experiment to explain each of the following : (a) The source of sound is a vibrating body. (b) Do sounds pass through a vacuum ? (c) Sound is transmitted by a wave motion.

What evidence is there for believing that sound does or does not pass through solids and liquids ? (O)

CHAPTER 25

PITCH AND INTENSITY

25.01. When a tuning-fork is giving out sound, each of its prongs is vibrating backwards and forwards. At each vibration of a prong the air in front of it is compressed; this air compresses the next layer of air, which in turn compresses the following one, and in this way a sound wave is sent out through the air. The number of sound waves produced in each second, or the frequency of the sound, thus depends upon the number of vibrations per second of the fork, or as it is called, the frequency of the fork. What would be the effect upon the sound produced if the frequency of the fork could be altered?

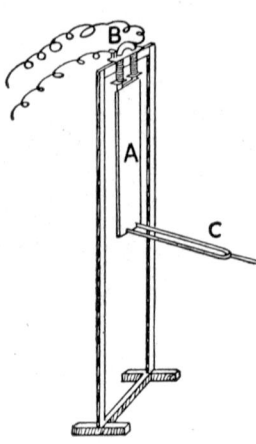

Instead of altering the frequency of one tuning-fork we may use a number of forks whose frequencies are known. If a number of forks are taken in turn and made to vibrate, it is found that the greater the frequency of the fork the higher is the note which it emits. Moreover, if two forks are taken, whose frequencies are (say) 256 per second and 512 per second, it will be found that the second fork gives a note which is the octave of the first. **The frequency of the sound waves determines the pitch of the sound,** and by doubling the frequency of the sound waves a note is produced which is the octave of the first note.

Fig. 25.01. — Determination of the Frequency of a Tuning-fork by means of a Falling Plate.

The frequency of a tuning-fork is often marked on the fork. The method of determining its frequency is as follows:

A strip of paper is covered with soot by holding it over a

smoky flame. This paper is attached to the front of a heavy steel plate A (figure 25.01), supported from an electromagnet B. A bristle is attached to one prong of the tuning-fork C, and the fork is so supported in front of the plate that when the latter is allowed to fall, the bristle rubs the soot away and marks a line on the paper. The tuning-fork is maintained in vibration by an electrical method, the details of which do not concern us here, and since the vibration of the fork is at right angles to the direction of fall of the plate, the bristle marks a wavy line on the paper as the plate falls. The trace obtained is shown in figure 25.02.

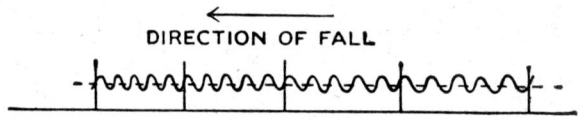

DIRECTION OF FALL

FIG. 25.02.—WAVE TRACE OBTAINED WITH THE FALLING PLATE.

The length of a wave on the wave trace is the distance fallen by the plate during the corresponding vibration of the fork, and the fact that the plate gains speed as it falls is shown by the greater wave length of the waves near the top of the plate. The waves are marked off in sets of five, and the lengths of the various sets are measured. Column I of the following table shows the results of such an experiment, and column II the average length of a wave in each of the successive sets. If n is the frequency of the fork, each vibration takes $\frac{1}{n}$ seconds, and since a wave length is the distance fallen by the plate in this time, the average velocity is found by dividing the wave length by $\frac{1}{n}$; i.e. by multiplying it by n. Hence, the average velocities are as shown in column III (see page 328).

The fork marks the first 5 waves in the time between time zero and $\frac{5}{n}$ seconds, so the average velocity for the first set of waves may be taken as that at the time $\frac{2\cdot5}{n}$. The other figures in column IV are obtained in a similar way. Plotting

I Length of 5 Waves (cm.)	II Average Length of 1 Wave (cm.).	III Average Velocity (cm. per sec.)	IV Time (seconds)
2·20	0·440	0·440n	2·5/n
2·60	0·520	0·520n	7·5/n
2·97	0·594	0·594n	12·5/n
3·34	0·668	0·668n	17·5/n
3·74	0·748	0·748n	22·5/n
4·10	0·820	0·820n	27·5/n
4·46	0·892	0·892n	32·5/n

the average velocities against the corresponding times given in column IV, figure 25.03 is obtained. During $\frac{30}{n}$ seconds the

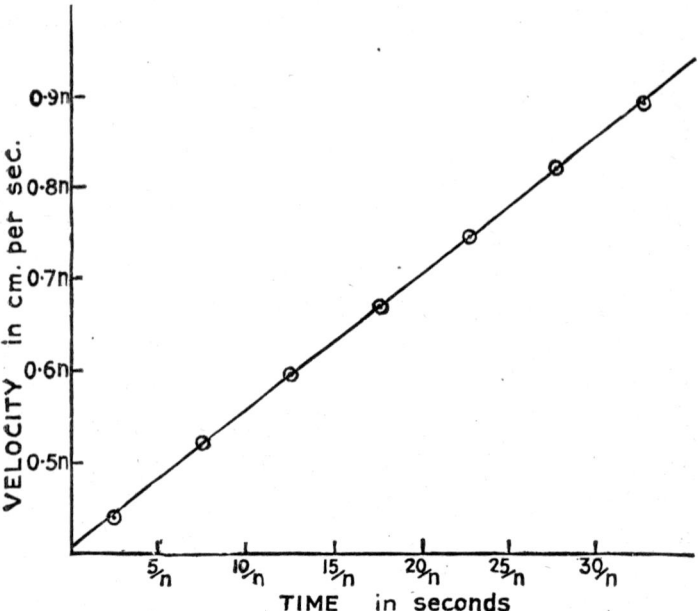

Fig. 25.03.—Velocity-time Graph for the Falling Plate.

velocity of the plate increases from $0.408n$ cm. per second to $0.858n$ cm. per second. Its acceleration is therefore,

$$\frac{0.858n - 0.408n}{\dfrac{30}{n}} = \frac{0.450n^2}{30} \text{ cm. per sec. per sec.}$$

In books on mechanics it is shown that the acceleration of a freely falling body, such as the steel plate, is 981 cm. per sec. per sec. Hence,

$$\frac{0.450n^2}{30} = 981, \text{ so } n = 256.$$

That is, the fork vibrates 256 times per second.

25.02. There are other methods of determining the frequency of a note. One of the simplest of these is by means of the apparatus known as *Savart's wheel* (after Félix Savart, 1791–1841). A wheel, the rim of which is fitted with a number of teeth, is turned rapidly by means of an electric motor. When a card is held against the rim of the wheel, the card receives a blow each time one of the teeth passes it. Each movement of the card compresses the air near it and starts a compression wave in the air, and the number of waves produced per second is equal to the number of teeth which strike the card per second. Hence, if the electric motor makes s revolutions per second, and the wheel has r teeth, the frequency n of the note produced is :

$$n = r.s.$$

The number of revolutions of the motor per second is determined by means of a watch and a revolution counter, by finding the number of revolutions in a given time, say 1 minute.

The Savart wheel may be used for determining the frequency of a note emitted by a musical instrument such as a piano, for the frequency depends only on the pitch of the note. It is therefore only necessary to adjust the speed of the Savart wheel until it gives a note of the same pitch as that given by the piano. The frequencies of the two notes are then equal, and that of the piano note is found by measuring the frequency of the note given by the wheel.

If two toothed wheels are attached to the same axle, the frequencies of the notes they produce will be in the same ratio as the numbers of teeth on the wheels. If one wheel has double the number of teeth of the second, it produces a note which is the octave of that given by the second wheel. Increasing the speed of the motor raises the pitches of both notes, but at any given speed the first wheel produces a note an octave higher than that of the second.

25.03. The siren (figure 25.04) works in a similar way. A disc A is attached to the shaft B of an electric motor, by means

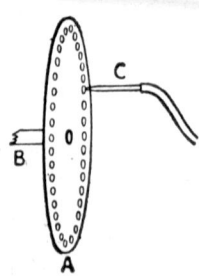

FIG. 25.04.—SIREN.

of which it is rotated. Around the rim of the disc are pierced a number of small holes, and a current of air is directed by the tube C on to these holes as the disc rotates. Each time a hole passes the tube a puff of air passes through the disc, compresses the air on the far side, and starts a compression wave. These waves, following one another at regular short intervals, produce a musical note. If the disc rotates at the rate of s revolutions per second, and contains r holes, the frequency n of the note emitted is given by the formula, $n = r.s.$

By using a thick disc, and directing the jet of air obliquely against the sides of the holes, the disc may be driven by the jet of air instead of by an electric motor. The speed of the disc can then be regulated by altering the pressure of the air at the jet, but the arrangement is very sensitive to changes of this pressure, and it is not easy to keep the speed constant. In factory sirens where the loudness, and not the pitch of the note, is important, the siren is driven in this way by jets of steam.

25.04. When a locomotive passes through a station with its whistle sounding, the pitch of the note appears, to observers on the platform, to fall suddenly as the engine passes. Similarly, the hum of a fast-moving motor-car appears to an onlooker to be of a lower pitch when it is receding than when it is approaching. This sudden fall of pitch is evidently caused by the motion of the source of sound past the observer, for people in the train or motor-car observe no alteration of pitch. The phenomenon is called the **Doppler effect** (after the Austrian physicist, Christian Doppler, 1803–1853). Its explanation is as follows:

Let us suppose first that the source of sound is stationary at A (figure 25.05) and that it emits a note of frequency n. If

the velocity of sound is V the waves travel a distance V in
1 second, so an observer at B, a distance V from A, receives
a wave at the instant when the wave emitted 1 second later
is starting from A.   Since n waves are emitted per second there
are n waves between the points A and B.

Let us now suppose that the source of sound is moving towards

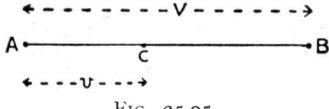

FIG. 25.05.

B with a velocity v, so that in 1 second it travels from A to C,
where the distance AC is v units of length.   The motion of the
source of sound makes no difference to the speed with which
the sound travels, so while the source is moving from A to C
the first wave is travelling from A to B.   The last wave emitted
during the second of time, however, starts from C, so n waves
are crowded into the length CB.   There are now n waves in a
length $(V - v)$, so in a length V there will be a number of
waves n_1, where

$$n_1 = \left(\frac{V}{V - v}\right)n \quad . \quad . \quad . \quad . \quad . \quad . \quad (1)$$

During 1 second the train of waves moves forward a distance V,
and all the waves in this length of wave train reach the ear of
the stationary observer during 1 second.   He therefore hears a
note of frequency n_1.

After the source of sound has passed the observer at B
(figure 25.06) the source of sound moves from A to C in 1 second.

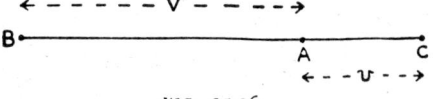

FIG. 25.06.

The first wave sent out in this second reaches B at the same
instant that the nth wave is leaving C, so the n waves now
occupy a length $(V + v)$.   Since a length V of the wave train
reaches the observer in 1 second, the number of waves he receives
in 1 second is:

$$n_2 = \left(\frac{V}{V + v}\right)n.$$

The ratio of the frequencies of the notes he hears is, therefore :

$$\frac{n_1}{n_2} = \left(\frac{V}{V-v}\right)n \Big/ \left(\frac{V}{V+v}\right)n$$

$$\therefore \frac{n_1}{n_2} = \frac{V+v}{V-v}.$$

Suppose, for example, that a train passes through a station at 88 ft. per second (60 miles per hour). Taking the velocity of sound as 1100 ft. per second, we have :

$$\frac{n_1}{n_2} = \frac{1100 + 88}{1100 - 88} = \frac{27}{23}.$$

The pitch of the note heard as the train recedes would in this case be more than a tone of the musical scale lower than that heard as it approaches.

It is clear that, if the velocity of sound is known, and n_1 and n are measured, formula (1) above would enable v, the velocity of the source of sound, to be calculated. It is usually much simpler to measure v than the frequencies n_1 and n, so this method is seldom employed with sound waves. The Doppler effect is used, however, to measure the velocities with which stars are approaching the earth. By experiments beyond the scope of this book it has been shown that light also consists of a wave motion, and the frequencies of various kinds of light waves are known. When light waves are emitted from stars which are travelling rapidly towards the earth, the frequency appears to be too high, and by measuring the apparent frequency of these waves, the velocity of approach of a star may be determined.

If sound is emitted from a source which is stationary, and the observer travels towards the source of sound, the pitch of the note heard is raised. Thus, if A (figure 25.07) is the posi-

Fig. 25.07.

tion of a source which emits n waves per second, n waves will occupy the distance AC, where AC contains V units of length. A stationary observer at C would receive n waves per second.

If the observer moves from B to C in 1 second with a velocity u, he receives not only the n waves which reach B during a second, but also the waves between B and C. Since BC is u units of length, there are $\frac{u}{V}.n$ waves in the length BC, so the observer receives n_1 waves in 1 second, where

$$n_1 = n + \frac{u}{V}.n$$

$$\therefore \ n_1 \doteq \left(1 + \frac{u}{V}\right).n$$

$$\therefore \ n_1 \doteq \left(\frac{V + u}{V}\right)n.$$

This formula gives the frequency of the sound observed by the moving observer. In the same way it may be shown that the frequency n_2 of the sound heard by an observer moving away from the source of sound with a velocity u is given by the formula :

$$n_2 = \left(\frac{V - u}{V}\right).n.$$

25.05. In the case of the sounds emitted by such sources as a tuning-fork or a piano, each sound has a definite pitch with which is associated a definite frequency, but this is not true of all sounds. The crack of a whip, or the sound made by rubbing two objects together has no definite pitch, and the sound waves do not form a regular series with a particular wave length and frequency. Such sounds as these are called **noises,** and the sounds which possess a particular pitch and frequency are called **musical notes.**

25.06. Besides differing in pitch, sounds differ in loudness, or intensity. **The loudness of a sound depends upon the energy of the sound waves reaching the ear.**

The motion of a gas molecule in a gas through which sound waves are passing can be imitated by means of the apparatus shown in figure 25.08. A lead bob A is fastened to the lower end of a spiral spring B. When the bob is pulled downwards to the position C and is released, it flies upwards, overshoots its initial position at A, and continues to move up and down between the positions C and D. The distance AC or AD is called the *amplitude* of the vibration. Since the motion of the bob is in a vertical direction, its motion corresponds to that of a molecule in a gas through which sound waves are travelling vertically upwards or downwards.

The force exerted by the spring at any instant is a force tending to restore the bob to its initial position A, and this force varies directly as the distance of the bob from A. A body which moves under the action of such a force is said to move with *simple harmonic motion*.

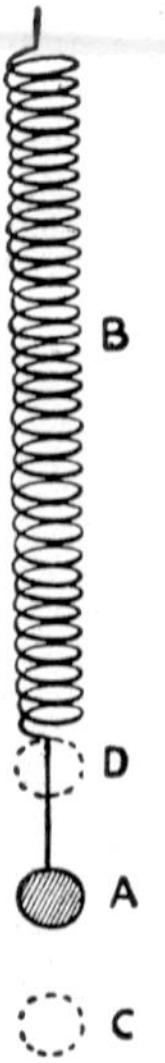

To find the work done by the spring in pulling the bob from C to A, the average force is multiplied by the distance CA. If F is the restoring force exerted by the spring when the bob is at C, the average force is $\dfrac{F}{2}$, so the work done in pulling the bob back from C to A is $\dfrac{Fa_1}{2}$, where a_1 is the distance CA, or the amplitude of the motion. Hence, the kinetic energy of the bob when it passes through the position A is $\dfrac{Fa_1}{2}$.

If the amplitude of vibration of the bob is increased to a_2, the restoring force exerted by the spring at the lowest position of the bob becomes $F \times \dfrac{a_2}{a_1}$, so the kinetic energy gained by the bob will then be, $\dfrac{F.a_2}{a_1} \times \dfrac{a_2}{2}$. Let E_1 and E_2 be the kinetic energies of the bob in the two cases.

FIG. 25.08.

$$\frac{E_1}{E_2} = \frac{Fa_1}{2} \bigg/ \frac{Fa_2{}^2}{2a_1}$$

$$\therefore \frac{E_1}{E_2} = \frac{a_1{}^2}{a_2{}^2}.$$

In words, **the energy of a body which vibrates with simple harmonic motion varies directly as the square of the amplitude of vibration.**

Each molecule in a gas through which sound waves are passing vibrates with simple harmonic motion, and since the energy of the sound wave consists of the sum of the energies of the vibrating molecules, its energy varies directly as the square of the amplitude of vibration of the individual molecules.

Extremely loud sounds cause a tingling sensation in the ear, and still louder sounds are painful, and may cause damage to the ear. The human ear is an extremely sensitive instrument for detecting sound waves, for it is able to perceive sounds whose intensity is about one million-millionth of that of the loud sounds which cause pain.

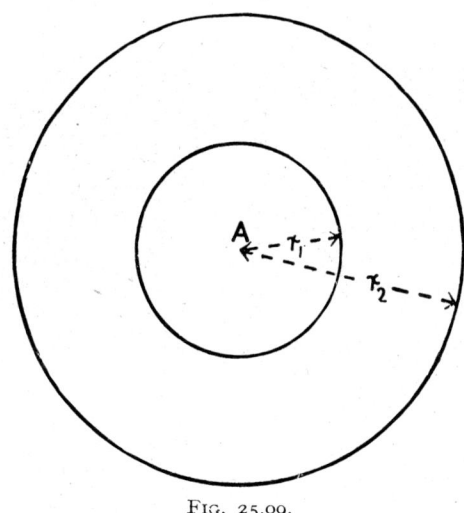

Fig. 25.09.

25.07. The intensity of a sound wave decreases as it moves away from the source of sound. Suppose that sound waves are sent out by a source of sound at A (figure 25.09). The waves spread out as spheres around the point A, so at a given instant a sound wave forms a sphere of radius r_1; a little later the same wave forms a sphere of radius r_2. Assuming that none of the sound energy is converted into other forms of energy, the same quantity of sound energy crosses the first and second spheres per second. If Q units of energy cross each sphere per second, the quantity crossing unit area of the first sphere is

$\dfrac{Q}{4\pi r_1{}^2}$; that crossing unit area of the second sphere, $\dfrac{Q}{4\pi r_2{}^2}$. These quantities of energy are in the ratio

$$\frac{E_1}{E_2} = \frac{Q}{4\pi r_1{}^2} \bigg/ \frac{Q}{4\pi r_2{}^2} = \frac{r_2{}^2}{r_1{}^2}$$

In other words, **the energy received on unit area varies inversely as the square of the distance from the source.** A sound is thus only one-quarter as loud at double the distance from the source, one-ninth as loud at three times the distance, and so on.

The above rule is only true if the sound waves are able to spread out freely in all directions. If the sound waves are produced at the end of a long tube, for example, they are unable

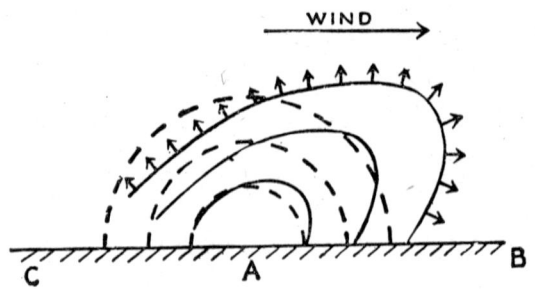

FIG. 25.10.—THE EFFECT OF THE WIND ON SOUND WAVES.

to spread, and even faint sounds may be heard at considerable distances.

In the open air the wind plays a considerable part in determining how far away from the source sounds may be heard. In still air sound waves spread out from a source near the ground as shown by the semicircles in figure 25.10. When a wind is blowing, however, the waves are carried forward by the wind. Near the ground the velocity of the wind is smaller than it is higher up, where the obstacles at the surface of the earth— trees, buildings, hills, etc.—have less effect upon the motion of the air. Consequently, the waves are carried forward faster by the wind farther from the ground, and the form of successive waves is similar to that shown in the figure. Waves, however, advance at right angles to the face of the wave, so the directions in which various parts of the wave are travelling are those shown by the small arrows. It is clear that the wave to the right of A is directed downwards, and will be perceived by an observer at B; the waves on the left, however, are directed upwards and will pass over the head of an observer at C. If the person at C climbs a ladder he may reach a position in the path of the sound waves, and hear the sounds which were not perceptible nearer the ground.

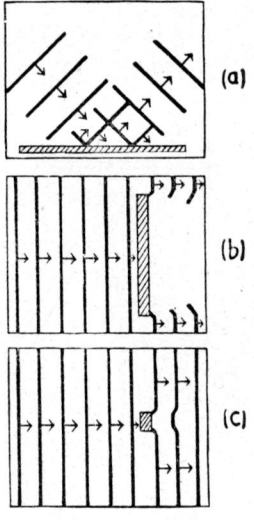

FIG. 25.11.—THE REFLEC- TION OF WAVES.

25.08. By means of the ripple tank it may be shown that water waves are reflected when they meet an obstacle [figure 25.11 (a)]. If such waves meet an object whose length is considerably greater than the wave length of the wave train, the water behind the object remains still as shown in figure 25.11 (b); but an object whose length is smaller than the wave length makes little difference to the progress of the waves [figure 25.11 (c)].

The same facts are true of sound waves. The wave lengths of many sound waves are so large, however, that the waves bend round any but large objects. The frequency of the middle C of the musical scale, for example, is 256 per second. The velocity of sound is 1100 ft. per second, so if l is the wave length of the waves,

$$V = n.l$$
i.e. $1100 = 256.l$
$$\therefore\ l = \frac{1100}{256} = 4 \text{ ft. approximately.}$$

To prevent sound waves of this pitch from bending round an object, the object must be considerably more than 4 ft. in length and breadth.

If the pitch is higher, however, the wave length of the sound waves is shorter, and smaller objects will form sound " shadows." The sounds produced by a watch, for example, consist chiefly of high-pitched notes, and a book placed between a watch and the ear cuts off the sound completely. If the book is placed behind the watch, however, the waves are reflected to the ear, and the watch can be heard at a greater distance. In a building a short distance from a busy street, the noise of the traffic is heard as a deep rumble, because the high-pitched sounds are shut off by the intervening buildings, whereas the longer waves of the lower notes bend round the obstacles.

To demonstrate the reflection of sound the apparatus shown in figure 25.12 may be used. Since sound waves of short wave length bend less readily round the reflecting object, such waves are reflected best, and to produce such waves a Galton whistle may be used. To detect the waves, gas is burned at a narrow jet. The gas burns steadily, but when the gas pressure is increased the flame becomes unstable and flares. Such a flame is adjusted until it is just on the point of flaring, and the arrival of sound waves then disturbs the steady flow of gas, and causes the flame to duck and flare.

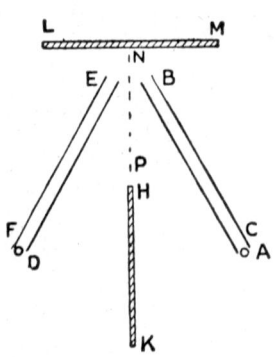

FIG. 25.12.—THE REFLECTION OF SOUND WAVES.

The whistle A is placed just inside the metal tube BC, and the sensitive flame D at the end of a similar tube EF. A screen HK shields the flame from sound waves travelling in the direction of the flame, and a second screen LM is used to reflect into the tube EF the sound waves travelling down the tube BC. It is found that, when the flame is disturbed, the two tubes make equal angles with the normal PN to the reflecting board, and that the tubes and the normal lie in one plane. In other words, sound obeys the same laws of reflection as light, and as in the case of the reflection of light:

(1) The reflected sound ray, the incident ray, and the normal to the reflector at the point of incidence lie in one plane;

(2) The angle of reflection is equal to the angle of incidence.

Sound waves may be reflected also by large spherical mirrors. The sound waves from a watch placed at the principal focus of a concave mirror may be reflected as a parallel beam across a room, and brought to a focus at the ear by means of a second mirror.

25.09. Out of doors, sound waves are sometimes reflected from a large distant object such as a cliff or wood. Since the sound takes an appreciable time to travel to the distant reflecting surface and back again, the reflected sound is received after the original sound has died away, and in such cases an *echo* is said to be produced.

In a large hall used for music or public speaking echoes are occasionally very troublesome. If the sound is reflected backwards and forwards for several seconds between the ceiling and the walls, the echoes of one word are heard while the speaker is pronouncing the next, and it is impossible to follow what is being said. To reduce the echoes in such cases, the walls or ceiling may be covered with a layer of some material such as felt, which absorbs most of the sound waves falling upon it. If an audience is present, the echoes are much reduced, since clothes are good absorbers of sound. For this reason it is often much easier to speak before a large audience than in a nearly empty hall.

It might be imagined that the best-designed hall for public speaking would be one in which echoes were completely absent. This is not so, however, because a certain amount of reflection aids in producing a sufficient volume of sound. In the open air, where echoes are usually absent, it is difficult to make sounds audible to a large crowd. It is found in practice that those halls are best, where the echo can be heard for about 2 seconds after the original sound.

By studying the behaviour of waves in models of buildings, it is possible to calculate whether any particular design of building will be suitable for music or speaking. Sound waves may be photographed as they pass through such models. To do this, a sound is produced by an electric spark, and a very short time later a second spark produces light, by means of which the interior of the model is photographed. Light is refracted in the air at those points where it is compressed by the sound wave, and the latter is shown on the photograph as a pair of dark and light bands. The upper picture in figure 25.13 was obtained in this way.

A simpler method is to photograph the water waves in a ripple tank, in which stands a model of the proposed building.

The apparatus used for this purpose is shown in figure 25.14, and the lower photograph in figure 25.13 was obtained in this way.

25.10. If the velocity of sound in a given medium is V and the sound waves are reflected back to the source by a reflecting surface at a distance s, the waves travel a distance $2s$, and therefore arrive back at the source after a time t, where

$$t = \frac{2s}{V}.$$

Hence, if the velocity of the sound waves is known, the distance of the distant reflecting surface may be calculated by measuring t.

In water, sound travels at 5000 ft. per second, so if sounds are produced under water, the waves are reflected from the bottom of the water after a very short interval of time.

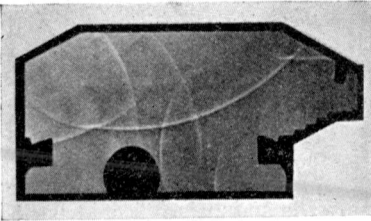

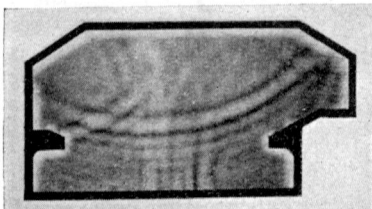

[From " Modern Acoustics," by A. H. Davis, by courtesy of G. Bell & Sons, Ltd.

FIG. 25.13.—SOUND WAVES IN A MODEL BUILDING.

[From " Modern Acoustics," by A. H. Davis, by courtesy of G. Bell & Sons, Ltd.

FIG. 25.14.—RIPPLES IN A MODEL BUILDING.

Nevertheless, apparatus has been developed for measuring the interval between the time at which sound waves are emitted and that at which the echo arrives, and such apparatus is used for measuring the depths of the ocean below the ship containing it. Echo sounding has also been applied to assist in the discovery of wrecks on the floor of the ocean.

25.11. In figure 25.15 (*a*) and (*b*) are shown sections through two waves travelling across the surface of water. The wave length of the second set of waves is six-sevenths that of the first set. Let us suppose that both of these wave trains are caused to pass in the same direction across a water surface at the same time, as shown diagrammatically in figure 25.15 (*c*). At certain points, such as at A and B, a crest of one set of waves coincides with a trough of the other set, and here the effect of one set of waves counteracts that of the second set, and there is little disturbance of the water surface. At other points such as C, D, and E the crests of one set of waves coincide with crests of the other set, and at such points the depth of the waves is increased. The resulting appearance of the water surface is that shown in figure 25.15 (*d*). This resultant train of

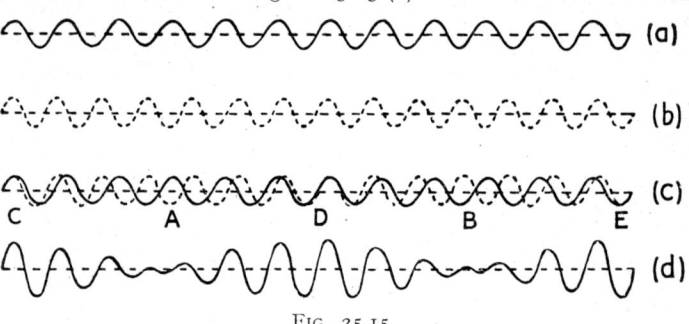

FIG. 25.15.

waves travels over the surface as a whole, so at any given point on the water surface the water is alternately almost at rest and then considerably disturbed.

Sound waves behave in a similar way, the compressions of one set of waves serving to neutralize rarefactions of the other set at some points, and to reinforce compressions in the other set at other points. When two notes of nearly equal frequencies are sounded (*e.g.* by means of two tuning-forks of nearly equal pitches) the two notes are heard as one, but the intensity of this note alternately increases and decreases. These alternations of intensity are called **beats**.

Let us suppose that N beats are produced per second by two forks whose frequencies are such that the first makes x vibrations in the time during which the other makes $(x + 1)$ vibrations, and suppose that at a given instant each fork is sending out a compression. These two waves reinforce one another and produce an intense sound. When the first fork has completed x vibrations it is sending out a compression, and the other fork has completed $(x + 1)$ vibrations and is sending out a compression which reinforces that from the first fork. This will occur each time the first fork completes x vibrations, so the sounds emitted by the forks reinforce one another each time the first fork completes x vibrations. There are N beats per second, so the first fork completes Nx vibrations per second; that is, its frequency is Nx. Similarly, the frequency of the second fork is $N(x + 1)$. Hence, the difference between the two frequencies is $[N(x + 1) - Nx]$, or N. **The number of beats produced per second is equal to the difference between the frequencies of the sources of sound.**

When only a few beats per second are heard, the effect upon the ear is not unpleasant. Two notes of nearly the same pitch may, however, produce a large number of beats per second, and if the number of beats is greater than about 16, the separate beats are not distinguishable and a discordant, unpleasant noise is heard.

By using the phenomenon of beats, it is possible to judge accurately whether two notes are of the same pitch. If their frequencies are exactly equal no beats are heard when they are sounded together, but if their frequencies differ only slightly, slow beats are produced. A slightly greater difference of frequency causes more rapid beating, and a still greater difference leads to the notes being heard as a discord.

When two notes of nearly equal frequencies are sounded together the difference of frequency may be found by counting the number of beats produced per second. To find which note has the higher frequency, it is necessary to alter the frequency of one of the sources of sound, and to count the beats again. Thus, if two tuning-forks produce 3 beats per second, and the frequency of one of them is known to be 256 per second, the frequency of the other is either 253 or 259 per second. The second fork is next loaded by attaching a small piece of wax to one of the prongs. The wax decreases the frequency of the fork, and if it is now found that the two forks give 6 beats per second, its frequency is either 262 or 250 per second. If the piece of wax is so small that it could not reduce the frequency by more than 3 or 4 vibrations per second, it is obvious that it has decreased the frequency from 253 to 250 per second, and not from 259 to 250, so the frequency of the first fork without the wax must be 253 per second.

EXAMPLES 25

1. Explain the action of a Savart wheel. How may it be used to determine the frequency of a tuning-fork ?

2. What is meant by the Doppler effect ? A locomotive passes through a station with the whistle sounding. If the speed of the locomotive is 60 m.p.h. and the frequency of the note emitted is 2000 per second, calculate its apparent frequency to an observer on the station (a) while the locomotive is approaching, (b) while it is receding. Take the speed of sound as 1100 ft. per second.

3. On what factors does the intensity of a sound depend ? The " inverse square law " describes how the intensity of a sound decreases when the distance from the source increases, if the waves spread out as concentric spheres round the source. How would you expect the intensity to decrease when the distance from the source increases (a) if the source is a locomotive at the middle of a tunnel, (b) if the source is just above the surface of a lake ? Give reasons.

4. At a certain point in the open air near a wooded valley an echo can be heard if a loud, high-pitched sound is produced, but no echo is heard when the sound is a low note of similar intensity. Explain how the echo is produced, and account for the fact that none is heard in the second case.

SCHOOL CERTIFICATE QUESTIONS

5. How would you determine the frequency of a tuning-fork ? Describe the experiment you would carry out, state the data you would require, and explain the calculations you would make. (L)

6. Describe how sound is transmitted from a sounding body to the ear. Explain the action of a speaking tube. (L)

7. How are echoes produced ? Make a careful diagram illustrating how the waves from a source of sound are reflected at a plane surface. An observer at a certain distance from a cliff notes that the interval between the sound he makes and its echo is 3 seconds.

He then walks 550 ft. nearer to the cliff and finds that the corresponding interval is 2 seconds. Calculate (a) the velocity of sound, (b) the observer's original distance from the cliff. (J)

8. Explain what is meant by (a) *frequency*, (b) *wave length* of a sound in air. Deduce the relation between these quantities and the velocity of the sound. Describe a siren and explain how it can be used (a) to determine the frequency of a note of a given tuning-fork, (b) to investigate the connection between a note and its octave. (J)

9. How would you show that sound waves are reflected by a hard surface in accordance with a definite law ? State this law. Explain why the sound of your voice appears to you to be much louder when you are speaking in an empty hall than when you are speaking in the same hall filled with people. (J)

10. Describe a method by which the velocity of sound in air can be determined. The wind is blowing from the north ; why are sounds which I make more audible to the south of me than to the north ? I stand in a position where I can hear a clear echo of the sound of the clap of my hands. After careful listening I find I can keep time at clapping again as each echo reaches me. A companion standing beside me counts that I make 80 claps in 1 minute. The velocity of sound in air is 1120 ft. per second. Find the distance from me of the object causing the echo. (O)

11. (a) Give a drawing of a transverse wave train of wave length 3 cm. and amplitude 1 cm. (b) If these waves are propagated at a speed of 300 metres per second, find their frequency. (c) Assuming that these waves represent a train of sound waves, give a drawing of a wave system representing a louder sound of higher pitch. (d) In what way or ways do the waves which you have drawn differ from sound waves ? (O)

12. Describe and explain the phenomenon of " beats." You are given two tuning-forks of nearly the same frequency. Assuming that the frequency of one of these forks is known, how would you determine that of the other ? (C)

CHAPTER 26

THE VIBRATION OF A STRETCHED STRING—RESONANCE AND FORCED VIBRATIONS

26.01. In many musical instruments sound is produced by causing a tightly stretched wire or string to vibrate. The sonometer (figure 26.01) enables the laws relating to the vibration of such wires to be determined. The wire A is held at each end by a peg, and passes over two fixed bridges D and E.

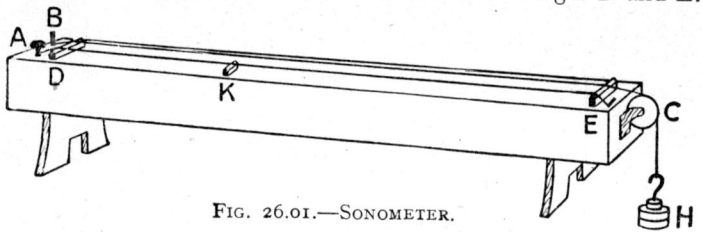

FIG. 26.01.—SONOMETER.

The string B passes at one end over a pulley C, and supports weights H. By adding or removing weights, the tension of this string may be varied. A movable bridge K can be placed at any desired position, to alter the length of wire which vibrates. By plucking either string, it can be caused to vibrate and emit sound.

The following table shows the results obtained in an experiment in which the tension of the wire was kept constant, while its length l was altered. The frequency n of the vibrating wire was obtained in each case by altering its length until it vibrated in unison with a tuning-fork of known frequency.

Referring to the first and fourth lines of the table it will be seen that when the frequency is doubled the length of the wire is about halved, so the product of n and l is the same. The third column shows the product of n and l for each pair of readings. Allowing for experimental errors these products are equal for all the sets of readings. Hence :

If the tension of a wire remains constant its frequency of vibration varies inversely as the length of the wire.

n (Vibrations per second)	l (cm.)	$n \times l$
160	79·5	12720
192	66·3	12730
256	49·7	12720
320	39·8	12730
384	33·1	12710
512	24·9	12750

26.02. The wire passing over the pulley was next used, and its length was kept constant while the tension was altered. The following results were obtained, The frequencies were

n (Vibrations per second)	T (Tension in grams weight)	$\dfrac{\sqrt{T}}{n}$
192	1770	0·220
256	3130	0·219
320	4910	0·219
384	7040	0·219
512	12500	0·218

found by means of tuning-forks of known frequencies. The first and second columns give the experimental results ; the third column is found by dividing the square root of the tension by the frequency. Since the values in this column remain constant :

The frequency of vibration of a wire varies directly as the square root of its tension when its length remains constant.

26.03. When one of the sonometer wires is replaced by a heavier wire, the pitch of the note emitted is lower. The next table shows results obtained using wires of different sizes. In each case the tension applied to the wire was 10,000 gm.-wt. The mass of unit length of each wire was determined by cutting off a measured length and weighing it, and the results are set out in the first column. The second column shows the length

m (Grams per centimetre)	l Length of String (cm.)	n Frequency	n_{100} Frequency for length 100 cm.	$\sqrt{m}$	$n_{100} \times \sqrt{m}$
0·0031	88·6	320	283	0·0557	15·8
0·0046	72·2	320	231	0·0678	15·7
0·0063	62·4	320	200	0·0794	15·8

of wire required to give a note of the same pitch as a tuning-fork of frequency 320 per second. The fourth column gives the frequency of the note which would have been emitted if the wire had been kept at the same tension while its length was increased to 100 cm. (The method of calculation is illustrated in the example below.) The square root of the mass per unit length of the wire is shown in the fifth column, and the last column gives the results obtained by multiplying the square root of the mass per unit length by the frequency emitted by a wire 100 cm. long. The values shown in this column are equal. Hence :

For wires, whose tensions are equal and whose lengths are equal, the frequency of vibration varies inversely as the square root of the mass per unit length.

EXAMPLES.—(1) *A wire of length 88.6 cm. emits a note of frequency 320 per second when the tension in the wire is 10,000 gm.-wt. Find the frequency of the note emitted by the same wire if its length is increased to 100 cm. and the tension is decreased to 4900 gm.-wt.*

If the tension is kept the same the frequency varies inversely as the length. Hence, if n_1 is the new frequency, when its length is increased to 100 cm. while the tension remains the same,

$$n_1 \times 100 = 320 \times 88.6$$
$$\therefore n_1 = \frac{320 \times 88.6}{100} = 283.4 \text{ per second.}$$

If the tension changes and the length is kept at 100 cm., the frequency varies as the square root of the tension. Let n be the new frequency.

$$\frac{n}{283 \cdot 4} = \frac{\sqrt{4900}}{\sqrt{10,000}}$$

$$\therefore n = 283 \cdot 4 \sqrt{\frac{4900}{10,000}} = 198 \cdot 4 \text{ per second}$$

(2) *Two wires have masses 0·4 and 0·5 gm. per metre respectively. What length of the second wire must be used to obtain a note of the same frequency as that emitted by a 100-cm. length of the first wire, the tensions in the wires being equal?*

Let n_1 and n_2 be the frequencies of vibration of the two wires when the length of each is 100 cm. Since the tensions are equal and the lengths are equal,

$$n_1 \sqrt{\frac{0 \cdot 4}{100}} = n_2 \sqrt{\frac{0 \cdot 5}{100}}$$

$$\therefore n_2 = n_1 \sqrt{\frac{4}{5}}.$$

The frequency varies inversely as the length when the tension is constant. Hence, if the length of the second wire is altered from 100 cm. to l cm., its new frequency n is given by the equation :

$$n.l = n_2 \times 100.$$

$$\therefore n = \frac{100 n_2}{l} = \frac{100}{l} \sqrt{\frac{4}{5}} \times n_1.$$

But the frequency n is to be equal to n_1,

$$\therefore n_1 = \frac{100}{l} \sqrt{\frac{4}{5}} \times n_1,$$

whence $l = 89 \cdot 4$ cm.

26.04. When the wire of a sonometer is plucked at the middle point, the vibration produced is usually similar to that shown in figure 26.02 (*a*). The two ends of the wire remain stationary, and the movement at the middle of the wire is a maximum. It is possible, however, to make the wire vibrate in other ways, such as those shown in figure 26.02 (*b*), (*c*), and (*d*). To obtain a vibration of the type (*b*) the wire is touched with a feather at the middle point A, and plucked at B. To obtain the type of vibration (*c*) the wire is touched at C and plucked at D, and so on. Those points where no movement occurs are called *nodes* ; points where the movement is a maximum are called *anti-nodes*. In every case, however the wire vibrates, there are nodes at each end, but there may be 0, 1, 2, 3 or more nodes at other points on the wire. The existence of these nodes and antinodes may be demonstrated by placing small paper riders on the wire. When the vibration is of the type (c) the rider at the node E is undisturbed, while those at the points F and G are thrown off.

The nodes and antinodes of a vibrating string may be seen with the following arrangement. A steel knitting-needle, clamped at one end, passes through a solenoid, through which flows an alternating electric current. The free end of the knitting-needle is placed between the poles of a **U**-shaped permanent magnet, and is thus caused to vibrate with the same frequency as that of the electric current. A string, several metres long, is fastened at one end to the vibrating needle ; the other end

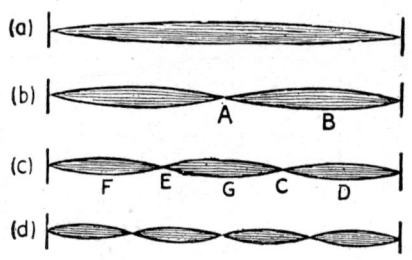

FIG. 26.02.—THE MODES OF VIBRATION OF A STRETCHED WIRE.

of the string passes over a pulley, and supports a scale pan. By adding weights to the scale pan the tension in the string is increased, and by suitably adjusting the tension any desired number of nodes may be obtained.

The string of a sonometer which is vibrating as shown in figure 26.02 (a) is vibrating with its lowest possible frequency, and is said to be emitting its *fundamental note*. When it vibrates as at (b), however, each half of the string vibrates as it would do if the string were clamped at A, and the frequency of vibration is thus equal to that of a string of one-half the length of the complete string, and vibrating with nodes at the ends only. In other words, the frequency of the note emitted is double that of the fundamental note. Similarly, the frequencies of the notes emitted by the string vibrating as at (c) and (d) are respectively three and four times the frequency of the fundamental note. These notes of frequencies 2, 3, 4 . . . times that of the fundamental are called its *harmonics*.

When a string is plucked, or bowed with a violin bow, its

motion is not usually one of the simple types shown in figure 26.02, but consists of a combination of several of these types at the same time. The note heard thus consists of the fundamental note together with several of its harmonics.

26.05. A string which is vibrating with nodes at various points along its length must have the nodes situated at equal distances apart. It is impossible, for example, for a string to vibrate as shown in figure 26.03 (*a*). If it did so, the two parts of the

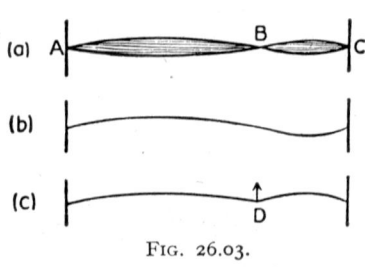

(a)

(b)

(c)

Fig. 26.03.

string, AB and BC, would be of different lengths, and would therefore have different frequencies. Hence, if the string were at one instant as shown at (*b*), it would a little later have some such form as that shown at (*c*). In this case, the two portions of the string would both exert forces on the string near D tending to move it in the direction shown by the arrow, and the string at this point could not remain stationary, as is required if the point D is to be a node.

26.06. Figure 26.04 (*a*) represents a wave ACD travelling

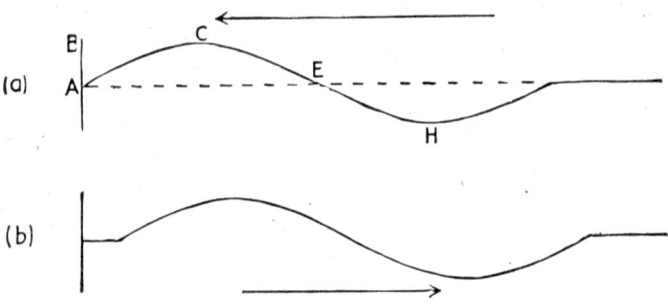

FIG. 26.04.—THE REFLECTION OF A WAVE IN A WIRE.

along a wire from right to left as shown by the arrow, and the wave is shown at the instant when it is arriving at the end of the wire at A. If this end of the wire is held rigidly, the portion AC of the wire exerts a force on the support tending to move it in the direction of the point B. The support therefore exerts an equal and opposite force on the wire, which tends to bring the wire AC back into the straight line AD. The crest ACE is by this means first flattened, and then, owing to the momentum obtained by the wire, converted into a trough. Similarly the trough EHD is converted into a crest when it in turn reaches the point A, and since the new trough formed at A has by this time begun to move back along the wire, the wave is reflected at the

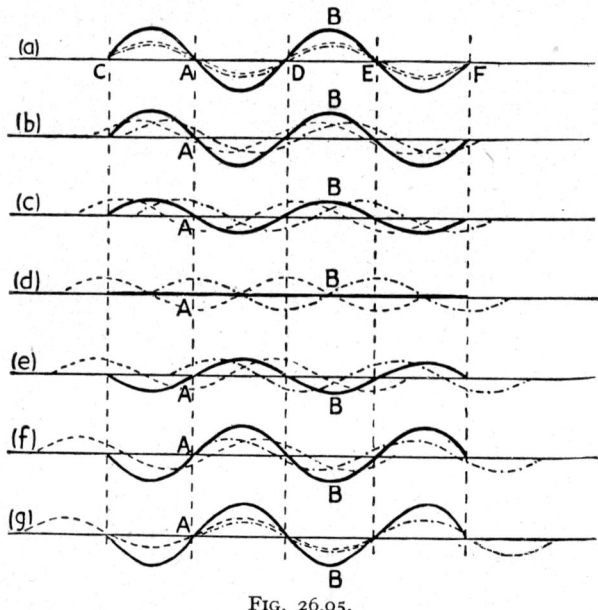

Fig. 26.05.

end of the wire and travels back as shown in figure 26.04 (*b*), with the trough preceding the crest.

It is not possible to follow the progress of waves along a wire because they travel too quickly to be followed by eye, but the reflection of a crest as a trough, and a trough as a crest, may be shown by supporting a length of rubber tubing vertically and producing waves at the lower end.

26.07. Let us now suppose that a series of waves are produced in a wire fixed at both ends. The waves are reflected at the fixed ends of the wire, so there will be a train of waves travelling in each direction along the wire. Figure 26.05 shows a section of the wire near the middle. The two wave trains are represented by the wavy dotted lines (the waves travelling from right to left), and by the dots and dashes (the waves travelling from left to right). At (a) the crests of one set of waves correspond with those of the other set. The two sets of waves then reinforce one another, and produce in the wire a curve as shown by the thick line. An instant later each wave has travelled on a short distance to the positions shown at (b). Here the crests no longer exactly correspond with one another, so the deformation of the wire is smaller. (c), (d), (e), (f) and (g) show the positions of the wave trains and the wire at successive short intervals of time. At (d) the wire has become straight ; at (g) it has reached a maximum of deformation, and is about to go through the successive states shown at (f), (e), (d), etc. until it is again in the shape (a).

Consider now what happens at particular points on the wire. Although either wave train separately would cause motion of the wire at A, the two wave trains together produce none at all at this point. A is a node. Other nodes lie at the points joined by the dotted straight lines in the diagram—at C, D, E, and F—and the distance between successive nodes is half a wave length of the wave trains. Midway between each pair of nodes is an antinode (e.g. at B), where the movement of the wire is a maximum.

The points C A D E F, where the wire is not displaced from its initial position, do not move along the wire, as do the points of no displacement in an ordinary wave system. The wire assumes the form of a wave, but the waves do not travel along it. For this reason such waves as these are called *standing waves*, or *stationary waves*.

26.08. The wire shown in figure 26.05 is stationary at the points C and F, so it would obviously make no difference to the vibrations between these points if the wire were clamped at C and F, and the rest of the wire were removed. We should then have a wire vibrating with three nodes at A, D, and E, and by comparing figure 26.05 with figure 26.02 (d) it will be seen that the vibration is similar in the two cases. Hence, another way of thinking of the vibration shown in figure 26.02 (d) is to regard it as produced by a set of waves travelling along the wire, and being reflected at both its ends.

- The waves which produce the stationary vibrations must be

such as produce nodes at the ends, and they may produce 0, 1, 2, 3, or more nodes in between. The distance between the nodes is half a wave length. Hence, if L is the length of the wire, and l the wave length of the waves, $\frac{1}{2}l = L$ when there are nodes at the ends only. If there is a node at the middle as well, $\frac{1}{2}l = \frac{1}{2}L$; if there are two nodes between the ends $\frac{1}{2}l = \frac{1}{3}L$; and so on. The wave length of possible waves in the vibrating wire are therefore such that $\frac{1}{2}l = L$, or $\frac{1}{2}l = \frac{1}{2}L$, or $\frac{1}{2}l = \frac{1}{3}L$, etc. ; that is, $l = \frac{2}{1}L$, or $\frac{2}{2}L$, or $\frac{2}{3}L$, or $\frac{2}{4}L$, etc., and the wave length will have these values according as there are 0, 1, 2, 3, etc., nodes between the ends.

26.09. Musical notes vary in quality or timbre as well as in pitch and loudness. Thus the note emitted by a violin may be distinguished from that produced by a piano or by the human voice, although both notes have the same pitch, and both are equally loud. The difference is due to the fact that the various harmonics are produced with different intensities by different instruments. Although the trained ear is able to distinguish harmonics of various pitches in the sound produced by an instrument, it is also possible to show their presence in other ways. One method depends upon the principle of resonance.

26.10. Imagine a boy sitting on a stationary swing, and suppose that the swing, when in motion, makes one complete vibration in 2 seconds (*i.e.* one complete forward and one complete backward movement in this time). Suppose that the boy receives small pushes from behind every 3 seconds. The first push will cause the swing to move forward slightly. It then swings backward once, forward once, and the next push occurs as it is moving backward again, and brings the swing to rest. If the force exerted at each push is small, the movement of the swing will also be small.

Suppose now that the same swing is pushed every 2·2 seconds. The second push occurs just after the swing has passed its lowest point during its forward movement, and assists the motion. The third push does the same. The fourth push, however, occurs 6·6 seconds after the first and the swing has then made 3·3 vibrations, or a little more than $3\frac{1}{4}$. The swing is therefore moving backwards at this instant and the push retards its motion, as do the next two pushes as well. Hence, the swing is again brought to rest. Since the first three pushes assist its motion, however, the movement of the swing is greater than in the first case.

N

If the pushes are applied at two-second intervals, however, each is applied at the instant when the swing is in its lowest position and moving forwards, so each assists the motion. Even if the force exerted at each push is small, the swing is made to move through bigger and bigger distances until a large movement is taking place. We have in this case an example of **resonance.**

When two tuning-forks of exactly equal frequencies are placed side by side and one is caused to vibrate, resonance occurs, and the second fork is found to be vibrating also. Each compression wave sent through the air from the sounding fork applies a small force to the prongs of the other. Since the two forks are of equal frequencies, each compression wave from the first fork reaches the second as it is completing a vibration, and assists its motion. Although the force exerted by each wave is small, the cumulative effect is sufficient to cause an appreciable vibration.

When a key of a piano is pushed down and held down, the corresponding wire in the instrument is free to vibrate. After the sound has died away, the note an octave lower may be sounded and "damped" by releasing its key. The original note can then be clearly heard. When the lower note is sounded, several harmonics are produced as well as the fundamental note. The first of these has a frequency double that of the fundamental, so its frequency is the same as that of the octave of the fundamental. It therefore produces resonance with the wire which was left free to vibrate.

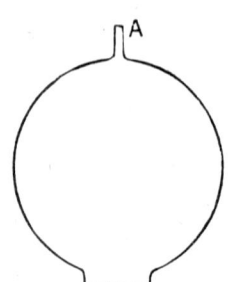

FIG. 26.06.—HELM-
HOLTZ RESONATOR.

Resonance is produced whenever one body transmits vibrations to a second body whose natural frequency of vibration is equal to, or nearly equal to, that of the first, and the more nearly equal their frequencies, the greater will be the vibration produced in the second body.

Resonators of the shape shown in figure 26.06 were used by Helmholtz to discover what harmonics were present when particular notes were sounded. Each resonator consisted of a metal sphere with two openings, and if a particular note contained a harmonic of frequency equal to the natural frequency of the resonator, the harmonic produced resonance, and could be heard by applying the ear to the resonator at **A.** The natural frequency of the resonator depends upon its size, and Helmholtz used a large number of resonators of various sizes to test for harmonics of different frequencies.

26.11. When a tuning-fork is sounded and its stem is held against a table, the table is set in vibration by the fork, and on account of its larger area it sets more air in motion than the fork, and thus produces a louder sound. The fork is at the same time quickly brought to rest. This is *not* a case of resonance, because the natural frequency of vibration of the table is not equal to that of the fork. The table has no definite natural frequency, for if it is struck, a noise, and not a musical note, is produced.

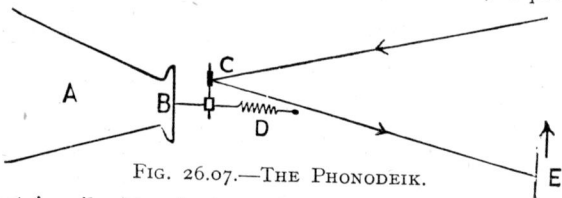

FIG. 26.07.—THE PHONODEIK.

It is set in vibration by *any* vibrating tuning-fork whose stem rests against it, and it vibrates with a frequency equal to that of whatever fork is used. The vibrations set up in the table are called **forced vibrations.**

A metal or glass diaphragm has a very high natural frequency of vibration, and such a diaphragm may be set into a state of forced vibration by other vibrating bodies. The fact that the vibrations of such diaphragms depend very little upon their own natural frequency of vibration, and chiefly upon that of the body which causes them to vibrate, is applied when diaphragms are used in such instruments as gramophones and wireless sets. A diaphragm is used in the phonodeik for a similar reason.

26.12. The phonodeik, designed by Professor Miller, is a modern form of apparatus for determining the amplitudes and pitches of the notes which make up any given sound.

Sound waves entering a cone A (figure 26.07) are concentrated upon a thin glass diaphragm B, and cause it to vibrate in time with the waves. Behind the diaphragm is mounted a small mirror C, which is able to rotate about a vertical axis. It is connected to the diaphragm by a fine wire passing round the axle which carries the mirror, and this wire is kept taut by the spring D. Each movement of the diaphragm thus causes the mirror to rotate.

In order to record the movements of the mirror, a beam of light is reflected from it to a spot on a photographic film E. The rotation of the mirror causes the spot of light to move from side to side across the film, along a line at right angles to the plane of the diagram. The film, however, moves at a steady speed in a vertical direction, as shown by the arrow, and the spot of light then traces a wavy line on the film.

Each of these curves is a graph of the positions of the centre of the diaphragm, and since the diaphragm moves in time with the air near it, such a graph also represents the displacement of the air particles as the sound waves pass through the gas.

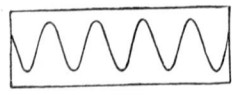

Tuning Fork

Specially designed instruments enable these graphs to be used to determine which notes are present in a given sound, and the intensity of each note.

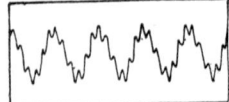

Tuning Fork (Struck violently)

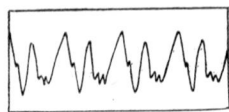

Reed Organ Pipe

[*From "Modern Acoustics," by A. H. Davis, by courtesy of G. Bell & Sons, Ltd.*

FIG. 26.08.—AIR VIBRATIONS PRODUCED BY DIFFERENT SOURCES OF SOUND.

EXAMPLES 26

1. A wire 100 cm. long, under a tension of 10,000 gm.-wt., vibrates with a frequency of 160 per second. What will be its frequency of vibration (a) if its length is reduced to 40 cm., (b) if its tension is increased to 14,400 gm.-wt., (c) if both the changes (a) and (b) are made ?

2. Wires made of the same material are of equal lengths and are under equal tensions. If the wires are of various diameters, calculate the law relating their frequencies and diameters.

3. Several wires are made of the same material. One wire has a diameter 0·105 cm. and is 100 cm. long. The other wire is to be tuned to give the same note as the first when the tensions in the two wires are equal. It is desired to make the second wire approximately 60 cm. long. Wires are available with diameters 0·105, 0·155, 0·222, 0·293 cm. Which wire is most suitable, and what is the exact length of the wire required ?

4. The vibrations of a stretched wire may be thought of as equivalent to two sets of waves travelling in opposite directions along the wire. Explain this statement.

5. A wire 100 cm. long vibrates in such a way as to produce (a) its fundamental note, (b) the first harmonic of the fundamental.

The frequency of the fundamental is 256. Calculate for the two cases the wave lengths of the waves in the wire, and their velocities along the wire.

6. On what does the *quality* of a musical note depend ? How may the presence of harmonics be detected ?

7. Distinguish between *resonance* and *forced vibrations*. Give two examples of each.

School Certificate Questions

8. Draw and briefly describe an apparatus suitable for studying the laws of vibration of strings. A string is tuned to give a certain note. Explain how you would obtain the octave of this note (*a*) by changing the vibrating length only, (*b*) by changing the tension only, (*c*) without changing length or tension. Give reasons in each case for the method you would use. (J)

9. Describe how you would investigate the relation between the frequency of vibration of a stretched string and its tension. What change must be made in the tension of a stretched string in order that its fundamental note may be raised an octave ? Where must a bridge B be placed under a sonometer wire AC, 90 cm. long, so that AB gives a note an octave higher than BC ? (J)

10. What is meant by the pitch of a musical note ? On what factors does the note emitted by a stretched wire, when plucked or bowed, depend ? Two stretched wires, A and B, of the same material and same diameter, give, when plucked, notes whose frequencies are in the ratio 1 to 2 respectively. If the length of A is twice that of B, compare the tensions in A and B. (J)

11. Explain carefully the terms *longitudinal, transverse, progressive, stationary*, as applied to wave motion. Illustrate each of the above terms by reference to the following example. A string of length 50 cm. is plucked and a note of frequency 250 is heard. Find the wave length of the vibration (*a*) in the string, (*b*) in the air. [Velocity of sound in air = 340 metres per second.] (J)

12. How would you investigate experimentally the relation between the tension and the vibration frequency of a stretched wire ? A stretched wire 3 ft. long is divided by two bridges so that the segments give notes of vibration frequencies in the ratio 3 : 4 : 5. Where must the bridges be placed ? (L)

13. How does the frequency of the note emitted by a string when vibrating transversely depend upon (1) its length, (2) its diameter, (3) its density, (4) the force with which it is stretched ? Two wires, one of steel and the other of brass, emit the same note when plucked. They are of the same length and stretched with the same force. If the diameter of the steel wire is 1 mm., calculate the diameter of the brass wire. [Density of steel 7·8, of brass 8·5 gm. per cubic centimetre.] (L)

CHAPTER 27

27.01. Let us suppose that a tuning-fork is placed at the end of a tube AB (figure 27.01), open at both ends, and suppose that at a given instant a compression wave sent out by the fork enters the tube. The compression wave in the tube is prevented from spreading by the walls of the tube, and it travels down the tube with little loss of intensity. When the compression reaches the far end of the tube, the air at that point is for an instant at a pressure greater than ordinary atmospheric pressure, and since the tube is open, the air is free to expand. Its sudden expansion causes a pressure wave to spread from the end of the tube into the surrounding air. During the expansion, however, the pressure decreases so quickly at the end of the tube, that, instead of the pressure being reduced merely to

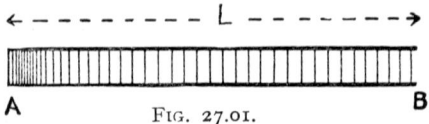

FIG. 27.01.

that of the surrounding air, it falls somewhat below it, and causes a rarefaction at the end of the tube. This rarefaction sets up a rarefaction wave which passes back along the tube, and the initial energy of the compression wave travelling down the tube is divided between the compression wave escaping from the tube, and the rarefaction wave which returns along it. The first compression wave may therefore be regarded as undergoing reflection at the open end of the tube with some loss of energy, but it is reflected, not as a compression, but as a rarefaction.

In a similar way it may be shown that when the rarefaction returning along the tube meets the end, it is reflected as a compression.

27.02. Suppose now that the frequency of the tuning-fork is such that it produces a second compression at the instant when the first wave has travelled to the end of the tube and returned. At this instant the first wave is being reflected at the end near the fork as a compression, and the second compression produced by the fork reinforces that formed by reflection. After this reinforced compression wave has been reflected and has returned, it is further reinforced by the third compression wave sent out by the fork, and so on. The fork thus produces resonance in the tube.

Let V be the velocity of sound, L the length of the tube, and n the frequency of the fork. The time required for a wave to travel to the other end of the tube and back again is $\dfrac{2L}{V}$. Hence, for resonance to occur this must be equal to the time required for the fork to complete one vibration.

$$\therefore \frac{1}{n} = \frac{2L}{V}$$

$$\therefore n = \frac{V}{2L}.$$

A tuning-fork whose frequency is that given by this formula will produce resonance in the tube. Other forks whose frequencies are twice, three times, four times, etc., that given by the above formula will also produce resonance.

Suppose that a certain fork has a frequency double that given above. Such a fork will have completed two vibrations by the time a wave has travelled down the tube and returned, and it therefore produces a third compression at just the right instant to reinforce that formed by reflection of the first. Similarly, the fourth compression reinforces the second, and so on.

It is not necessary that the original sound waves should be produced by a tuning-fork. Any other source of sound of suitable frequency would do just as well. The compression waves may even be formed by the material of the tube itself, and if the tube vibrates, those of its vibrations for which $n = \dfrac{V}{2L}$, or 2, 3, 4 . . . times this value, will produce resonance of the air in the pipe and form loud notes. Such a tube, open at both ends, produces a fundamental note of frequency $\dfrac{V}{2L}$, and harmonics whose frequencies are 2, 3, 4 . . . times that of the fundamental.

When a pipe, open at both ends, is sounding, the compressions and rarefactions cause a maximum amount of movement of the air at the ends of the tube, where the air can move freely. The ends of the tube are therefore antinodes, or points of maximum movement.

27.03. When a compression wave reaches the closed end of a pipe, the air near the end is compressed to a pressure greater than atmospheric pressure. This compressed air can only return to atmospheric pressure by forcing back the air behind it, and in doing so it starts a compression wave, which returns along the tube. Hence, a compression is reflected as a compression at the closed end. Similarly a rarefaction is reflected as a rarefaction.

When a tuning-fork causes a compression at the open end A of a pipe, the other end B of which is closed (figure 27.02), the

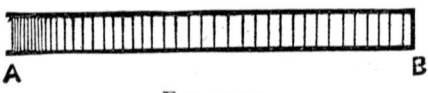

A   **B**

FIG. 27.02.

compression is reflected at B as a compression. This compression is reflected at A as a rarefaction, travels to B, and is reflected back as a rarefaction to A. At this end it is now reflected as a compression, and if at this instant the fork produces a further compression, this will reinforce the first one. To produce resonance in this case it is therefore necessary that successive compressions should be produced at intervals of time equal to that during which a sound wave travels four times the length of the tube. Let n be the frequency of a fork which produces resonance, L be the length of the tube, and V the velocity of sound. The time required for a wave to travel a distance of $4L$ is $\dfrac{4L}{V}$, and the time between successive vibrations of the fork is $\dfrac{1}{n}$,

$$\therefore \frac{1}{n} = \frac{4L}{V}$$
$$\therefore n = \frac{V}{4L}.$$

This equation gives the frequency of the fundamental note of such a tube.

A tuning-fork of frequency double that of the fundamental note does *not* produce resonance with this type of tube, for such a fork produces a compression at the instant when the first compression has travelled twice the length of the tube, and is being reflected at the open end as a rarefaction. The second compression wave merely destroys this rarefaction.

A tuning-fork of frequency three times that of the fundamental does, however, produce resonance. Its second compression is produced when the first wave has travelled four-thirds the length of the tube ; its third compression is produced after the first has travelled eight-thirds the length of the tube ; and its fourth compression is produced after the initial wave has travelled twelve-thirds, or four times the length of the tube. The first wave is then being reflected at the end near the fork as a compression, and this compression is reinforced by the fourth compression from the fork. Similarly, the second compression is reinforced by the fifth, the third by the sixth, and so on, and the tube resounds to the fork.

In the same way it may be shown that such a tube resounds to notes whose frequencies are 3, 5, 7, 9, etc., times that of the fundamental note, but not to notes of frequency 2, 4, 6, 8, etc., times its frequency. Since a closed tube of this kind emits only the fundamental note and its odd harmonics, the sound produced by a closed tube is different in quality from that produced by a tube which is open at both ends.

27.04. A tube of length L_1, closed at one end, resounds with a tuning-fork of frequency n to produce its fundamental note, if $n = \dfrac{V}{4L_1}$; where V is the velocity of sound. A tube of length L_2 resounds with the same fork to produce the first of its possible harmonics if $n = \dfrac{3V}{4L_2}$. These facts enable the velocity of sound to be measured in the laboratory. A long glass tube, open at both ends, is lowered into a tall gas jar containing water (figure 27.03), so that the lower end of the tube is closed by the water. The length of the air column in the tube can then be varied by raising or lowering the tube. A vibrating tuning-fork of known frequency n is held over the open end of the tube, and the shortest length of the air column for which resonance occurs is found. Let this length be L_1. The tube is in this case emitting its fundamental note, so $n = \dfrac{V}{4L_1}$.

The velocity of sound might be calculated from this equation, but the value so obtained would not be accurate, for the following reason. When a compression reaches the open end of a tube, it is reflected as a rarefaction, because at the open end the excess pressure is suddenly reduced, and the pressure falls from a value slightly above atmospheric pressure to one somewhat below it. This decrease of pressure occurs very quickly, but is not instantaneous. There is, therefore, a short delay after the compression reaches the end of the tube before the rarefaction is set up. A similar delay occurs when a rarefaction is reflected as a compression. The effect of these delays is the same as that which would be caused by lengthening the tube. Hence, the effective length of such a tube is not the same as its actual length L_1, but is equal to $(L_1 + a)$ where a is a small correction.

The correct equation for the resounding tube is, therefore, not $n = \dfrac{V}{4L_1}$, but $n = \dfrac{V}{4(L_1 + a)}$. Hence,

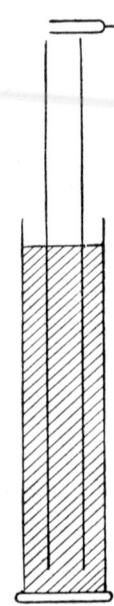

Fig. 27.03.—
Measurement
of the Veloc-
ity of Sound
by means of
a Resounding
Tube.

$$(L_1 + a) = \frac{V}{4n} . \quad . \quad . \quad . \quad . \quad . \quad (1)$$

Suppose, now, that the length of the tube is increased by drawing it farther out of the water. For a longer air column the frequency of the fundamental note is lower, so the tube can no longer resound to the fork with its fundamental note. When its length is correctly adjusted, however, it can resound by emitting the first of its possible harmonics. Let L_2 be the length of the air column when this occurs. Its effective length is then $(L_2 + a)$, so resonance occurs when

$$n = \frac{3V}{4(L_2 + a)}$$

$$\therefore (L_2 + a) = \frac{3V}{4n}.$$

Subtracting equation (1) above from this equation, we obtain:

$$(L_2 - L_1) = \frac{2V}{4n}$$

$$\therefore \quad V = 2n(L_2 - L_1).$$

From this equation the velocity of sound may be calculated. The value obtained is that for room temperature, and must be corrected to obtain that at $0°$ C., if the latter is required.

27.05. When resonance is obtained in a column of gas, the trains of waves travelling in both directions along the tube produce a set of stationary waves in the gas, similar to those in a vibrating wire. This fact is clearly demonstrated by means of **Kundt's tube** (after the German physicist, A. A. E. Kundt, 1839–1894). One end of a long glass tube (figure 27.04) is closed

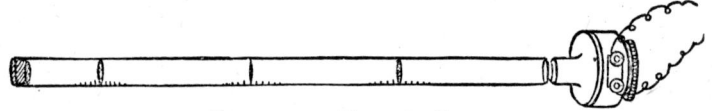

FIG. 27.04.—KUNDT'S TUBE.

by a cork. At the other end is placed a loud speaker, the diaphragm of which may be caused to vibrate with any desired frequency by means of an electrical circuit. The diaphragm produces sound waves of a similar frequency in the gas in the tube. When these sound waves are of a frequency which produces resonance, lycopodium powder, which is distributed along the bottom of the tube, is thrown into violent motion by the vibrating gas column. The lycopodium powder forms a series of sharp ridges near each antinode, and at the antinode a narrow disc of powder is thrown up right across the tube. The distance between successive nodes is half a wave length of the sound waves, so the wave length of the sound may be found by measuring the distance between the discs. If d is the distance, the wave length is $2d$, so the velocity of sound is given by the formula $V = 2n.d$, where n is the frequency of the waves. The velocity of sound in the tube may thus be calculated if n is known.

That the distance between successive antinodes is half a wave length may be seen as follows. Antinodes are formed at those points in the tube where a compression travelling in one direction meets a *rarefaction* travelling in the opposite direction.

The molecules in front of a compression are driven forward in
the direction of the wave, but the molecules in front of a rarefaction move back to fill up the rarefaction, and thus move in

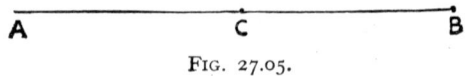

A   C   B

FIG. 27.05.

the opposite direction to that of the wave.   Hence, the molecules between a compression travelling in one direction, and a
rarefaction travelling in the other are displaced
the maximum amount, since both waves tend to
move them in the same direction.   That is, antinodes exist where compressions meet rarefactions.

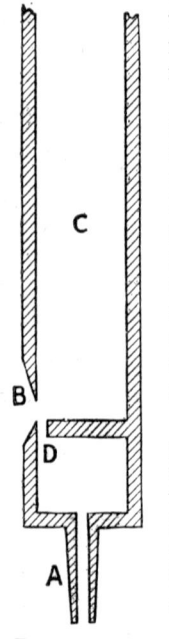

Suppose now that a compression travelling in
the direction AB (figure 27.05) reaches A at the
same instant as a rarefaction travelling in the
opposite direction, so that A is an antinode.   If
the distance AB is equal to a wave length, the
next rarefaction is at B, and as both waves
advance, the compression meets this rarefaction
at C, midway between A and B, and produces
an antinode there.   Hence, the antinodes are half
a wave length apart.   Similarly it may be shown
that successive nodes are half a wave length apart,
and are situated midway between the antinodes.

27.06.   Vibrating columns of air are used to
produce sound in organ pipes.   The column of air
in the pipe is caused to vibrate by forcing air
through the tube A (figure 27.06).   As it passes
the lip B, vibrations of various frequencies are
set up in the moving air, and the note sounded
by the pipe is composed of those frequencies
which produce resonance in the column of air C.

When such a vibration has been set up it is
maintained and reinforced by the stream of air
entering at A.   The lower end of such a pipe

FIG. 27.06.—
AN ORGAN
PIPE.

serves as an open end, for when a compression
wave, travelling down the tube C, reaches the end, the compressed
air at the bottom escapes at B, and produces a rarefaction which
returns along the tube.   The air escaping from B deflects the

jet of air entering at D. This air is moving rapidly, however, and the deflected jet passing through the holes at D and B sweeps out with it more of the air in the tube C, thus increasing the rarefaction produced at the reflection. Similarly, when a rarefaction reaches the lower end of the tube, a stream of air enters at B to produce a compression, so the rarefaction is reflected as a compression. The air entering at B, however, deflects into the tube the stream of air entering at D, and this air reinforces the compression produced by reflection.

27.07. When resonance occurs in a tube closed at one end, the air in contact with the closed end cannot move, and this

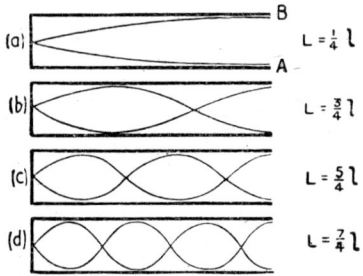

FIG. 27.07.—DIAGRAMMATIC REPRESENTATION OF THE STATIONARY WAVES IN A TUBE CLOSED AT ONE END.

point is always a node. At the open end there is a minimum of restriction of motion, and the open end is an antinode. There may be 0, 1, 2, . . . nodes at various other points in the tube as well, and the stationary waves are often represented by such diagrams as figure 27.07. The distance between the curved lines at any point in the tube represents the amplitude of vibration of the air molecules at the point. Thus, at the closed end of the tube there is a node in every case, and this is shown by drawing the lines to intersect there. The antinodes at the open end are shown by the fact that the curves are the maximum distance apart at these points. Note, however, that the motion of the vibrating molecules is *not* across the tube between the two lines (*e.g.* between the points A and B) but along lines parallel to the axis of the tube. The distances between the curved lines represent the magnitudes of the vibrations and nothing more.

When the air column vibrates as at (a), there is a node at the end of the tube only, and in the cases (b), (c), and (d) there are, in addition to the node at the end of the tube, one, two, and three nodes at points along its length. The distance between successive nodes is equal to half a wave length. Hence, the wave lengths in the four cases shown are $\frac{4}{1}$ times, $\frac{4}{3}$ times, $\frac{4}{5}$ times, and $\frac{4}{7}$ times the length of the tube, and the length of the tube L is related to the wave length l as shown in the figure. The velocity of sound, V, is equal to the frequency of the waves, n, multiplied by the wave length l, i.e. $V = n.l$. Hence, $n = \dfrac{V}{l}$, and the frequencies in the four cases are n_1, n_2, n_3, and n_4, where

$$n_1 = \frac{V}{l} = \frac{V}{4L}$$

$$n_2 = \frac{V}{\frac{4}{3}L}$$

$$n_3 = \frac{V}{\frac{4}{5}L}$$

$$n_4 = \frac{V}{\frac{4}{7}L}.$$

These four frequencies are in the ratio $1 : 3 : 5 : 7$, and since the first type of vibration is that which produces the fundamental note, the harmonics produced by such a tube are such as have frequencies 3, 5, 7 . . . times that of the fundamental. This result agrees, as it should do, with that obtained in section 27.03 by considering the reinforcement of the individual waves.

By means of similar diagrams it may be shown that a tube open at both ends produces all the possible harmonics, and not merely the odd ones.

EXAMPLES 27

SCHOOL CERTIFICATE QUESTIONS

1. Explain the phenomenon of the resonance tube. A vertical tube, 1 metre long, is filled with water which is allowed to run out gradually from the bottom. For how many positions of the water surface will it be possible to obtain resonance with a tuning-fork

of frequency 512 ? The velocity of sound in air may be taken as 330 metres per second. (C)

2. Describe a laboratory experiment by which you could determine the velocity of sound in air if you were provided with a tuning-fork of known vibration frequency. What conditions would affect the value observed ? (L)

3. Explain what you understand by the term *resonance*. Describe an experiment in which a column of air closed at one end is tuned to a fork by resonance, and explain with the aid of a diagram the mode of vibration of the air column. If the fork has a frequency of 440 and the minimum length of the resonant air column is 18·75 cm., find the velocity of sound in air. (O)

4. Explain fully what is meant by saying that the air in a tube *resounds* to a tuning-fork held near the end. The air in a cylindrical tube 32 cm. long, open at both ends, resounds most loudly to a certain tuning-fork. Calculate the frequency of the fork. If one end of the tube is then closed, what will be the wave length and frequency of the note emitted when the tube resounds ? [Take the velocity of sound in air as 336 metres per second.] (J)

5. Why does a vibrating tuning-fork sound louder when it is mounted on a hollow wooden box than when it is held in the hand by its stem ? What should be the approximate length of a box, open at one end, which should be used for a fork of vibration frequency 256 to ensure maximum loudness ? (Velocity of sound in air may be taken as 1100 ft. per second.) (J)

6. Explain and distinguish between the reinforcement of the sound emitted by a vibrating tuning-fork when (1) the stem of the fork is pressed on the top of a table, (2) the fork is held near the mouth of a glass tube of appropriate length, open at both ends. (L)

7. If the velocity of sound in air is 1120 ft. per second, what is the wave length in air of the note emitted by a tuning-fork of frequency 384 ? How would you determine this wave length experimentally ? (L)

8. Describe briefly the construction of an organ pipe. A given organ pipe, open at both ends, sounds a certain note. What will be the effect on the pitch if the top of the pipe be closed, and why ? Explain why the " bass " pipes of an air organ are long but the " treble " pipes are short. (J)

CHAPTER 28

MUSICAL INSTRUMENTS

28.01. The Piano.—Sound is produced in a piano by tightly strung wires, which are struck by felt-covered hammers operated from the keyboard. Each key of the keyboard operates a single hammer, and each hammer at the bass end strikes a single wire, which gives the appropriate note. The wires which produce the higher notes are shorter, and to produce sufficiently intense sounds these wires are arranged in groups of three, each group being struck by one hammer, and producing a single note.

To obtain notes of different pitches, wires under different tensions, of different lengths, or of different diameters might be used. In practice it is found advisable to arrange that all the wires are at about the same tension (160 lb.-wt.), and to obtain notes of different pitches by using wires of various lengths and diameters.

Wires of length about 5 cm. are used to give the highest note. Those which produce the next note are of the same diameter but somewhat longer; those for the next note longer again, and so on. If only the length of wire were altered, the length of wire required for the lower notes would be longer than that which could be stretched inside the piano-case. Hence, as soon as a note is reached, to produce which it is feasible to use a wire of the next larger diameter, this thicker wire is used instead of the thin wire used for the top notes. The thick steel wires used for producing the lowest notes are covered with layers of copper wire to increase their mass per unit length.

The sound produced by a vibrating wire is faint, and to give a sufficiently loud note the wires are attached to supports in a large board, called the sounding-board of the piano. This board is nearly as large as the piano, and the vibrations of the wires set up forced vibrations in it, of frequencies equal to those of the wires. Owing to its large area, the sounding-board displaces a large volume of air at each vibration, and produces loud sounds.

To enable it to support the tensions of the wires, the sounding-board is rigidly attached to an iron frame.

When the wires have been stretched in position, their frequencies of vibration will be such as produce approximately the correct notes of the scale, but tuning is still necessary to make their frequencies accurately correct, and this tuning is performed by altering the tensions in individual wires. To enable this to be done, one end of each wire is attached to, and wound round, a steel pin which fits in a socket in a heavy beam. By turning one of these pins in its socket, the tension in the wire attached to it may be adjusted to the required value.

28.02. The Violin.—Sounds are produced by the strings of a violin when they are set in vibration by bowing. There are four strings of various diameters. The strings are stretched from the body of the instrument across a bridge, and each is attached to a peg at the end of the neck of the violin. They are tuned by screwing these pegs, and thus altering the tensions. When tuned, they give the four notes of the musical scale : G, D, A and E. Other notes are produced by forcing the strings down with the fingers until they touch bridges on the neck of the violin. The length of string is thus shortened, and a note of higher pitch is produced.

As the bow is drawn across a string, the latter alternately adheres to the bow, and slips. The vibration of the string is therefore extremely complicated, and not only the fundamental note and various harmonics are produced, but a number of other tones as well. To distinguish between these tones and the harmonics, they are referred to as *overtones*. The harmonics are such notes as have frequencies 2, 3, 4 . . . etc. times that of the fundamental. The frequency of an overtone is often related to that of the fundamental, but not in this simple manner. Overtones are produced by all musical instruments, and it is the presence of these overtones and harmonics which gives the note emitted by each particular instrument its own peculiar quality.

The body of the instrument serves a purpose similar to that of the sounding-board of a piano. The body and the air inside it are set in vibration by the vibrating strings, and the large area exposed to the external air enables loud sounds to be produced. The design and methods of manufacture of the body of a violin are of the greatest importance if the vibrations produced in it are to be similar to those of the strings.

28.03. Wireless.—It is impossible to explain here how electric currents are converted into wireless waves, and how the latter are reconverted into electric currents, but the processes of transmitting and receiving may be dealt with briefly in so far as they are connected with sound.

At the studio, where broadcasting is taking place, sound waves produced by the performer are allowed to fall on the diaphragm A (figure 28.01) of a microphone. The diaphragm is caused to vibrate with forced vibrations of the same frequency as that of the sound waves falling on it. Behind the thin metal plate which

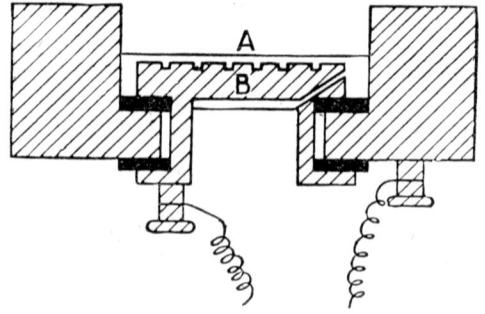

FIG. 28.01.—A CONDENSER MICROPHONE.

forms the diaphragm is a second plate B. The two plates are insulated from one another and form a condenser, the two plates of which are kept at different electrical potentials. When the diaphragm vibrates, the distance between its centre and the plate B is alternately increased and decreased, and this causes momentary changes of the potential. These changes of potential are used to produce electric currents in wires leading from them.

If the diaphragm is to respond equally to notes of various frequencies, resonance must not be set up in the air between the plate B and the diaphragm, whatever may be the frequency of the waves falling on the diaphragm. For this reason a number of grooves are cut in the plate B. When the air above this plate vibrates, the grooves cause eddies in it, and the kinetic energy of the air vibrations is quickly absorbed in the production of these eddies.

The wireless waves produced by means of the electric currents from the microphone travel out through space, and are again converted into electrical currents in receiving circuits. If these currents are passed through a coil of wire placed near a magnet, each change of current produces a movement of the coil, and the movements of the coil correspond to those of the diaphragm of the microphone transmitter. The motion of the coil thus produces waves in the air near it of a frequency similar to that of the waves falling on the microphone. The intensity of the waves set up by such a small object as a coil of wire would be small, but a louder sound is produced by attaching the coil to a diaphragm, which is set in forced vibration by the coil.

28.04. The Gramophone.—When a gramophone record is being produced a disc of soft wax is rotated upon a revolving table, and a sharp needle bears on the wax. The arm which carries the needle moves slowly from the edge towards the centre of the wax disc, and the needle cuts a spiral groove from the outside to the centre. If no sound were being recorded this groove would be smooth. The sound waves of the music being recorded fall on a microphone and produce electric currents which are used to cause the needle to vibrate from side to side with a frequency equal to that of the sound waves. The actual path traced by the needle is thus not smooth, but contains indentations corresponding to the vibrations of the needle. After suitable treatment, the wax disc is then used to produce a mould in which gramophone records may be moulded. Each of these records carries wavy markings similar to those of the original.

To play the record, it is placed upon the revolving table of a gramophone, and a needle point is made to traverse the groove in the record. This needle vibrates from side to side in the irregular groove, reproducing the movements of the needle by which the recording was done, and the movements of the needle are communicated by it to a diaphragm. This, in turn, sets up vibrations in the air, and these are of a similar frequency to that of the sounds received by the microphone during recording.

28.05. The Speaking Trumpet.—This is a cone, open at both ends, and is used for producing loud sounds. The speaker applies his mouth to the narrow end of the cone, and he is then able to make his voice heard at greater distances than he could do without the assistance of the trumpet. It is a common belief that this is due to the fact that the speaking trumpet directs the sound in a particular direction, but the true explanation is that the trumpet enables louder sounds to be produced than those produced without its aid.

It is difficult to break a ping-pong ball which is free to move, because the ball rebounds before its sides are driven in. In a similar way the vocal chords are unable to exert a large force on the air near them, because the pressure waves set up by the movement of the vocal chords escape quickly from the open mouth. When a speaking trumpet is used, however, such waves have to travel to the open end before the air can expand freely, and in the confined space of the trumpet more intense vibrations of the air may be produced. The sounds produced by the trumpet appear louder because they are louder ; not because they are directed by the trumpet. The horn of a gramophone acts in a similar way to enable loud sounds to be produced by the movement of the diaphragm.

EXAMPLES 28

1. How is sound produced in a piano ? Describe the construction of the instrument and explain (a) how notes of different pitches are produced by it, (b) how the piano is tuned, (c) the function of the sounding-board.

2. With the aid of a diagram explain the construction of a microphone, and its use in broadcasting.

3. Explain the function of the horn of a gramophone.

School Certificate Questions

4. When a violin string is bowed a musical note is heard. Describe what is taking place at the violin and in the air between it and the listener. Explain what determines (a) the loudness, (b) the pitch, of the note heard.   (L)

5. Describe the steps in the process by which the needle on a rotating gramophone disc produces the sensation of sound to a listener.   (L)

ANSWERS

HEAT

EXAMPLES 1 (p. 15)

(**1**) 0·29 in. ; (**2**) 0·42 in. ; (**3**) 214° C. ; (**4**) 199·78 cm. ; (**5**) 11·9973 in., 12·0105 in. ; (**6**) 200·41 c.c. ; (**7**) 200·030, 0·0015% ; (**8**) 100·15 cm. ; (**9**) 2 : 1 ; (**10**) 30·164 ; (**11**) 266° C.

EXAMPLES 2 (p. 31)

(**1**) 120 c. ft. ; (**2**) 1273 c.c. ; (**3**) 25·9 lb.-wt. per square inch ; (**4**) 1134, 1183 c.c. ; (**5**) 3025 c.c. ; (**6**) 106° C., 201° C. ; (**7**) 0·75 sq. cm. ; (**8**) 130 c. in., 30·8 c. in. ; (**10**) 2 cm. of mercury, 107° C. ; (**11**) 0·00821 gm. ; (**12**) 91 lb.-wt. per square inch ; (**13**) 21·3 times per minute ; (**14**) 34·2° C.

EXAMPLES 3 (p. 42)

(**5**) 167° F., − 49° F., 62·6° F. ; (**6**) 37·8° C., − 23·3° C., 537·8° C. ; (**7**) − 40° ; (**8**) 0·0000155 ; (**11**) − 21·2° C. ; (**14**) 35° C., 43·3° C. ; (**16**) 70 cm. of mercury, 273° C.

EXAMPLES 4 (p. 55)

(**2**) 0·00085 per degree C., 106·8 c.c. ; (**3**) 0·000475 per degree C., 0·000500 per degree C. ; (**4**) 0·000028 per degree C. ; 0·00104 per degree C. ; (**5**) 0·0364 ; (**6**) 2·77 gm. ; (**7**) 0·195 cm. ; (**8**) 0·133 sq. mm. ; (**9**) 0·000518 per degree C., 0·000545 per degree C.

EXAMPLES 5 (p. 69)

(**1**) 36·7° C. ; (**2**) 14·9° C. ; (**3**) 252·2 ; (**4**) 1·46*d*. ; (**5**) 0·120 ; (**6**) 43·4° C. ; (**7**) 0·213, 6·04 gm. ; (**8**) 2 : 5 ; (**10**) 23 cal. per second, 50 cal. per second ; (**11**) 835° C. ; (**12**) 30·8° C. ; (**13**) 1·7° C.

EXAMPLES 8 (p. 107)

(**3**) 336,000 ft.-lb., 456,000 joules ; (**5**) 4·26 joules per calorie ; (**6**) 159° C. ; (**8**) 0·24° C. ; (**10**) 89·9 metres ; (**13**) 20·1° F. ; (**14**) 140 minutes.

EXAMPLES 9 (p. 116)

(**2**) 658° C., 76° C. per minute, 16,720 cal. per minute, 4½ minutes, 75 cal. per gram ; (**5**) 75 cal. per gram ; (**6**) 200° C. ; (**7**) 65° C. ; (**8**) 41·3 gm. ; (**9**) 79·4 cal. per gram ; (**10**) 81·1 cal. per gram ; (**11**) 2680 ft. per second ; (**13**) 0·505 ; (**14**) − 183° C.

Examples 10 (p. 131)

(1) + 0·6° C. ; (4) 600 cal. per minute ; 1200 cal. per minute ; 540 cal. per gram ; (5) 66% ; (6) 978 B.Th.U. per lb. ; (7) 0·57 ; (8) 265 gm. ; (9) 0·27 ; (10) $\frac{1}{16}$, $9\frac{1}{2}$ minutes.

Examples 11 (p. 141)

(9) 4·2 mm. of mercury.

Examples 12 (p. 150)

(4) 8·5% ; 75%.

LIGHT

Examples 14 (p. 170)

(12) 5 ft. from mirror ; (13) 2 ft., 7 ft. ; (15) 16° 42′, $\frac{1}{2}$; (16) 5.

Examples 15 (p. 187)

(6) 0·04 cm. ; (8) 2 cm. long ; (9) 37·5 cm. from lens, $1\frac{1}{2}$ cm. long ; (10) $16\frac{2}{3}$ cm. ; (11) 30 cm., 60 cm. ; (12) $-\frac{3}{7}$, $-\frac{2}{3}$; (13) 120·0, 111·9 cm. from lens, 8·1 times ; (15) 8 in. from lens ; (16) 11·4 in. ; (17) 200 cm. beyond lens, 8 cm. long ; (18) 16 in. farther from lens.

Examples 16 (p. 199)

(2) 10 cm., 20 cm. from the lens ; (4) 60 cm. ; (5) 5D ; (6) 5 cm. ; (7) $31\frac{1}{4}$ cm., $18\frac{3}{4}$ cm. ; (10) − 5D, 20 cm. ; (11) − $3\frac{1}{3}$D ; (12) 50 cm. from object, $47\frac{1}{2}$ cm. ; (13) 20 cm., $6\frac{2}{3}$ cm. from lens on same side as object ; (14) $26\frac{2}{3}$ cm., $13\frac{1}{3}$ cm.

Examples 17 (p. 219)

(5) 22° 1′, 40° 30′ ; (17) 41° 48′ ; (22) 10·2 ft. ; (24) 1·47 ; (25) 9 cm., 1·5.

Examples 18 (p. 239)

(7) 15 cm. in front of mirror, + $\frac{1}{2}$; (8) 15 cm. in front of mirror, $2\frac{1}{2}$ cm. ; (9) 16 cm. in front of mirror ; (10) 5 cm. behind mirror, $\frac{1}{2}$ cm. ; (11) $\frac{50}{101}$ ft. behind mirror, $\frac{6}{101}$ ft. long, 0·57 in. ; (12) 2·77 in. ; (14) 5 in. ; (15) 240 cm., 48 cm. ; (17) $2\frac{1}{2}$ cm. in front, 5 cm. behind mirror ; (18) 60 in. ; (20) 4 in., 2 in. ; (22) 5·8 in., 2·2 in. ; (23) 1 ft. ; (24) 8 in.

Examples 19 (p. 257)

(1) 8·33 cm., 8·40 cm., 9·09 cm. ; (2) lenses of power − $3\frac{1}{3}$D ; (3) lenses of power + $2\frac{2}{3}$D ; (4) lenses of power − $2\frac{2}{3}$D ; (5) (*a*) $F = +\,2$D, (*b*) $F = -\,1$D ; (9) $f = 46$ cm. ; (12) 8 in., 2·4 in. ; (13) 2 in. ; (14) 11 ft., 7·57 sq. ft.

Examples 20 (p. 276)

(1) 21 ; (9) 6 in. ; (10) 35 in., $2\frac{1}{2}$ times ; (11) $4\frac{1}{6}$ cm., 25 cm. ; (13) 1·16 in.

EXAMPLES 21 (p. 285)

(1) 90 c.p., 17·6 c.p. ; **(2)** 8, 2 ; **(3)** 100 cm. from screen on side of 40 c.p. lamp ; **(4)** 50 cm. from weaker source ; **(5)** 1·08 : 1, 5·2 and 6 ft. ; **(7)** (*a*) 40 cm. from 24 c.p. lamp, (*b*) 60 cm. from 6 c.p. lamp, 120 cm. from 24 c.p. lamp.

EXAMPLES 22 (p. 302)

(1) 15° 42′.

SOUND

EXAMPLES 24 (p. 325)

(2) 1129 ft. per second.

EXAMPLES 25 (p. 343)

(2) 2174, 1852 per second ; **(7)** 1100 ft. per second, 1650 ft. ; **(10)** 420 ft. ; **(11)** 10,000 per second.

EXAMPLES 26 (p. 356)

(1) 400, 192, 480 per second ; **(3)** 0·155 cm. diameter, 67·7 cm. ; **(5)** 200 cm., 100 cm., 512 metres per second, 512 metres per second ; **(9)** 30 cm. from A ; **(10)** equal ; **(11)** 100 cm., 136 cm. ; **(12)** 15 in. and 9 in. from ends ; **(13)** 0·958 mm.

EXAMPLES 27 (p. 366)

(1) 3 ; **(3)** 330 metres per second ; **(4)** 525 per second, 128 cm., 262·5 per second ; **(5)** 12·9 in. ; **(7)** 35 in.

INDEX